Cambridge International GCSE

Chemistry

No doubt about it, Cambridge International GCSE Chemistry is tough. But never fear — this brilliant all-in-one CGP book has the formula for exam success!

There are clear notes, examples and exam-style questions for every topic, plus a set of realistic practice papers at the end of the book. Everything you need.

Both the Core and Extended courses are covered — you'll see the supplement content for the Extended course marked throughout the book.

How to access your free Online Edition

This book includes a free Online Edition to read on your PC, Mac or tablet. You'll just need to go to **cgpbooks.co.uk/extras** and enter this code:

3102 5597 0350 6926

By the way, this code only works for one person. If somebody else has used this book before you, they might have already claimed the Online Edition.

Complete
Revision & Practice

Everything you need to pass the exams!

Contents

Section 1 — The Particulate Nature of Matter

Section 2 — Experimental Techniques

Section 3 — Atoms, Elements and Compounds

Section 4 — Stoichiometry

Section 5 — Electricity and Chemistry

Section 6 — Chemical Energetics

Section 7 — Chemical Reactions

Section 8 — Acids, Bases and Salts

Section 9 — The Periodic Table

Section 10 — Metals

Section 11 — Air, Water, Sulfur and Carbonates

Section 12 — Organic Chemistry

Practical Skills

Practice Papers

Supplement

Some of the content in the specification is 'Supplemental'. This content will only be assessed if you're taking the Extended version of the Cambridge International GCSE. We've marked up all the content that's only for the Extended course with purple brackets, like the ones on this box, or the example below:

S Information or questions with a bracket like this are for the Extended Course only.

Supplement

Published by CGP

From original material by Paddy Gannon.

Editors:
Mary Falkner, Emily Forsberg, Rob Hayman, Sarah Pattison.

With thanks to Emma Clayton, Chris Elliss and Glenn Rogers for the proofreading.

ISBN: 978 1 78908 476 4

With thanks to Emily Smith for the copyright research.

Graph to show trend in Atmospheric CO_2 Concentration and global temperature on page 116 based on data by EPICA community members 2004 and Siegenthaler et al 2005.

Printed by Bell and Bain Ltd, Glasgow.

Clipart from Corel®

Illustrations by: Sandy Gardner Artist, email sandy@sandygardner.co.uk

Based on the classic CGP style created by Richard Parsons.

States of Matter

Materials can be solids, liquids or gases. The particles in solids, liquids and gases are arranged differently.

The **Three States of Matter** — Solid, Liquid and Gas

1) Materials come in three different forms — solid, liquid and gas. These are the three states of matter.
2) Which state you get (solid, liquid or gas) depends on how strong the forces of attraction are between the particles of the material.
3) How strong the forces are depends on three things:
   - the material
   - the temperature
   - the pressure.

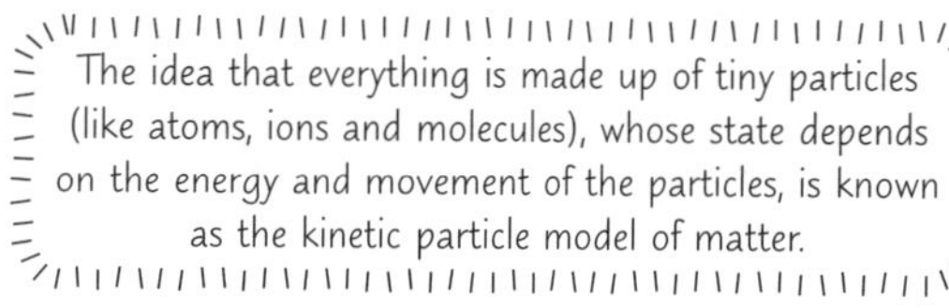

The idea that everything is made up of tiny particles (like atoms, ions and molecules), whose state depends on the energy and movement of the particles, is known as the kinetic particle model of matter.

Solids

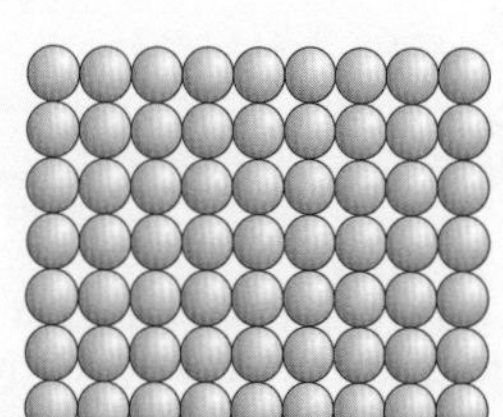

1) In solids, there are strong forces of attraction between particles, which hold them close together in fixed positions to form a very regular lattice arrangement.
2) The particles don't move from their positions, so all solids keep a definite shape and volume, and don't flow like liquids.
3) The particles vibrate about their positions — the hotter the solid becomes, the more they vibrate (causing solids to expand slightly when heated).

Liquids

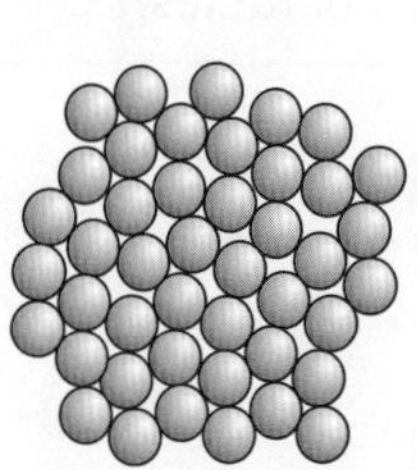

1) In liquids, there is a weak force of attraction between the particles. They're randomly arranged and free to move past each other, but they tend to stick closely together.
2) Liquids have a definite volume but don't keep a definite shape, and will flow to fill the bottom of a container.
3) The particles are constantly moving with random motion. The hotter the liquid gets, the faster they move. This causes liquids to expand slightly when heated.

Gases

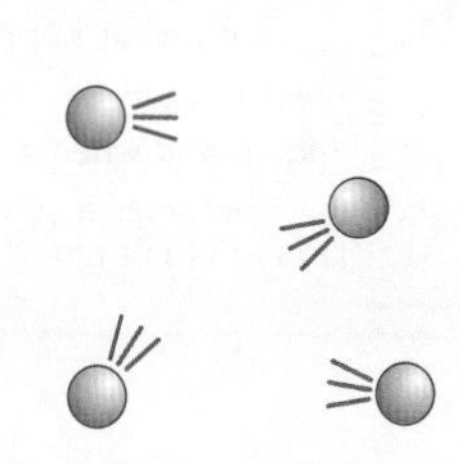

1) In gases, the force of attraction between the particles is very weak — they're free to move and are far apart. The particles in gases travel in straight lines.
2) Gases don't keep a definite shape or volume and will always fill any container.
3) The particles move constantly with random motion. The hotter the gas gets, the faster they move. Gases either expand when heated, or their pressure increases.

Gases can be compressed easily as the particles are far apart and can be squeezed closer together.

Changes of State

Substances don't just stay in one state. They can change depending on how much energy they have.

Substances Can **Change** from **One State to Another**

If you heat or cool a substance it can change state. Here are the state changes you need to know:

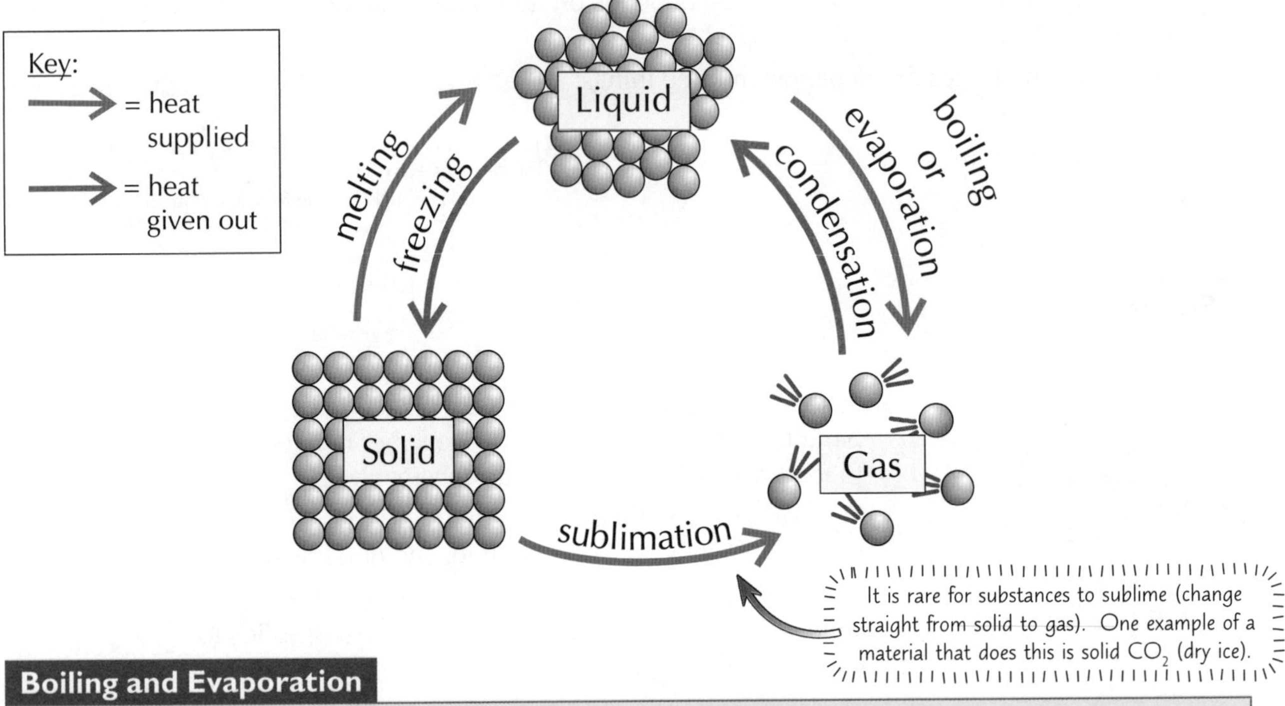

Boiling and Evaporation

1) Boiling and evaporation are both changes of state that involve a liquid changing to a gas.
2) Boiling happens when a liquid is heated to its boiling point. When you boil it, all of the liquid will gradually turn into a gas.
3) Evaporation can happen at temperatures lower than the liquid's boiling point. More energetic particles that are near the surface of the liquid can escape and become gas particles.

Supplement

Changing the **Energy** of Particles Can Cause a Change of **State**

1) When a solid is heated, its particles gain more kinetic energy.
2) This makes the particles vibrate more, which weakens the forces that hold the solid together. This makes the solid expand.
3) At a certain temperature, the particles have enough energy to break free from their positions. This is called melting and the solid turns into a liquid.
4) When a liquid is heated, the particles get even more kinetic energy.
5) This energy makes the particles move faster, which weakens and breaks the bonds holding the liquid together.
6) At a certain temperature, the particles have enough kinetic energy to break their bonds. This is called boiling and the liquid turns into a gas.
7) The amount of energy needed to cause a substance to change state depends on the strength of the forces between the particles.

The opposite happens if you cool a substance — the particles lose energy and the forces between the particles get stronger. That's what happens when a gas becomes a liquid and when a liquid becomes a solid.

Supplement

Changing state happens with changing temperature

You need to know the terms for all those changes of state. Obviously some will be a bit more familiar than others, but that cycle diagram at the top of the page is a really good way of remembering them all.

Movement of Particles

Gases and liquids are made up of particles that can move. This explains a lot of their behaviour.

Colliding Gas Particles Create **Pressure**

1) The particles in a gas constantly move about randomly.
2) As the particles move, they bump into each other — and whatever else gets in the way.
3) When the particles collide with something, they exert a force on it.
4) In a sealed container the gas particles hit the container walls, creating an outward pressure.
5) The size of this pressure depends on the number of gas particles present and how fast they are moving.
6) The faster the particles move, the more often they hit the container walls. They also hit the walls harder.
7) So the faster the particles are moving and the more particles that are present, the greater the pressure will be.

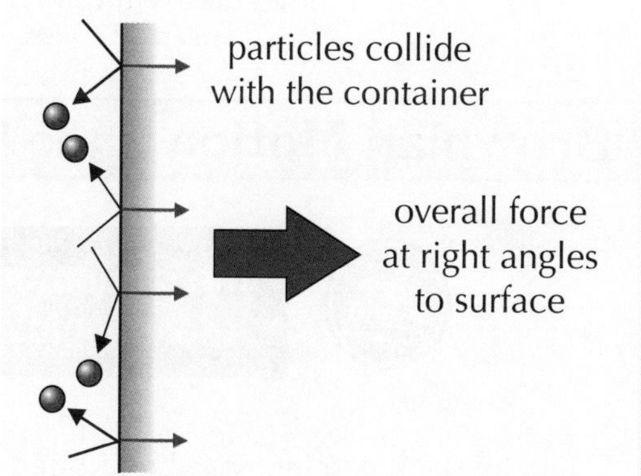
particles collide with the container
overall force at right angles to surface

Increasing the Temperature Makes Particles Move **Faster**

1) If you heat a gas, the particles move faster and gain more kinetic energy.

2) This increase in energy means the particles hit the container walls harder and more frequently. This produces a larger force on the walls, creating more pressure.

3) The opposite is true too — if you cool a gas, the particles will move more slowly, causing the pressure to decrease.

Diffusion is Caused by the **Random Movement** of Particles

KEY TERM

Diffusion is when a substance moves from an area of higher concentration (where there's lots of it) to an area of lower concentration (where there's less of it).

Diffusion does not require any energy input — it occurs passively over time as particles move around.

Diffusion happens because the particles in a liquid or gas move around randomly. They constantly bump into each other and bounce around until they're evenly spread out.

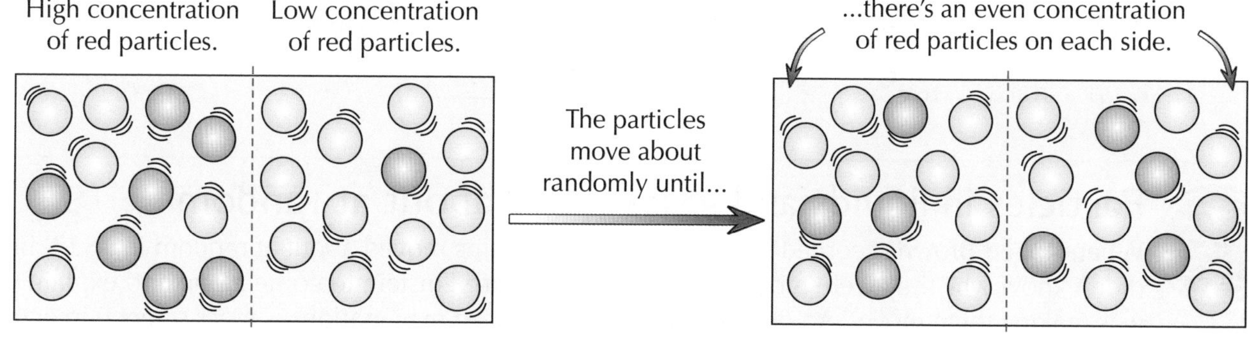
High concentration of red particles.
Low concentration of red particles.
The particles move about randomly until...
...there's an even concentration of red particles on each side.

Movement of Particles

Supplement

The Rate of Diffusion Depends on Molecular Mass

1) How fast a substance diffuses through a gas or a liquid depends on its molecular mass.
2) Small, light molecules move faster through gases or liquids than large, heavy molecules.
3) So small molecules will diffuse faster than large ones.

Brownian Motion is the Random Movement of Particles

The random zigzag movement of any particle suspended (floating) in a liquid or gas is called Brownian motion.

1) In 1827, a scientist called Robert Brown noticed that tiny grains of pollen floating in water appeared to move about at random.

2) In 1905, Albert Einstein explained that the pollen grains were moving because the tiny, fast-moving water molecules in the liquid were randomly bombarding the pollen grains and pushing them about.

3) Einstein's work provided evidence for the idea that liquids and gases are made up of particles (like atoms and molecules) which are constantly moving around randomly. This idea is known as the kinetic particle model of matter.

Supplement

Smoke Particles Moving in Air Give Evidence for Brownian Motion

1) Large, heavy particles, like smoke particles, can be moved by smaller, lighter particles travelling at high speeds, like the gas molecules that make up air.
2) Lots of small air particles collide with the smoke particles, sending them off in random directions.
3) This is why smoke particles in air appear to move around randomly when you watch them in the lab.

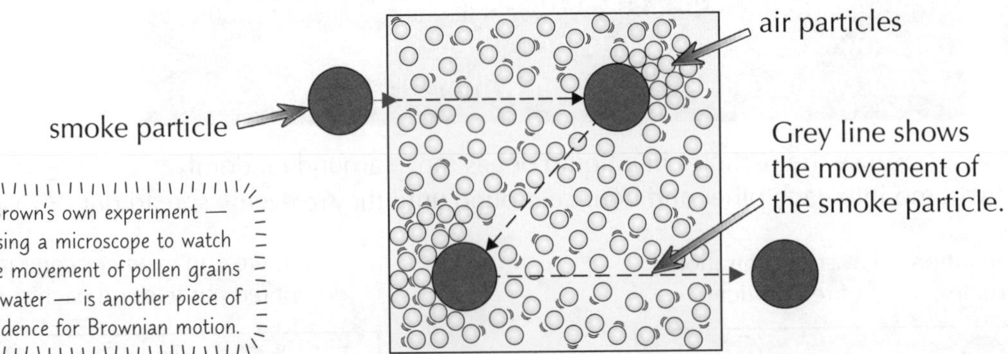

Brown's own experiment — using a microscope to watch the movement of pollen grains in water — is another piece of evidence for Brownian motion.

Particles in liquids and gases move about at random

When Robert Brown recorded how floating pollen grains moved about at random in 1827, he didn't know why they were moving. It took 78 years for Einstein to come along and explain what was making them move. An observation, followed by an explanation — that's science in action.

Warm-Up & Exam Questions

Well, that's the end of the first section. Here's a page of questions to check you've learnt it all. Have a go at the warm-up questions first, then move on to the exam questions.

Warm-Up Questions

1) Describe the arrangement of particles in a liquid.
2) Why does increasing the temperature of a gas in a sealed container increase its pressure?
3) What is the name for the random movement of particles that are suspended in a liquid or gas?

Exam Questions

1 The diagram below shows a substance changing between solid, liquid and gas states.

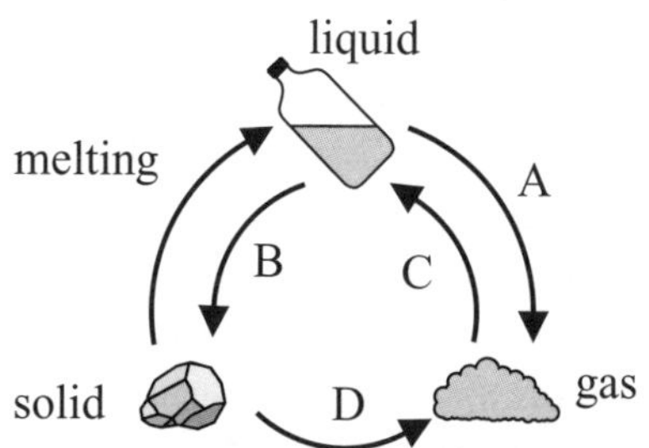

(a) Give the letter of the arrow that represents **sublimation**.

[1]

(b) Give the name of the process represented by arrow **C**.

[1]

S (c) Describe what happens to the particles in a solid when it is heated to the point of melting.

[4]

[Total 6 marks]

2 Lead ions react with iodide ions in solution to form the solid, yellow salt lead iodide.

$$Pb^{2+}_{(aq)} + 2I^{-}_{(aq)} \rightarrow PbI_{2(s)}$$ (relative masses: Pb = 207, I = 127)

A teacher took a shallow dish and filled it with deionised water. She placed a crystal of lead nitrate at one end of the tray and a crystal of potassium iodide at the other end.

As the crystals dissolved, lead ions and iodide ions diffused across the dish. After 30 minutes, a line of yellow lead iodide had formed in the tray.

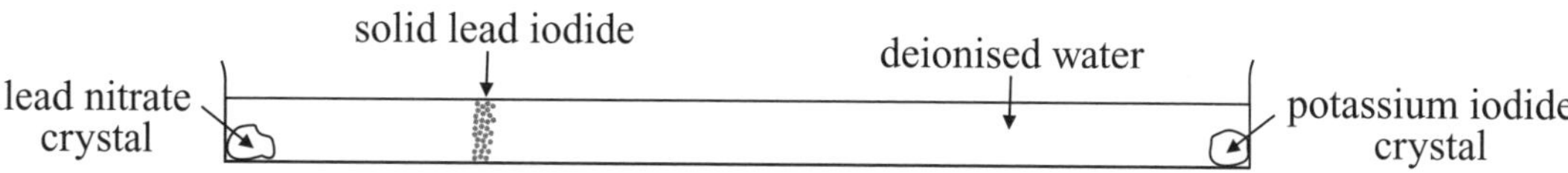

(a) What is meant by **diffusion**?

[1]

S (b) Explain why the line of lead iodide did not form in the centre of the tray.

[3]

[Total 4 marks]

Taking Measurements

As part of your assessment, you'll sit a paper that will test your practical (experimental) skills. There are a few things you need to know about practical work. These pages are about using apparatus to take measurements.

Three Ways to Measure Liquids

There are a few methods you might use to measure the volume of a liquid. Whichever method you use, always read the volume from the bottom of the meniscus (the curved upper surface of the liquid) when it's at eye level.

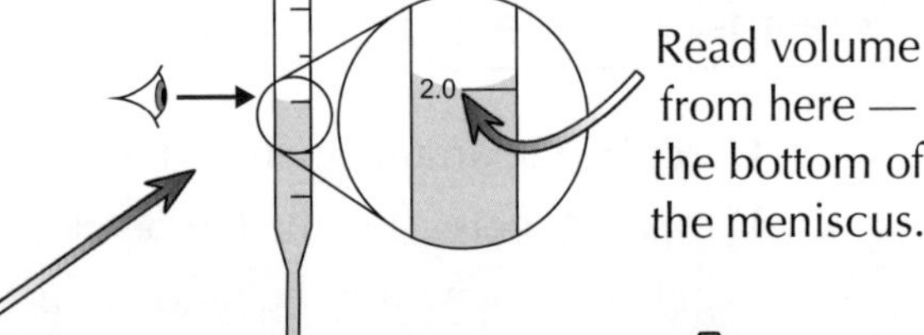
2.0
Read volume from here — the bottom of the meniscus.

Pipettes are long, narrow tubes that are used to suck up an accurate volume of liquid and transfer it to another container. A pipette filler attached to the end of the pipette is used so that you can safely control the amount of liquid you're drawing up. Pipettes are often calibrated to allow for the fact that the last drop of liquid stays in the pipette when the liquid is ejected. This reduces transfer errors.

pipette filler

10 cm^3

Burettes measure from top to bottom (so when they're filled to the top of the scale, the scale reads zero). They have a tap at the bottom which you can use to release the liquid into another container (you can even release it drop by drop). To use a burette, take an initial reading, and once you've released as much liquid as you want, take a final reading. The difference between the readings tells you how much liquid you used.

Burettes are used a lot for titrations. There's loads more about titrations on page 81.

Measuring cylinders are the most common way to measure out a liquid. They come in all different sizes. Make sure you choose one that's the right size for the measurement you want to make. It's no good using a huge 1000 cm^3 cylinder to measure out 2 cm^3 of a liquid — the graduations will be too big, and you'll end up with massive errors. It'd be much better to use one that measures up to 10 cm^3.

If you only want a couple of drops of liquid, and don't need it to be accurately measured, you can use a dropping pipette to transfer it. For example, this is how you'd add a couple of drops of indicator into a mixture.

Solids Should Be Measured Using a Balance

1) To weigh a solid, start by putting the container you're weighing your substance into on the balance.
2) Set the balance to exactly zero and then start weighing out your substance.
3) It's no good carefully weighing out your solid if it's not all transferred to your reaction vessel — the amount in the reaction vessel won't be the same as your measurement. Here are a couple of methods you can use to make sure that none gets left in your weighing container...

- If you're dissolving the solid in a solvent to make a solution, you could wash any remaining solid into the new container using the solvent. This way you know that all the solid you weighed has been transferred.
- You could set the balance to zero before you put your weighing container on the balance in order to find the mass of the empty container, then reweigh the weighing container after you've transferred the solid. Use the difference in mass to work out exactly how much solid you added to your experiment.

Taking Measurements

To Collect **Gases**, the System Needs to Be **Sealed**

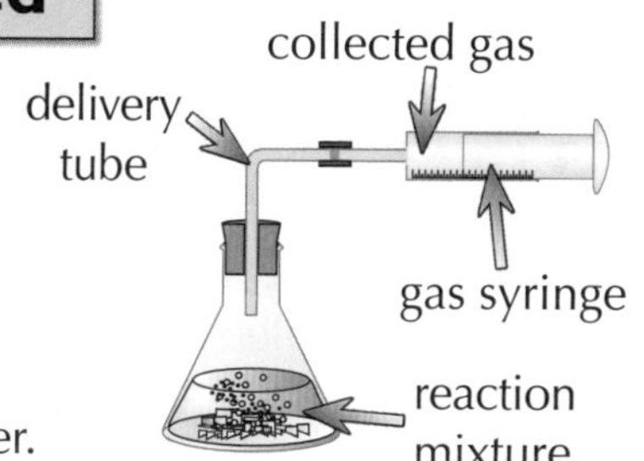

1) There are times when you might want to collect the gas produced by a reaction in order to measure it. For example, to investigate the rate of the reaction.
2) One way to measure the volume of a gas that's been produced is to collect it in a gas syringe (see page 64).
3) You could also collect it by displacing water from a measuring cylinder. Here's how you do it...

- Fill a measuring cylinder with water, and carefully place it upside down in a container of water. Record the initial level of the water in the measuring cylinder.
- Position a delivery tube coming from the reaction vessel so that it's inside the measuring cylinder, pointing upwards. Any gas that's produced will pass through the delivery tube and into the measuring cylinder. As the gas enters the measuring cylinder, the water is pushed out.
- Record the level of water in the measuring cylinder and use this value, along with your initial value, to calculate the volume of gas produced.

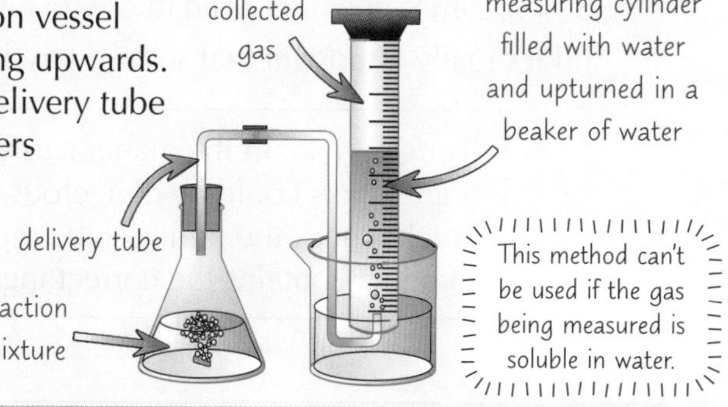

This method can't be used if the gas being measured is soluble in water.

4) When you're measuring a gas, your equipment has to be sealed or some gas could escape and your results wouldn't be accurate.
5) If you just want to collect a sample to test (and don't need to measure a volume), you can collect it over water as above using a test tube. Once the test tube is full of gas, you can stopper it and store the gas for later.

If the delivery tube is underneath the measuring cylinder rather than inside it then some of the gas might escape out into the air.

Measure **Temperature** Accurately

You can use a thermometer to measure the temperature of a substance:

1) Make sure the bulb of the thermometer is completely submerged in any mixture you're measuring, but not touching the inside of the container.
2) If you're taking an initial reading, you should wait for the temperature to stabilise first.
3) Read your measurement off the scale on a thermometer at eye level to make sure it's correct.

You May Have to Measure the **Time Taken** for a Change

1) You should use a stopwatch to time experiments. Most of them measure to the nearest 0.01 s, so they are sensitive. (You can use a clock to measure time, but these are only accurate to the nearest second.)
2) Always make sure you start and stop the stopwatch at exactly the right time. For example, if you're investigating the rate of an experiment, you should start timing at the exact moment you mix the reagents and start the reaction. If you're measuring the time taken for a precipitate to form, you should watch the reaction carefully so you can stop timing the moment it goes cloudy.

WORKING SCIENTIFICALLY

Have your stopwatch ready before you try to time something

To make sure your results can be trusted by other scientists, you have to make sure all your measurements are accurate. So make sure you learn all the tips on these two pages for improving accuracy — e.g. using the right size of measuring cylinder for the volume of liquid you want.

Purity

Substances are often not 100% pure — they might have other stuff that you can't see mixed in with them.

Pure Substances Contain Only **One Thing**

1) In everyday life, the word 'pure' is often used to mean 'clean' or 'natural'.
2) In chemistry, it's got a more specific meaning — a substance is pure if it's completely made up of a single element or compound.
3) If you've got more than one compound present, or different elements that aren't all part of a single compound, then you've got a mixture.
4) So, for example, fresh air might be thought of as nice and 'pure', but it's chemically impure, because it's a mixture of nitrogen, oxygen, argon, carbon dioxide, water vapour and various other gases.
5) Lots of mixtures are really useful — alloys (see page 96) are a great example. But sometimes chemists need to obtain a pure sample of a substance.
6) And it's really important that some everyday substances are pure.

> For example, in the manufacture of drugs or foods, using impure ingredients could be dangerous for consumers. This means a company might check the purity of the ingredients before using them, or check the product contains the correct ingredients (and nothing else) after it is made.

You Can Test for **Purity** Using **Melting Points**

1) Every pure substance has a specific, sharp melting point and boiling point. For example, pure ice melts at 0 °C, and pure water boils at 100 °C.
2) You can use this to test the purity of a sample of a substance, by comparing the actual melting point of the sample to the expected value.
3) If a substance is a mixture then it will melt gradually over a range of temperatures, rather than having a sharp melting point, like a pure substance.
4) Impure substances will melt over a range of temperatures, because they are effectively mixtures.

> You can also use the boiling point to test for purity, but boiling points tend to be harder to measure.

Example: The melting points of four powdered solids, A, B, C and D, are shown below.

Solid	**A**	**B**	**C**	**D**
Melting point / °C	82	72-79	101	63

Which of the four solids, A, B, C or D, is a mixture?

Answer: B — Solid B must be a mixture, because it melts over a range of temperatures (rather than melting at a specific temperature, as the other three solids do).

5) Impurities will usually decrease the melting point and increase the boiling point of a substance. For example, seawater (water containing salts and other compounds) melts at about –2 °C and boils at about 100.4 °C.

Pure substances are made up of one element or compound...

...so their melting points and boiling points are specific. There are many different ways to extract a pure substance from a mixture. You'll learn about some of these techniques over the next few pages.

Chromatography

Chromatography is a method used to separate a mixture of soluble substances and identify them.

Chromatography **Separates Mixtures...**

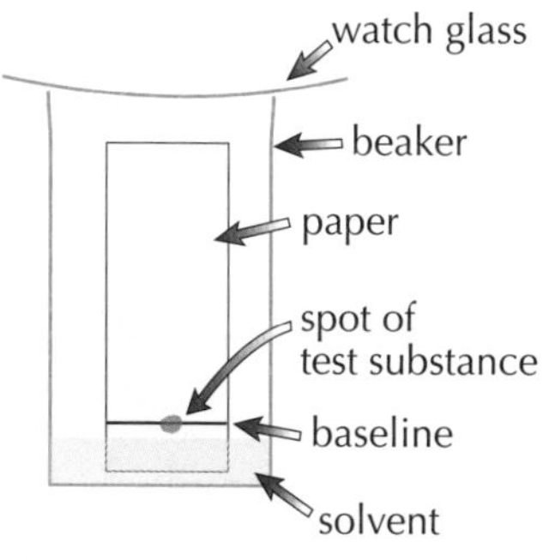

1) In paper chromatography, a spot of the test substance is added to chromatography paper. It is put on a baseline, which has been drawn in pencil. Then the end of the paper is placed in a solvent, with the solvent just below the baseline.
2) The solvent travels up the paper and carries the test substance with it. The furthest point the solvent reaches is called the solvent front.
3) Chromatography works because different substances will move up the paper at different rates.
4) Some will stick to the paper and others will dissolve more readily in the solvent and travel more quickly.

The distance the substances travel up the paper depends on the solvent and the paper you use.

5) The resulting pattern is called a chromatogram.

Chromatography is often carried out to see if a certain substance is present in a mixture. You run a pure sample of a substance that you think might be in your mixture alongside a sample of the mixture itself. If the sample travels the same distance as one of the spots, they're likely to be the same.

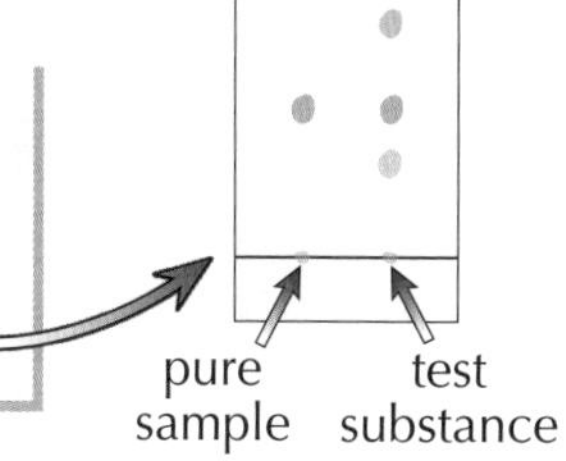

You Can Calculate the R_f **Value** for Each Chemical

Supplement

1) You need to know how to work out the R_f values for the spots on a chromatogram.
2) An R_f value is the ratio between the distance travelled by the dissolved substance (the solute) and the distance travelled by the solvent.
3) You can find R_f values using the formula:

$$R_f = \frac{\text{distance travelled by substance}}{\text{distance travelled by solvent}}$$

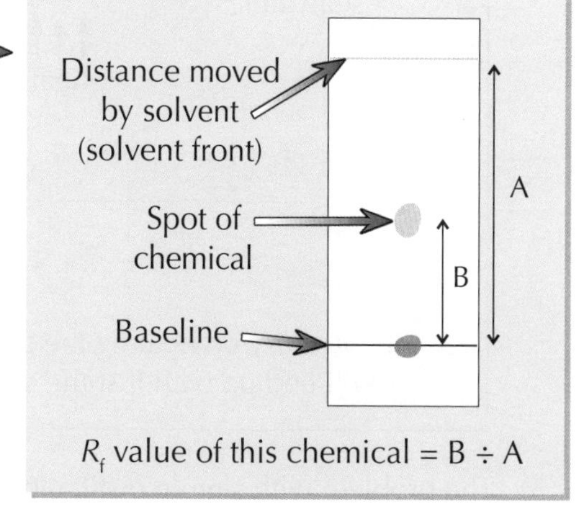

R_f value of this chemical = B ÷ A

4) To find the distance travelled by the solute, measure from the baseline to the centre of the spot.
5) If you know that you have chemicals in your mixture that are colourless (e.g. amino acids), you might have to spray the chromatogram with a chemical called a locating agent to show where the spots are.

Supplement

If the test substance doesn't separate, it might be pure...

A pure substance won't be separated by chromatography — it will move as one blob (while a mixture should give you multiple blobs). However, if a spot remains on the baseline, even after the solvent has run all the way up the paper, you might have a mixture in which some components are insoluble in that solvent.

Simple Distillation

Distillation is used to separate mixtures which contain liquids. This first page looks at simple distillation.

Simple Distillation is Used to **Separate Out Solutions**

1) Simple distillation is used for separating out a liquid from a solution.
2) The solution is heated. The part of the solution that has the lowest boiling point evaporates.
3) The vapour is then cooled, condenses (turns back into a liquid) and is collected.
4) The rest of the solution is left behind in the flask.

Example:

1) You can use simple distillation to get pure water from seawater.
2) As the seawater is heated, the water evaporates. Then it is condensed and collected.

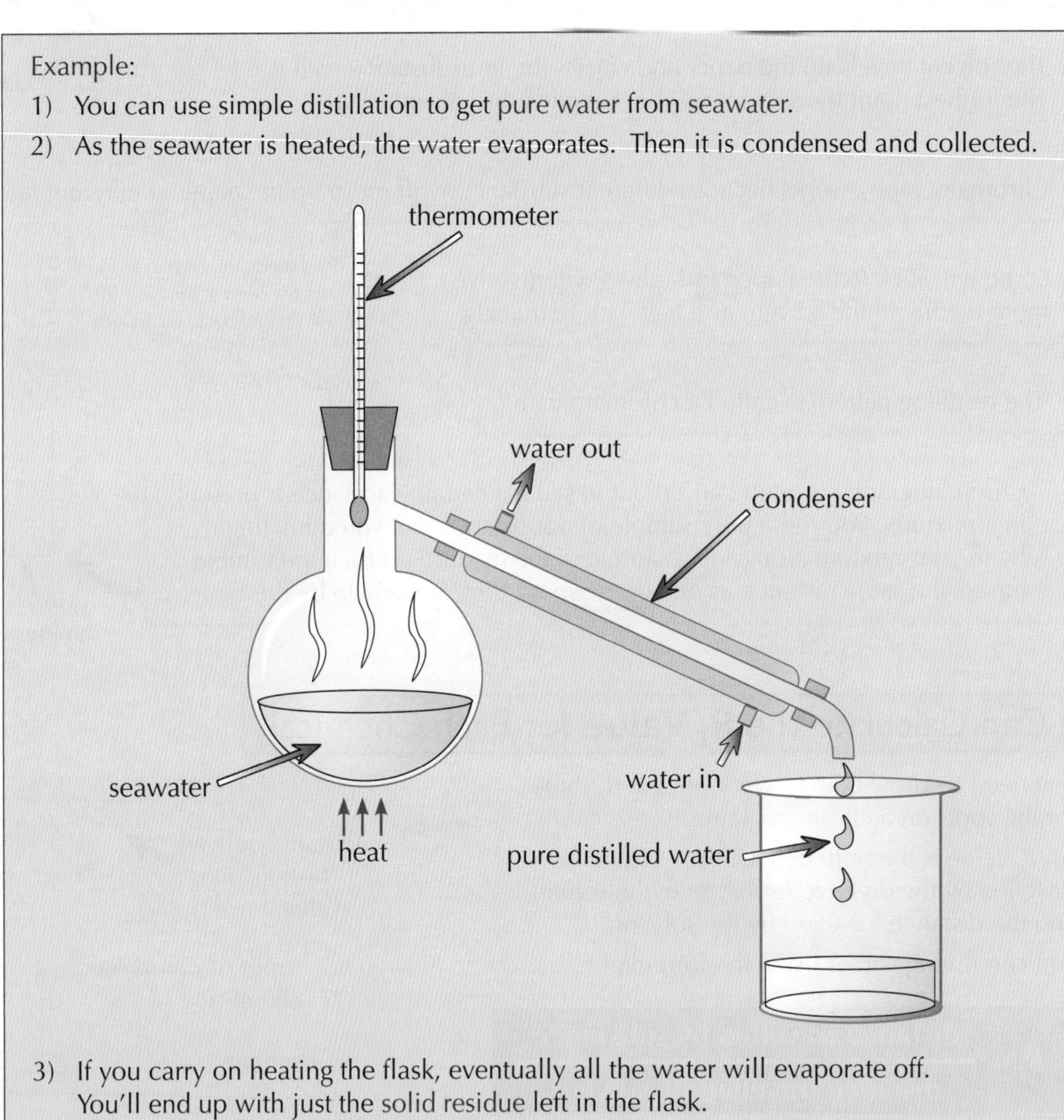

3) If you carry on heating the flask, eventually all the water will evaporate off. You'll end up with just the solid residue left in the flask.

5) The problem with simple distillation is that you can only use it to separate things with very different boiling points.
6) If you have a mixture of liquids with similar boiling points, you need another method to separate them out — like fractional distillation (see next page).

Heating ⟶ Evaporating ⟶ Cooling ⟶ Condensing

You might have used distilled water in Chemistry lessons. Because it's been distilled, there aren't any impurities in it (like ions, see page 23) that might interfere with experimental results. Clever stuff.

Fractional Distillation

Another type of distillation is fractional distillation. This is more complicated to carry out than simple distillation, but it can separate out mixtures of liquids even if their boiling points are close together.

Fractional Distillation is Used to Separate a Mixture of Liquids

If you've got a mixture of liquids you can separate it out using fractional distillation.
Here is a lab demonstration that can be used to model the fractional distillation of petroleum at a refinery.

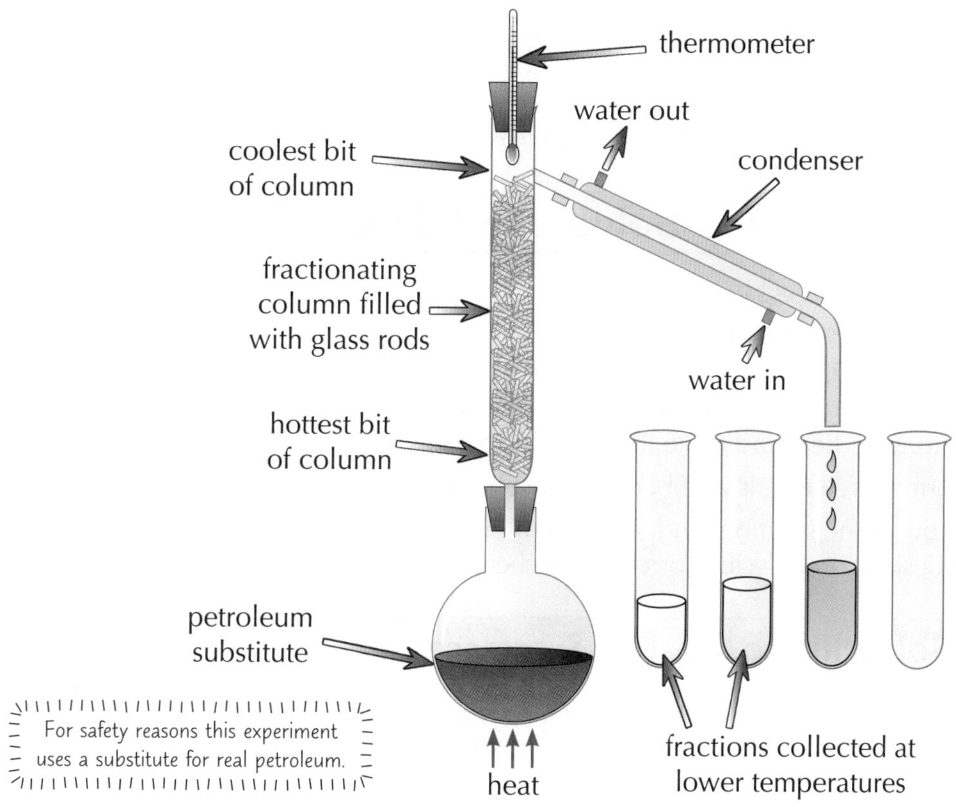

1) You put your mixture in a flask and stick a fractionating column on top. Then you heat it.
2) The different liquids will all have different boiling points — so they will evaporate at different temperatures.
3) The liquid with the lowest boiling point evaporates first. When the temperature on the thermometer matches the boiling point of this liquid, it will reach the top of the column.
4) Liquids with higher boiling points might also start to evaporate. But the column is cooler towards the top. So they will only get part of the way up before condensing and running back down towards the flask.
5) When the first liquid has been collected, you raise the temperature until the next one reaches the top.

Fractional distillation can be used to separate a mixture of ethanol and water. The boiling point of ethanol is 78 °C and the boiling point of water is 100 °C, so the mixture is heated to a temperature between those two.

This method is used to concentrate the alcohol produced by fermentation (see p.135) in alcoholic drinks like vodka and whisky.

Fractional distillation is used in the lab and industry

The industrial method for fractional distillation of petroleum isn't quite as simple as the one shown here. If you really want to find out what goes on in oil refineries, have a look at page 123.

Filtration and Crystallisation

If you've mixed a solid with a liquid, it should be pretty easy to separate them out again. Which method you'll need to use depends on whether or not the solid can dissolve in the liquid.

Filtration is Used to Separate an **Insoluble Solid** from a **Liquid**

Filter paper folded into a cone shape.
The solid is left in the filter paper.

1) If the product of a reaction is an insoluble solid, you can use filtration to separate it out from the liquid reaction mixture.
2) It can be used in purification as well. For example, solid impurities can be separated out from a reaction mixture using filtration.
3) All you do is pop some filter paper into a funnel and pour your mixture into it. The liquid part of the mixture runs through the paper, leaving behind a solid residue. You should wash the solid with distilled water and leave it to dry.

Crystallisation Separates a **Soluble Solid** from a **Solution**

evaporating dish

Here's how you crystallise a product from an aqueous solution...

1) Pour the solution into an evaporating dish and gently heat the solution. Some of the water will evaporate and the solution will get more concentrated.
2) When you see crystals start to form (the point of crystallisation), remove the dish from the heat and leave the solution to cool.
3) The salt should form more crystals as it becomes insoluble in the cold, highly concentrated solution.
4) Filter the crystals out of the solution, and leave them in a warm place to dry. You could also use a drying oven or a desiccator (a desiccator contains chemicals that remove water from the surroundings).

You Can Use **Solubility** to Separate Substances

1) Substances have different solubilities in different solvents. Some substances dissolve better in organic solvents (e.g. hexane) and others dissolve better in inorganic solvents (e.g. water).
2) If you have two substances dissolved in water, one of which is more soluble in organic solvents, you can separate them by adding an organic solvent and shaking the mixture. The second substance will dissolve into the organic solvent instead.
3) Organic and inorganic solvents don't mix, so they will form two layers of solutions that can be separated using a separating funnel.
4) You can use crystallisation to separate each substance from its solution.

solution with organic solvent
solution with inorganic solvent
Open the tap to drain off the bottom layer.

Choose the Right **Purification Method**

You might have to pick one of the techniques covered in this section to separate a mixture. The best technique to use will depend on the properties of the substances in the mixture.

Example: A mixture is composed of two substances, X and Y.
Substance X is a liquid at room temperature. It has a melting point of 5 °C and a boiling point of 60 °C. Substance Y is a solid at room temperature. It has a melting point of 745 °C and a boiling point of 1218 °C. Substance Y dissolves completely in substance X.

Suggest a purification method you could use to obtain:
a) A pure sample of substance X, b) A pure sample of substance Y.

Answer: a) To get X on its own, you need to distil it from the solution. You can use simple distillation here — there's no need for fractional distillation as there's only one liquid in the solution.

b) To get a soluble solid like substance Y out of a solution, you should use crystallisation.

If you distilled the mixture to evaporate off substance X, you might still be left with traces of it in the flask — crystallisation's a better way of getting a pure sample of a solid from a solution.

Warm-Up & Exam Questions

Practical work — you either love it or you hate it. Whichever it is, you need to know how to do it. Have a go at these questions and see how much of this section you can remember.

Warm-Up Questions

1) Name one piece of apparatus you could use to measure the volume of a liquid.
2) What is meant by a pure substance in chemistry?
3) What effect will impurities in a substance have on its boiling point?
4) Which technique could you use to separate a mixture of liquids with similar boiling points?
5) Name a separation technique that could be used to separate a soluble solid from a solution.

Exam Questions

1 The table on the right gives the boiling points of three liquids.

Liquid	Boiling point / °C
Methanoic acid	101
Propanone	56
Water	100

(a) State why simple distillation cannot be used to separate water from a solution of water and methanoic acid.

[1]

(b) The apparatus on the right was used to separate a mixture of propanone and water.

Complete the table using the options below.

no liquid **water** **propanone** **both liquids**

Temperature on thermometer	Contents of the flask	Contents of the beaker
30 °C	....	....
65 °C	....	....
110 °C	....	....

[3]

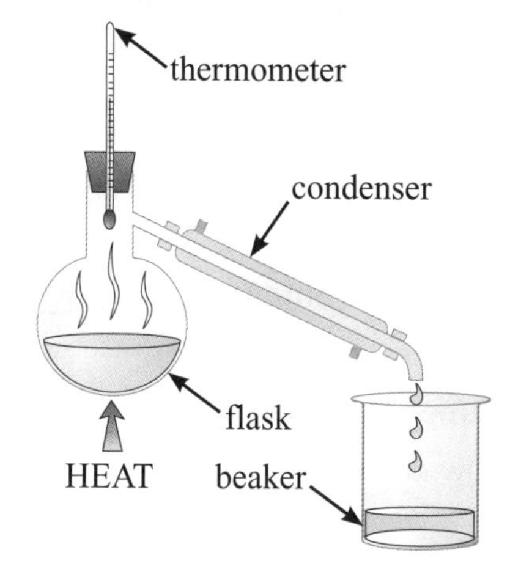

[Total 4 marks]

2 A scientist used chromatography to analyse the composition of five inks. Four of the inks were unknown (**A-D**). The other was an ink called sunrise yellow. The results are shown in the diagram on the right.

solvent front

9.0 cm

12.0 cm

A B C D Sunrise yellow

NOT TO SCALE

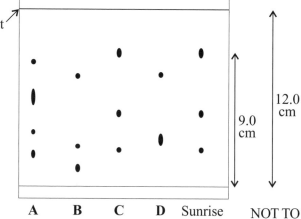

(a) Explain how the diagram shows that none of the inks are pure substances.

[1]

(b) Which of the inks, **A-D**, could be the same as sunrise yellow? Explain your answer.

[2]

Supplement

(c) Calculate the R_f value for the spot of chemical in sunrise yellow which is furthest up the chromatogram.

[2]

[Total 5 marks]

Revision Summary for Sections 1 & 2

That's the end of Sections 1 & 2 — time to put yourself to the test and find out how much you really know.

- Try these questions and tick off each one when you get it right.
- When you've done all the questions for a topic and are completely happy with it, tick off the topic.

States of Matter and Changes of State (p.1-2)

1) Describe the arrangement and movement of particles in a solid.
2) A substance keeps the same volume, but changes its shape according to the container it's in. Is it a solid, a liquid or a gas?
3) Are the forces of attraction between the particles in a liquid stronger or weaker than those in a gas?
4) Name the process that takes place when a liquid turns into a solid.
5) Give the starting and finishing states of matter of a substance that has condensed.
6) [S] Describe what happens to the particles of a substance when it changes from a liquid to a gas.

Movement of Particles in Liquids and Gases (p.3-4)

7) Describe how the particles of a gas create pressure when it is in a sealed container.
8) What happens to the pressure of a gas in a sealed container if you increase the temperature?
9) True or false? Diffusion is when a substance moves from an area of lower concentration to an area of higher concentration.
10) [S] Describe how the molecular mass of a substance affects the rate at which it diffuses through air.
11) What is Brownian motion?
12) [S] Give one example of an experiment that shows Brownian motion in action.

Taking Measurements (p.6-7)

13) What is a burette used for?
14) Name a piece of apparatus that can be used to measure mass.
15) How can you use a measuring cylinder to measure the volume of gas produced by a reaction?

Purity and Methods of Purification (p.8-12)

16) Explain why air isn't considered a pure substance, according to the scientific definition of pure.
17) Give one example in everyday life where it is important that a substance is pure.
18) A substance melts over a range of temperatures. Is it likely to be a pure substance or a mixture?
19) What causes different substances to separate out during a chromatography experiment?
20) What is the name of the pattern of spots generated by paper chromatography?
21) [S] Why might you need to use a locating agent when analysing paper chromatography results?
22) Draw the apparatus you would use to carry out a simple distillation.
23) What type of mixture would you separate using fractional distillation?
24) Where is the hottest part of a fractionating column — at the top or at the bottom?
25) a) When would you use filtration to separate a mixture?
    b) Describe how to carry out filtration.
26) Describe how to carry out crystallisation.
27) You have a mixture of two substances dissolved in water, one of which is more soluble in organic solvents. Describe how you could separate them.

Atoms and Isotopes

All substances are made of atoms. They're really tiny — too small to see, even with a microscope.

Atoms Contain Protons, Neutrons and Electrons

The atom is made up of three subatomic particles — protons, neutrons and electrons.

- Protons are heavy and positively charged.
- Neutrons are heavy and neutral.
- Electrons have hardly any mass and are negatively charged.

Relative mass (measured in atomic mass units) measures mass on a scale where the mass of a proton or neutron is 1.

Particle	Relative mass	Relative charge
Proton	1	+1
Neutron	1	0
Electron	0.0005	–1

The Nucleus

1) It's in the middle of the atom and is made up of protons and neutrons.
2) It has a positive charge because of the protons.
3) Almost the whole mass of the atom is found in the nucleus.
4) Compared to the overall size of the atom, the nucleus is tiny.

Protons and neutrons are still tiny — they're just heavy compared to electrons.

The Electrons

1) Electrons move around the nucleus in energy levels called shells.
2) Electrons are negatively charged.
3) They're tiny, but their orbitals cover a lot of space.
4) The size of their orbitals determines the size of the atom.
5) Electrons have virtually no mass.

The Atom

1) Neutral atoms have no charge overall.
2) The charge on the electrons is the same size as the charge on the protons — but opposite.
3) This means the number of electrons always equals the number of protons in a neutral atom.
4) If some electrons are added or removed, the atom becomes charged and is then an ion.

Proton Number and Nucleon Number Describe an Atom

These two numbers tell you how many of each kind of particle an atom has.

The proton (atomic) number is the number of protons in the nucleus of an atom.

The nucleon (mass) number is the total number of protons and neutrons in the nucleus of an atom.

$^{23}_{11}\text{Na}$

nucleon number — 23; proton number — 11; element symbol — Na

1) Atoms of the same element all have the same number of protons — so atoms of different elements will have different numbers of protons.
2) To find the number of neutrons in an atom, just subtract the proton number from the nucleon number.

Atoms and Isotopes

Isotopes are the Same Except for an Extra **Neutron** or Two

Isotopes are atoms of the same element which have the same proton number but a different nucleon number.

1) Isotopes must have the same proton number but different nucleon numbers.
2) If they had different proton numbers, they'd be different elements altogether.
3) A very popular example of a pair of isotopes is carbon-12 and carbon-13.

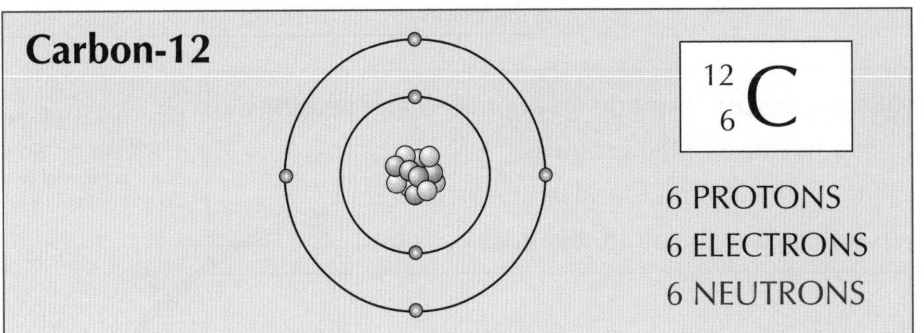

Remember — the number of neutrons is just the nucleon number minus the proton number.

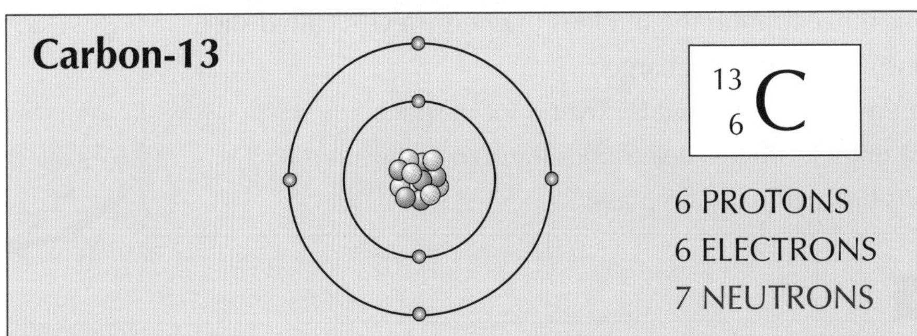

As all the isotopes of an element have the same number of electrons in their outer shell, they will have the same properties — they'll react in the same way.

See page 17 for more on how electrons affect reactivity.

Isotopes can be **Radioactive** or **Non-Radioactive**

1) Some isotopes are stable, but others are unstable and will undergo radioactive decay.
2) As these atoms decay, they release energy and small particles until they reach a point where they become stable.

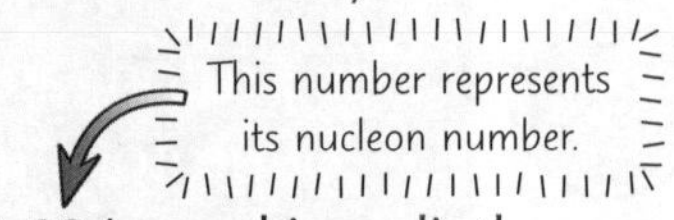

3) Some radioactive isotopes are used in medicine. For example, cobalt-60 is used in radiotherapy to treat cancer and iodine-131 can be used to treat a range of thyroid diseases.
4) They are also used in industry — for things like scanning metal machinery for faults or damage.

Isotopes of an element have different numbers of neutrons

If you're struggling to recall how an isotope is defined, try using the letters in 'isotope' as a memory aid — i**S**oto**P**es of the same element have the **S**ame **P**roton number but different nucleon numbers.

Electron Shells

The fact that electrons occupy 'shells' around the nucleus is what causes the whole of chemistry.

Electron Shell **Rules:**

1) Electrons always occupy shells (sometimes called energy levels).

2) The lowest energy levels are always filled first.

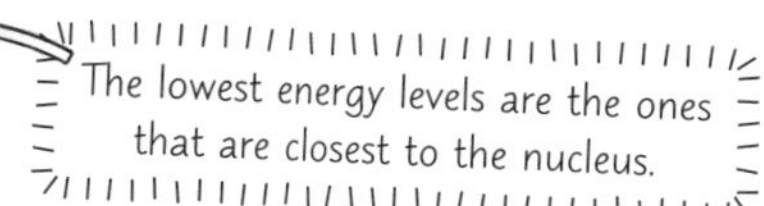

The lowest energy levels are the ones that are closest to the nucleus.

3) Only a certain number of electrons are allowed in each shell:

1st shell: 2 2nd shell: 8 3rd shell: 8

Electron Shells can be Shown as **Diagrams** or **Numbers**

1) Electronic structures can be shown as diagrams like this:

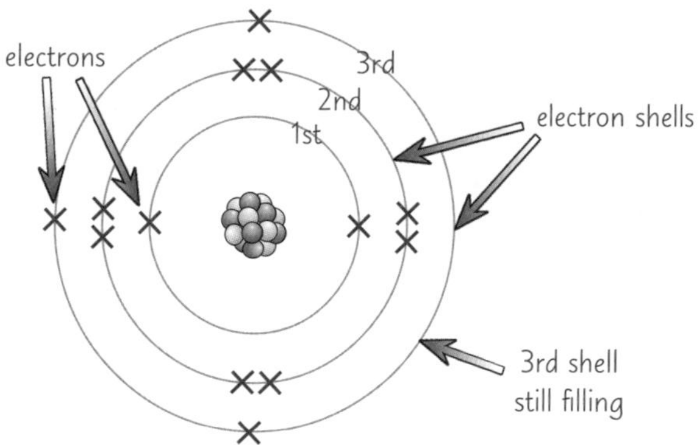

2) They can also be shown as numbers like this: 2,8,3.
3) Both electronic structures shown above are for aluminium.

The **Outer Shell Electrons** Control **Reactivity**

1) The electrons in the outer shell of an atom are involved in forming bonds with other atoms.
2) Atoms will form bonds which allow them to gain or lose enough electrons to be left with a full outer shell — like a noble gas element.
3) Noble gases (see page 93) are unreactive as they already have a full outer shell.

> Example: Chlorine has 7 electrons in its outer shell. So when it reacts, it will gain 1 electron in order to have the structure of the closest noble gas, argon.

Electron shells — probably the most important thing in chemistry

It's important to learn the rules for filling electron shells, so here's a recap. The energy of the shells increases with increasing number (so shell 1 is the lowest energy level). You fill the shell with the lowest energy first. The 1st shell hold a maximum of 2 electrons and the 2nd and 3rd shells both hold a maximum of 8 electrons.

Electron Shells

You can easily work out the electronic structures for the first 20 elements of the periodic table (things get a bit more complicated after that). This page will show you how to do just that.

Working Out **Electronic Structures**

1) The electronic structures of the first 20 elements are shown in the diagram below. They're not hard to work out. Here are a couple of examples:

Example: Finding the electronic structure of nitrogen

- The periodic table tells you that the atomic (proton) number of nitrogen is seven. That means nitrogen has seven protons, so it must have seven electrons.
- Follow the 'Electron Shell Rules' on the previous page. The first shell can only take 2 electrons and the second shell can take a maximum of 8 electrons.
- So the electronic structure of nitrogen must be 2,5.

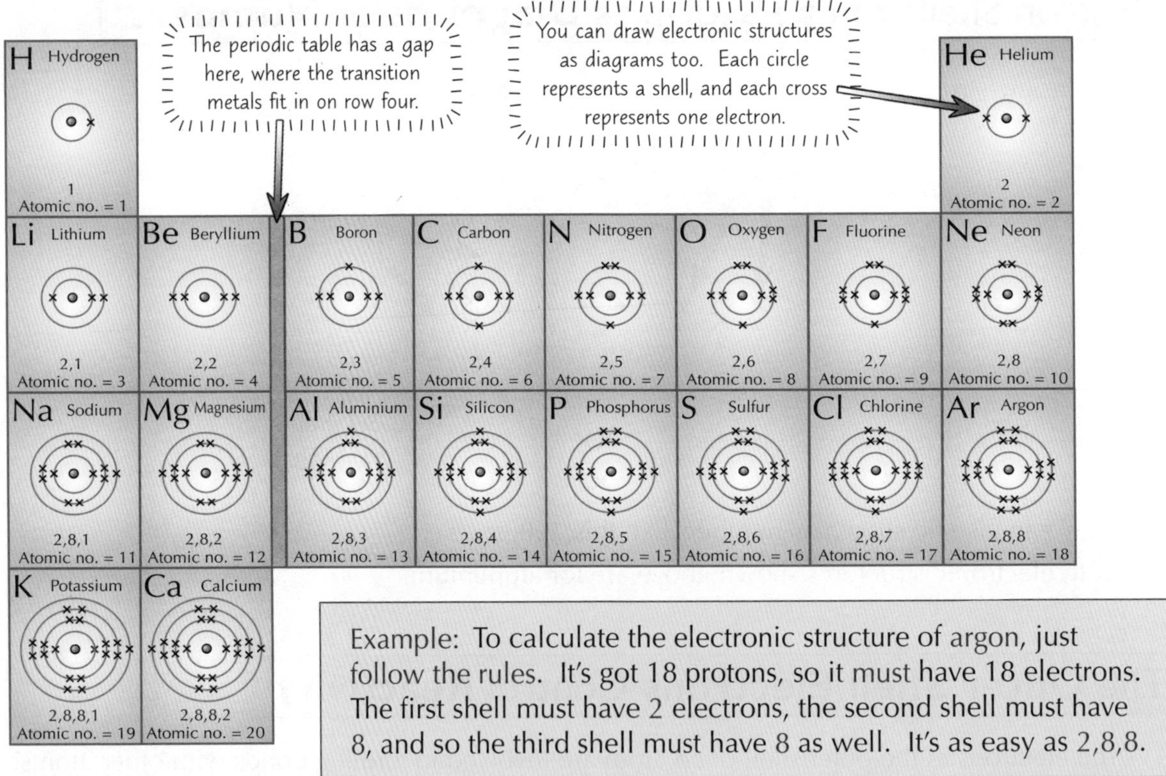

Example: To calculate the electronic structure of argon, just follow the rules. It's got 18 protons, so it must have 18 electrons. The first shell must have 2 electrons, the second shell must have 8, and so the third shell must have 8 as well. It's as easy as 2,8,8.

2) You can also work out the electronic structure of an element from its period and group:
   - The number of shells which contain electrons is the same as the period of the element.
   - The group number tells you how many electrons occupy the outer shell of the element.

Example: Sodium is in period 3, so it has 3 shells occupied. The first two shells must be full (2,8). It's in Group 1, so it has 1 electron in its outer shell. So its electronic structure is 2,8,1.

For a neutral atom, total number of electrons = atomic number

Electronic structures may seem complicated, but once you know how to do them, they're not too bad.

The Periodic Table

The periodic table was developed by chemists as a way of displaying all the elements according to their similar properties and atomic structure.

The Periodic Table Helps you to See Patterns in Properties

1) Once protons and electrons were discovered, the atomic (proton) number (see p.15) of each element could be found, based on the number of protons in its nucleus.

2) The modern periodic table (see below) shows the elements in order of ascending atomic number.

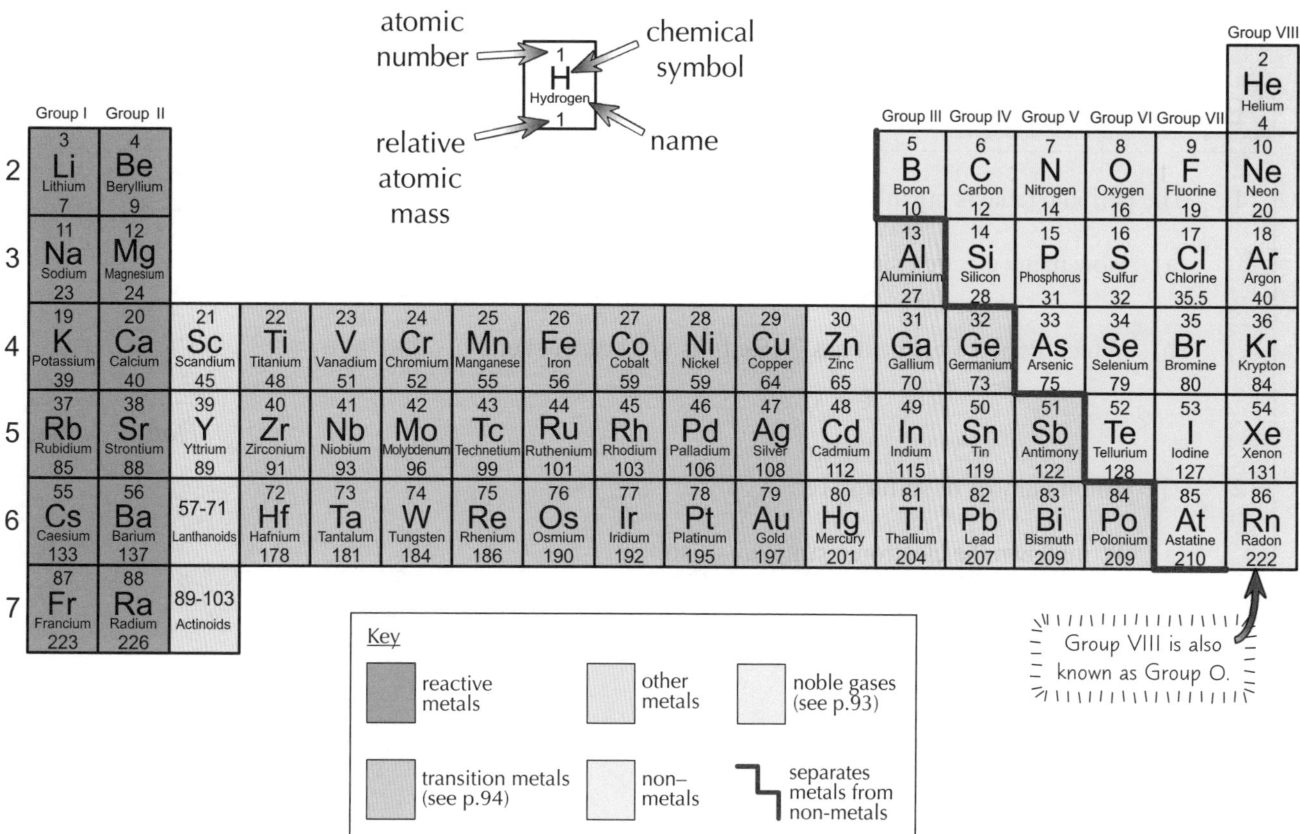

3) The periodic table is laid out so elements with similar chemical properties form columns called groups.

4) The group to which the element belongs corresponds to the number of electrons in its outer shell.

> For example, Group I elements have 1 outer shell electron, Group VII elements have 7, etc. (Helium is the exception to this — it's in Group VIII but has a full outer shell of 2 electrons.)

5) The rows are called periods. Each new period represents another full shell of electrons.

6) The period to which the element belongs corresponds to the number of shells of electrons it has.

The modern periodic table is vital for understanding chemistry

The periodic table can look overwhelming at first, but it makes a lot of sense when you get used to it. You'll find a copy at the back of the multiple choice and theory papers, so don't worry about memorising it all. Just make sure you know how to use it to find information about an element.

Warm-Up & Exam Questions

Lots of information there about atoms, protons, neutrons and electrons. Understanding it all is crucial to understanding the rest of chemistry, so have a go at these questions before moving on.

Warm-Up Questions

1) State the relative charge and relative mass of a neutron.
2) What does the nucleon number tell you about an atom?
3) A neutral atom of potassium has a proton number of 19 and a nucleon number of 39. Give the number of electrons, protons and neutrons in the atom.
4) How many electrons can be held in: a) the first electron shell? b) the second electron shell?

Exam Questions

1 The periodic table is organised into horizontal periods and vertical groups.

(a) How many electron shells would a Period 3 element have?

[1]

(b) Which Period 3 element has 7 electrons in its outer shell?

[1]

[Total 2 marks]

2 The proton number of sulfur is 16.

(a) Write down the electronic structure of sulfur.

[1]

(b) Draw a diagram to show how the electrons are arranged in a single sulfur atom.

[1]

[Total 2 marks]

3 Sodium has a proton number of 11.

(a) Sodium is in Group I.
Name another element that would have the same number of outer shell electrons.

[1]

(b) How many electrons does sodium need to lose so that it has a full outer shell?

[1]

[Total 2 marks]

4 Carbon has several isotopes. These include carbon-12 and carbon-13.
Details about the carbon-13 isotope are shown on the right.

$^{13}_{6}C$

(a) Explain what isotopes are.

[2]

(b) Give the number of protons, neutrons and electrons that carbon-13 contains.

[3]

(c) Details of element **X** are shown on the right.
Explain how you can tell that element **X** is not an isotope of carbon.

$^{13}_{7}X$

[1]

[Total 6 marks]

Elements, Compounds and Mixtures

There are only about 100 or so different elements, which doesn't sound too bad.
But they can join together in a variety of different combinations, which makes life more complicated.

Elements Consist of One Type of Atom Only

Quite a lot of everyday substances are elements:

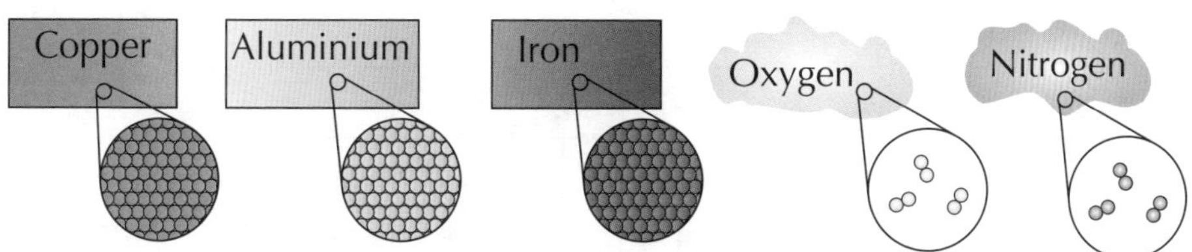

Nitrogen is the most common element in the air (about 78%).

Compounds are Chemically Bonded

carbon + oxygen → carbon dioxide

C + OO → OCO

1) A compound is a substance made of two or more different elements which are chemically joined (bonded) together.
2) For example, carbon dioxide is a compound formed from a chemical reaction. One carbon atom reacts with two oxygen atoms to form a molecule of carbon dioxide, with the formula CO_2.
3) It's very difficult to separate the two original elements out again.
4) The properties of a compound are often totally different from the properties of the original elements.
5) For example, if a mixture of iron and sulfur is heated, the iron and sulfur atoms react to form the compound iron sulfide (FeS).
6) Iron sulfide is not much like iron (e.g. it's not attracted to a magnet), nor is it much like sulfur (e.g. it's not yellow in colour).

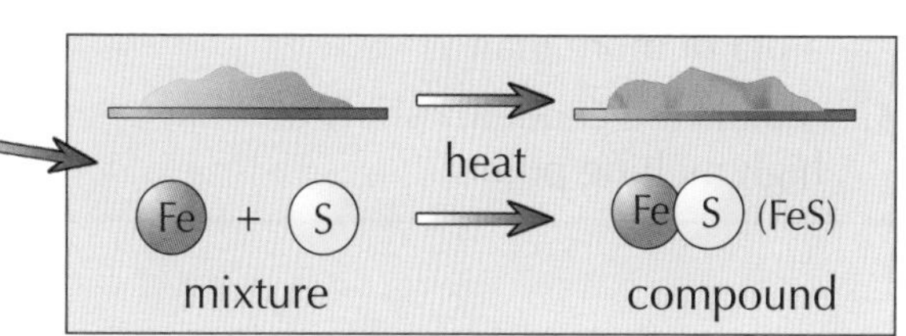

Mixtures are Easily Separated — Not Like Compounds

1) Unlike in a compound, there's no chemical bond between the different parts of a mixture. The parts can be separated out by physical methods such as distillation (see pages 10-11).
2) The properties of a mixture are just a mixture of the properties of the separate parts. E.g. a mixture of iron powder and sulfur powder will show the properties of both iron and sulfur. It will contain grey magnetic bits of iron and bright yellow bits of sulfur.
3) Mixtures aren't chemically pure. In chemistry, a substance is pure if it's completely made up of a single element or compound.

Iron and sulfur mixed together, but unreacted.

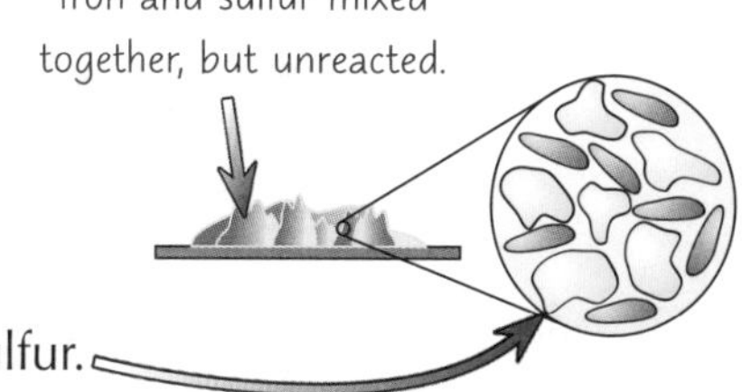

There's more about purity on page 8.

Every object in the universe is made up of elements

Of course, they can be combined in a lot of different ways, but everything from stars to paperclips to you is made up of just over 100 elements. That's mind-blowing when you think about it.

Metals and Non-Metals

Not all elements are the same and how they behave can depend on which of these groups they're in.

The Elements can be Classified as **Metals** or **Non-Metals**

The periodic table can be split into two parts — the metals are on one side and the non-metals are on the other.

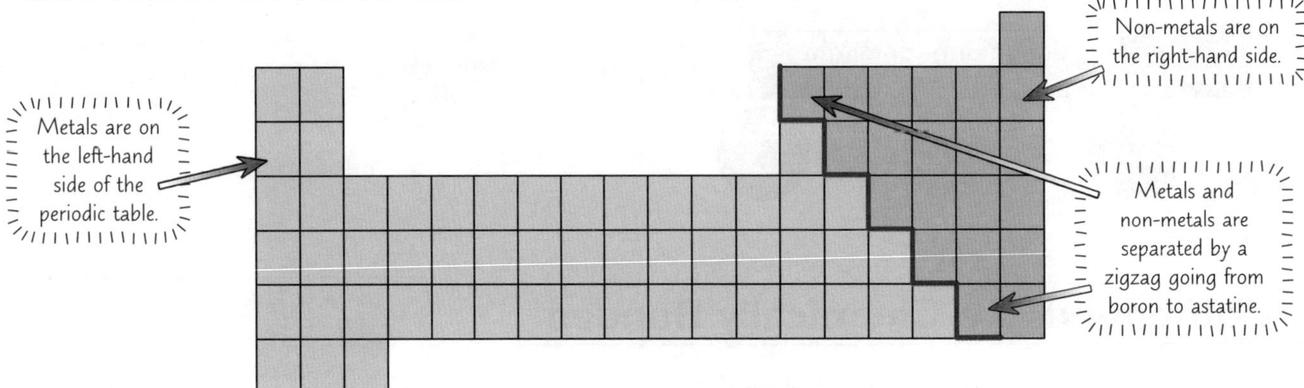
Metals are on the left-hand side of the periodic table.
Non-metals are on the right-hand side.
Metals and non-metals are separated by a zigzag going from boron to astatine.

Metals

1) The elements on the left of the zigzag are all classified as metals.
2) Metals conduct electricity.
3) Metal oxides are basic. This means they will neutralise acids. Metal oxides that dissolve in water will form solutions with a pH of more than 7.
4) Metals are generally shiny and have high melting points.

Non-metals

1) The elements on the right of the zigzag are all classified as non-metals.
2) Non-metals are poor conductors of electricity.
3) Non-metal oxides are acidic. This means that they will neutralise bases. Non-metal oxides that dissolve in water will form solutions with a pH of less than 7.
4) Non-metals are generally dull and have low melting points.

You can read all about pH on page 75.

Alloys are a **Mixture** of **Elements**

1) Pure metals are made up of a single element, such as iron, copper or zinc.
2) In contrast, alloys contain a mixture of elements.

For more about alloys, turn to page 96.

KEY TERM

An alloy is a mixture of a metal with other elements.

3) Many of the metals we use in everyday life are alloys. For example, brass is an alloy of copper and zinc used in plumbing, decoration and to make certain musical instruments.

REVISION TIP

Metals have quite different properties from non-metals

If you're staring at the periodic table and trying to remember where the line dividing metals from non-metals should go, just remember: BAt stairs. Imagine you're standing inside square B (boron). Draw a staircase that will take you down to inside square At (astatine). That's your dividing line.

Ions and Ionic Bonding

Time to find out how particles bond together to form compounds. There are a few types of bonding that you need to know about — they're covered in the rest of this section. First up, ionic bonding...

Simple Ions Form When Atoms Lose or Gain **Electrons**

1) Ions are charged particles — they can be formed from single atoms (e.g. Na^+) or groups of atoms (e.g. NO_3^-).
2) When atoms gain or lose electrons to form ions, they are trying to get a full outer shell (also called a 'stable electron structure').
3) Negative ions (anions) form when atoms gain electrons — they have more electrons than protons. Positive ions (cations) form when atoms lose electrons — they have fewer electrons than protons.
4) The number of electrons lost or gained is the same as the charge on the ion. E.g. If 2 electrons are lost, the charge is 2+. If 3 electrons are gained, the charge is 3–.

You calculate the number of protons and neutrons in an ion in the same way as for an atom (see page 15).

Transfer of Electrons Produces an **Ionic Compound**

1) Most of the time, when a metal reacts with a non-metal (such as when a Group I metal reacts with a Group VII element), the metal atom loses electrons to form a positive ion (cation) and the non-metal gains these electrons to form a negative ion (anion).
2) These oppositely charged ions are strongly attracted to one another by electrostatic attractions.
3) This attraction is called an ionic bond.

Ionic Compounds All Form in a **Similar Way**

You can use 'dot and cross' diagrams to show what happens to the electrons when ionic bonding happens. For example, here's what happens when sodium reacts with chlorine to form sodium chloride:

The sodium atom gives up its outer electron, becoming an Na^+ ion.
The chlorine atom picks up the electron, becoming a Cl^- (chloride) ion.

Na → Cl → [Na]$^+$ [Cl]$^-$

Na	Cl	Na+	Cl–
2,8,1	2,8,7	2,8	2,8,8
sodium atom	chlorine atom	sodium ion	chloride ion

NaCl (sodium chloride)

In this example, the dots represent the electrons from one of the atoms and the crosses represent the electrons from the other. (All electrons are really identical, but this is a good way of following their movement.)

Supplement

Ionic Compounds Have a **Lattice** Structure

1) Compounds with ionic bonding always have giant ionic structures.
2) The ions are held together in a closely packed 3D lattice arrangement by the attraction between oppositely charged ions.
3) These lattice structures are a regular arrangement of alternating positive and negative ions.

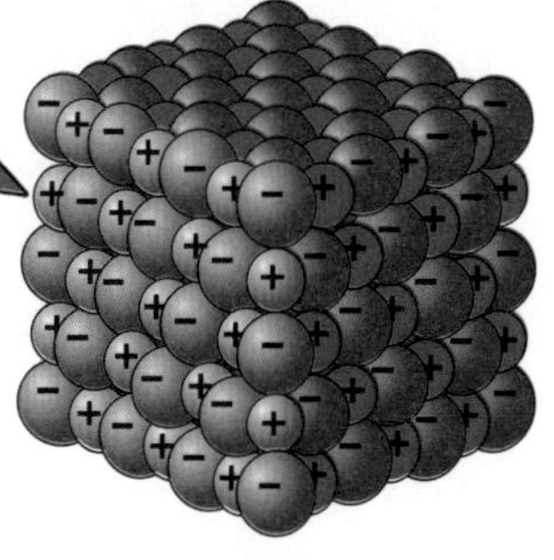

Supplement

Covalent Bonding

Ionic bonding (see p.23) isn't the only type you need to know about — there's covalent bonding too.

Covalent Substances Contain **Shared Pairs of Electrons**

1) Sometimes atoms make covalent bonds by sharing pairs of electrons with other atoms.
2) Sharing electrons allows atoms to gain a noble gas structure with a full outer shell.
3) Each covalent bond provides one extra shared electron for each atom.
4) In covalent bonding, there's a strong electrostatic attraction between the negatively charged shared electrons (the bonding pair) and the positively charged nuclei of the atoms involved.
5) The atoms in molecules are joined together by covalent bonds.

An electrostatic attraction is when two (or more) oppositely charged particles are attracted to each other.

Learn These **Important Examples:**

Hydrogen, H_2

A hydrogen atom has one electron in its outer shell. It can only fit one more electron in that shell...

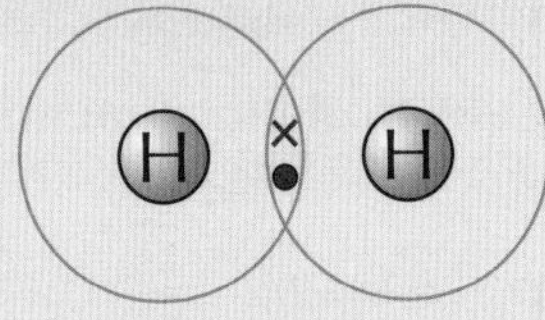

OR H—H

...so hydrogen atoms can form one covalent bond.

In covalent bonding, the diagrams only show the outer shell electrons.

Chlorine, Cl_2

A chlorine atom has seven electrons in its outer shell. It can only fit one more electron in that shell...

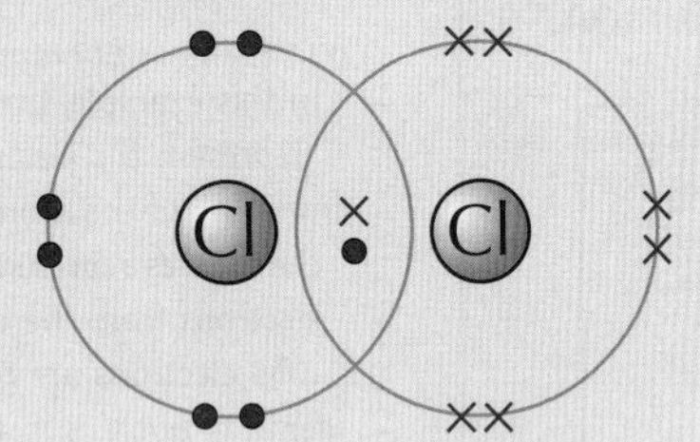

OR Cl — Cl

...so chlorine atoms also form one covalent bond.

Hydrogen chloride, HCl

This is very similar to H_2 and Cl_2.

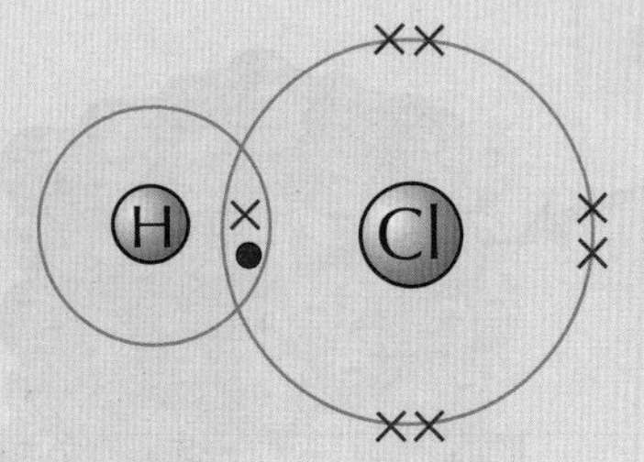

OR H—Cl

Each atom can only fit one more electron in its outer shell — so they form one covalent bond.

Covalent Bonding

Water, H_2O

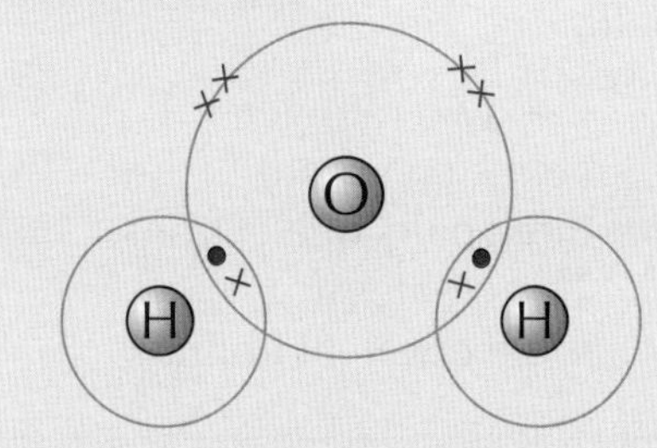

OR

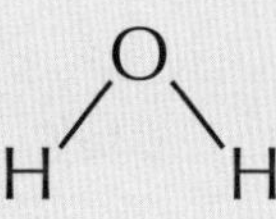

In water molecules, two hydrogen atoms each share a pair of electrons with an oxygen atom to form two covalent bonds.

Ammonia, NH_3

A nitrogen atom has five electrons in its outer shell. It can only fit three more electrons in that shell...

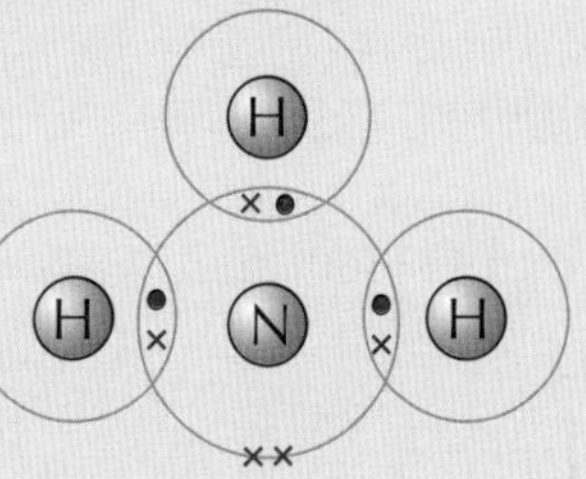

OR

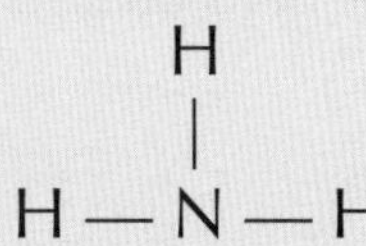

...so in ammonia, it forms three covalent bonds — one each with three hydrogen atoms.

Methane, CH_4

A carbon atom has four electrons in its outer shell. It can fit four more electrons in that shell...

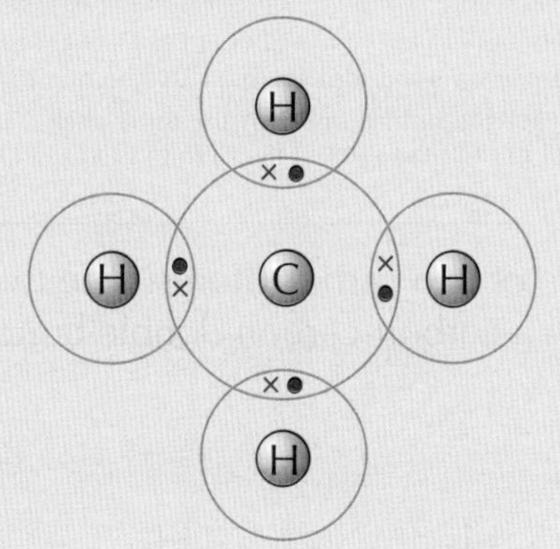

OR

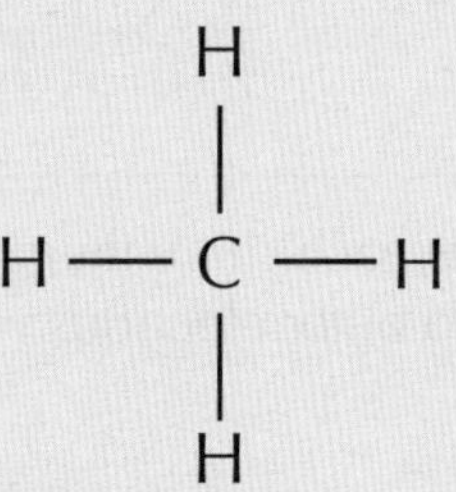

...so in methane, it forms four covalent bonds — one each with four hydrogen atoms.

Supplement

Carbon dioxide, CO_2

In carbon dioxide, two oxygen atoms each share two pairs of electrons with a carbon atom.

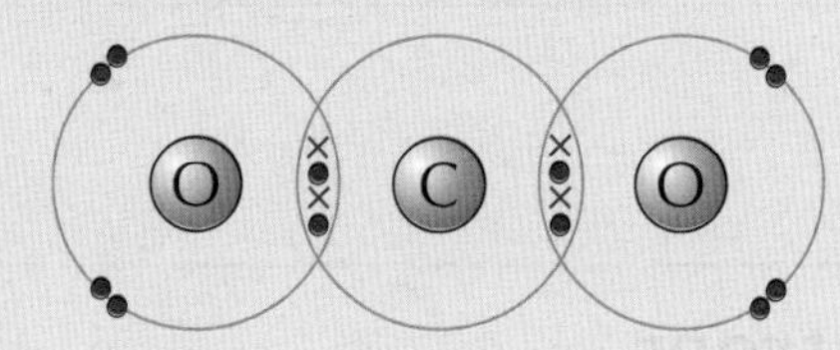

OR O=C=O

This forms two double covalent bonds.

Supplement

Covalent Bonding

Nitrogen, N_2

Again, a nitrogen atom can only fit three more electrons in its outer shell...

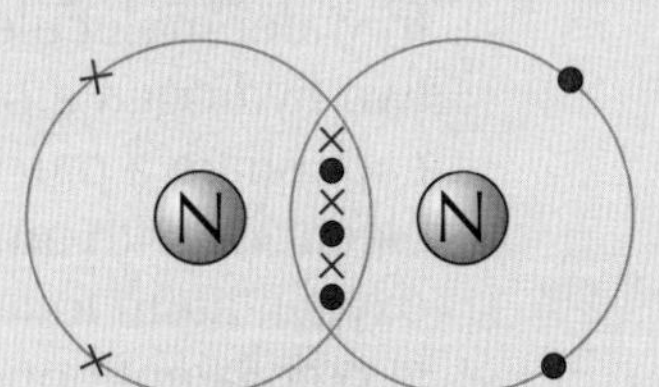

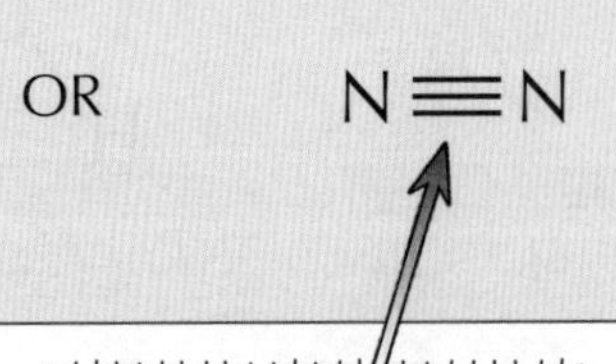

...so two nitrogen atoms can share three pairs of electrons. This creates a triple covalent bond.

This is the displayed formula of a molecule of nitrogen (see page 124 for more).

Methanol, CH_3OH

In methanol, three hydrogen atoms each share their outer electron with one carbon atom.
One hydrogen atom shares its outer electron with an oxygen atom.
The oxygen atom also shares one of its outer electrons with the carbon atom.

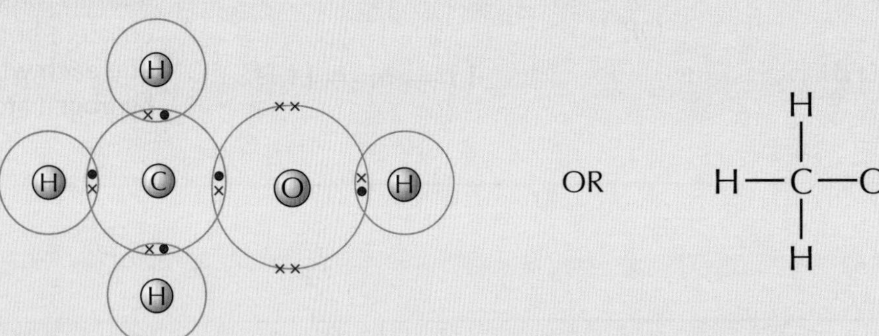

H—C—O—H (with H above and below the C)

When you've drawn a dot and cross diagram, it's a good idea to count up the number of electrons, just to double-check you've got the right number in the outer shell.

Ethene, C_2H_4

In ethene, 4 hydrogen atoms each share their outer electron with one of two carbon atoms. The two carbon atoms also share two outer electrons with each other, to form a carbon-carbon double bond.

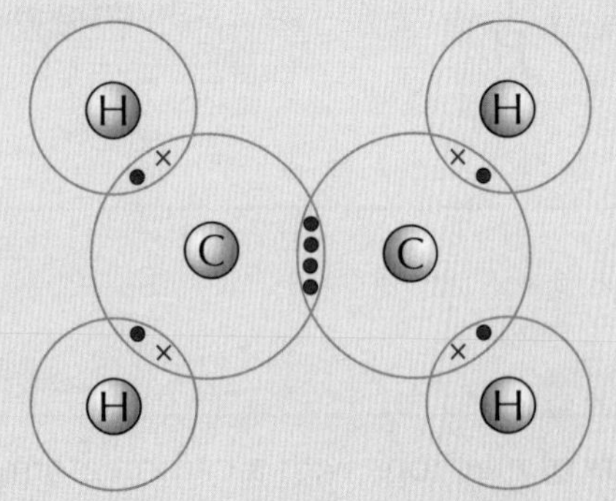

OR

H₂C=CH₂ displayed: each C bonded to two H, C=C

Supplement

Covalent bonding involves sharing electrons

You could be asked to draw a dot and cross diagram for a molecule in the exam. The ones on pages 24-26 are important examples that you need to know, so make sure you've learnt them.

Warm-Up & Exam Questions

Time for the next round of practice questions. Check you can get them all correct before moving on.

Warm-Up Questions

1) What is the definition of a compound?
2) What is the definition of an alloy?
3) How does a positive ion form from a neutral atom?
4) How many electrons are required to form a single covalent bond?

Exam Questions

1 Dot and cross diagrams show the position of electrons in covalent molecules.

Draw dot and cross diagrams for hydrogen chloride (HCl) and ammonia (NH_3).
Only show the outer electrons.

[Total 2 marks]

2 The diagram below shows the position of Element **Q** in the periodic table.

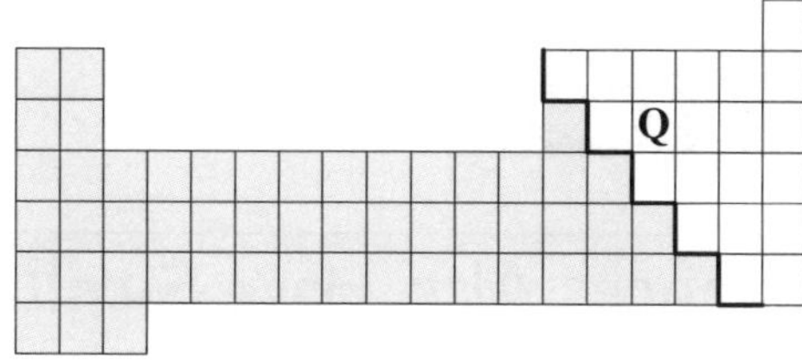

(a) State whether Element **Q** is a metal or a non-metal.
Explain why you have chosen this answer.

[1]

(b) Name two properties you would expect element **Q** to have.

[2]

[Total 3 marks]

3 The diagram below shows the electronic structures of sodium and fluorine.

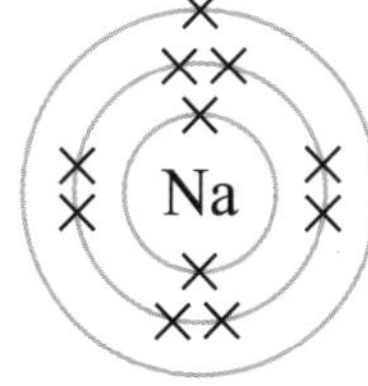

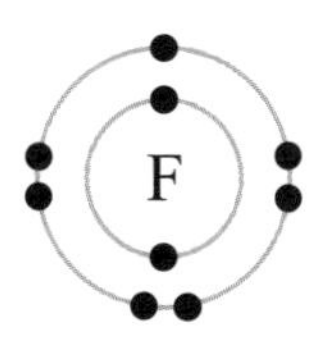

(a) Describe what will happen when sodium and fluorine react, in terms of electrons.

[2]

(b) When sodium and fluorine react they form an ionic compound.
Describe the structure of an ionic compound.

[3]

[Total 5 marks]

Properties of Ionic and Covalent Compounds

Ionic and covalent compounds bond in different ways — and that means their properties are different too.

Ionic Compounds All Have Similar Properties

1) Ionic compounds have high melting points and high boiling points, and do not readily form gases (they aren't very volatile).
2) This is because the ions in ionic compounds are held together by extremely strong ionic bonds. It takes lots of energy to break these bonds to separate the ions.
3) Ionic compounds generally do dissolve in water.
4) When they're solid, ionic compounds don't conduct electricity. However, they do conduct when they melt or are in solution.
5) This is because when they're solid, the ions are held in place. When ionic compounds melt or dissolve, the ions are free to move and carry electric charge.

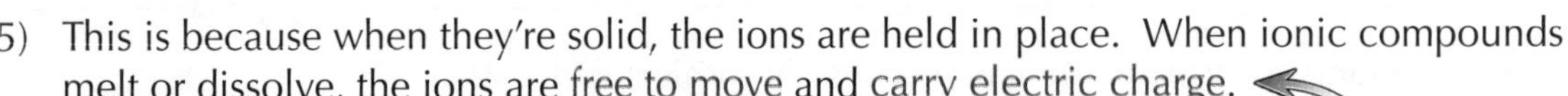

Ionic compounds generally don't dissolve in organic solvents though.

Electric current is a flow (movement) of charged particles, so if ions or electrons can move then the substance can conduct electricity.

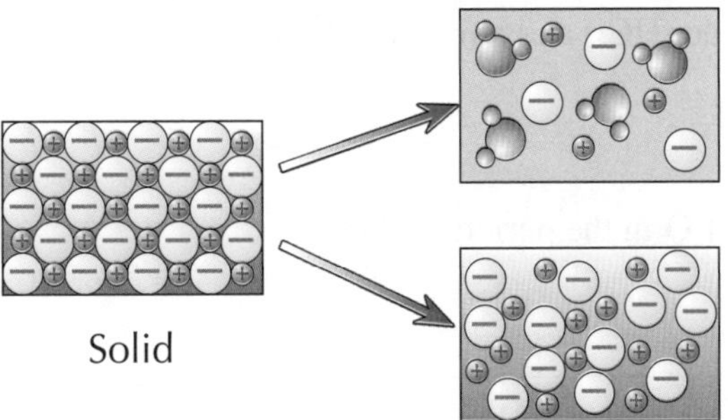

Simple Molecular Substances Also Have Similar Properties

1) Many substances containing covalent bonds have simple molecular structures, like the examples shown on pages 24-26.
2) Simple molecular substances are more volatile than ionic compounds. Their melting and boiling points are much lower and they are often gases or liquids at room temperature.
3) The atoms within the molecules are held together by very strong covalent bonds. By contrast, the forces of attraction between these molecules are very weak.
4) To melt or boil a simple molecular compound, you only need to break the weak intermolecular forces and not the covalent bonds. So the melting and boiling points are very low because the molecules are easily parted from each other.
5) As molecules get bigger, the strength of the intermolecular forces increases, so more energy is needed to break them, and the melting and boiling points increase.
6) Molecular compounds don't conduct electricity.
7) This is because they aren't charged, so there are no free electrons or ions.
8) Simple molecular compounds generally don't dissolve in water, but do dissolve in organic solvents.

Weak intermolecular forces — Chlorine — Oxygen

Simple molecules are more volatile than ionic compounds

Even though the atoms in a molecule are held together by strong covalent bonds, the molecules in a simple molecular substance are only held together by weak intermolecular forces. These intermolecular forces are all you need to break to boil the substance — so simple molecular substances have low boiling points.

Macromolecules

Molecules with covalent bonds aren't limited to just a few atoms. Atoms can bond covalently to each other to form giant structures (macromolecules) which have different properties depending on their structure.

Most **Giant Covalent** Structures Have Certain Properties

1) In giant covalent structures, all the atoms are bonded to each other by strong covalent bonds.
2) They have very high melting and boiling points as lots of energy is needed to break the covalent bonds.
3) They generally don't contain charged particles, so they don't conduct electricity.
4) They aren't soluble in water.

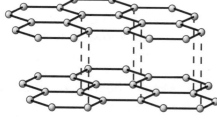

Apart from rare exceptions like graphite.

Graphite Contains **Sheets** of **Hexagons**

1) In graphite, each carbon atom only forms three covalent bonds, creating sheets of carbon atoms arranged in hexagons.
2) There aren't any covalent bonds between the layers — they're only held together weakly, so they're free to move over each other. This makes graphite soft and slippery, so it's ideal as a lubricating material.
3) Graphite's got a high melting point — the covalent bonds in the layers need loads of energy to break.
4) Only three out of each carbon's four outer electrons are used in bonds, so each carbon atom has one electron that's delocalised (free), which can move and carry electric charge. So graphite conducts electricity and is often used to make electrodes (see page 47).

Diamond is Very **Hard**

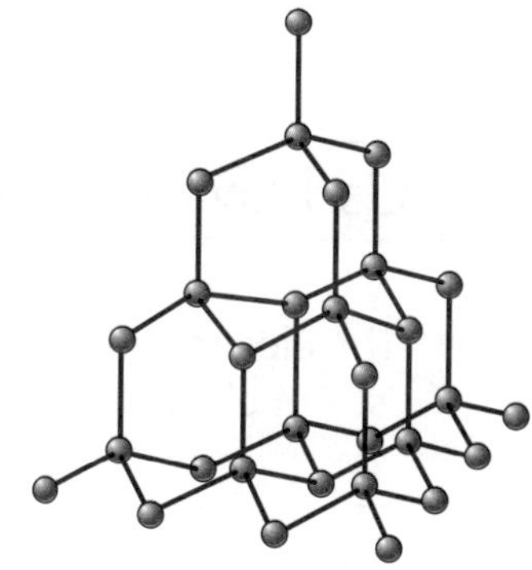

1) Diamond is made up of a network of carbon atoms that each form four covalent bonds.
2) The strong covalent bonds take lots of energy to break, so diamond has a high melting point.
3) The strong covalent bonds also hold the atoms in a rigid lattice structure, making diamond really hard — it's used to strengthen cutting tools (e.g. saw teeth and drill bits).
4) It doesn't conduct electricity because it has no free electrons or ions.

Supplement

Silicon Dioxide has a **Diamond-like Structure**

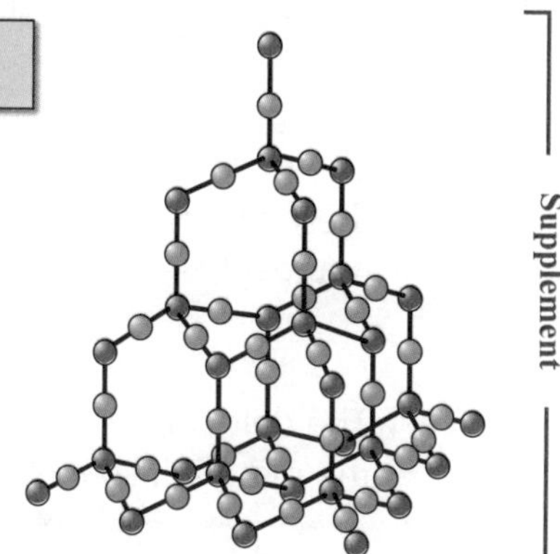

1) Silicon(IV) oxide (also known as silicon dioxide) has a macromolecular structure very similar to that of diamond.
2) The silicon atoms are positioned like the carbon atoms in diamond, with an oxygen atom between each one.
3) Silicon dioxide also shares many properties with diamond. It is hard, has a high melting point and has no free electrons, so doesn't conduct electricity.

Giant covalent structures have high melting and boiling points

To melt or boil a giant covalent structure, you have to break very strong covalent bonds. The high melting and boiling points of diamond, graphite and silicon are caused by the strength of their covalent bonds.

Metallic Bonding

You've seen ionic and you've seen covalent. Now it's for the last of the bond types — metallic bonding. This is quite different to the other two, but it's still all about the electrons.

Supplement

Metallic Bonding Involves Delocalised Electrons

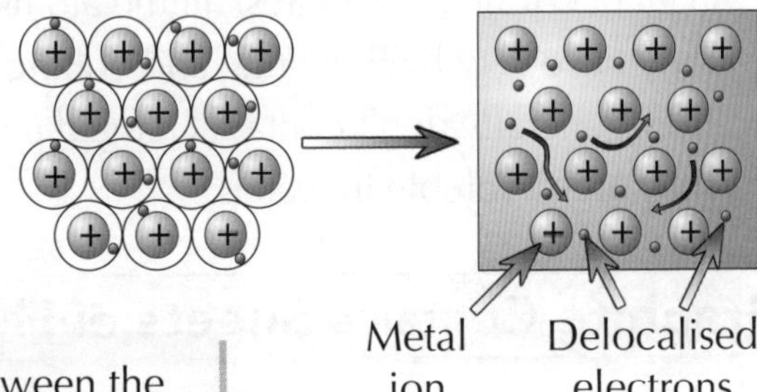

1) Metals also consist of a giant structure.
2) The electrons in the outer shell of the metal atoms are delocalised (free to move around).
3) There are strong forces of electrostatic attraction between the positive metal ions and the delocalised negative electrons.
4) These forces of attraction hold the atoms together in a regular structure and are known as metallic bonding. Metallic bonding is very strong.
5) Metallic bonding can thought of as a lattice of positive ions in a 'sea of electrons'.
6) Compounds that are held together by metallic bonding include metallic elements and alloys (see p.96).
7) It's the delocalised electrons in the metallic bonds which produce all the properties of metals.

Metals Have Certain Physical Properties

1) The electrostatic forces between the metal ions and the delocalised 'sea of electrons' are very strong, so need lots of energy to be broken.
2) This means that most compounds with metallic bonds have very high melting and boiling points, so they're generally shiny solids at room temperature. They aren't soluble in water either.
3) The metal atoms in the lattice are arranged into layers. In a pure metal, these layers can slide over each other (see page 96), making metals malleable — this means that they can be hammered or rolled into flat sheets.
4) The delocalised electrons carry electric charge through the material, so metals are good conductors of electricity.

Supplement

Metallic bonding is all about the delocalised electrons...

If you can't remember their properties, think about how metals are used. Copper is used in wires, so metals must conduct electricity. Aluminium is used to make foil, so metals must be malleable.

Warm-Up & Exam Questions

It's time to have a go at these exam questions to get you prepared for the real thing. Good luck.

Warm-Up Questions

1) True or false? Ionic compounds are very volatile.
2) Which forces are stronger in simple molecular substances — the covalent bonds between atoms or the intermolecular forces between molecules?
3) Describe metallic bonding.

S

Exam Questions

1 Graphite and diamond are both entirely made from carbon but have different properties.

(a) Explain why the structure of graphite makes it a useful lubricant.

[2]

(b) Explain why graphite is able to conduct electricity but diamond isn't.

[2]

(c) Using your knowledge of the structure of diamond, explain why it is useful as a cutting tool.

[2]

[Total 6 marks]

2 A chemist is investigating the properties of three pure solid substances, **A**, **B** and **C**.

(a) Substance **A** has a high melting point and is a good conductor when liquid.
However, it cannot conduct electricity when in its solid form.
What type of substance is **A**?

[1]

(b) The chemist knows substances **B** and **C** both contain covalent bonds.
Suggest how they could tell which substance has a giant macromolecular structure.

[2]

[Total 3 marks]

3 Magnesium oxide (MgO) is an ionic compound. Oxygen (O_2) is a simple molecule.

(a) Explain why molten MgO can act as an electrical conductor but oxygen gas can't.

[2]

(b) Explain why MgO melts at 2826 °C while O_2 melts at –218 °C.

[2]

[Total 4 marks]

4 Copper is a metallic element. It can be used to make the wires in electrical circuits.

(a) State a property of copper that makes it suitable for use in electrical circuits, and explain why it has this property.

[2]

(b) Explain why copper is also malleable.

[1]

[Total 3 marks]

Supplement

Supplement

Formulas of Compounds

It's important for chemists to know what elements are in a compound. That's why we have formulas.

A **Formula** Shows What **Atoms** are in a **Compound**

Just as elements can be represented by symbols, compounds can be represented by formulas. The formulas are made up of element symbols in the same proportions that the elements can be found in the compound.

1) For example, carbon dioxide, CO_2, is a compound formed from a chemical reaction between carbon and oxygen. It contains 1 carbon atom and 2 oxygen atoms.

Carbon + Oxygen ⟹ Carbon Dioxide

C + O O ⟹ O C O CO_2

Elemental oxygen goes around in pairs of atoms (so it's O_2).

2) Here's another example: the formula of sulfuric acid is H_2SO_4. So, each molecule contains 2 hydrogen atoms, 1 sulfur atom and 4 oxygen atoms.
3) There might be brackets in a formula, e.g. calcium hydroxide is $Ca(OH)_2$. The little number outside the bracket applies to everything inside the brackets. So in $Ca(OH)_2$ there's 1 calcium atom, 2 oxygen atoms and 2 hydrogen atoms.

Here are some examples of formulas which might come in handy:

- Carbon dioxide — CO_2
- Ammonia — NH_3
- Water — H_2O
- Sodium chloride — NaCl
- Carbon monoxide — CO
- Hydrochloric acid — HCl
- Copper(II) sulfate — $CuSO_4$
- Sulfur dioxide — SO_2
- Sulfuric acid — H_2SO_4

It is also possible to work out a molecule's formula from a diagram or a model. For example, the molecule to the right contains 2 carbon atoms, 5 hydrogen atoms, 2 oxygen atoms and 1 chlorine atom. So the formula is $C_2H_5O_2Cl$.

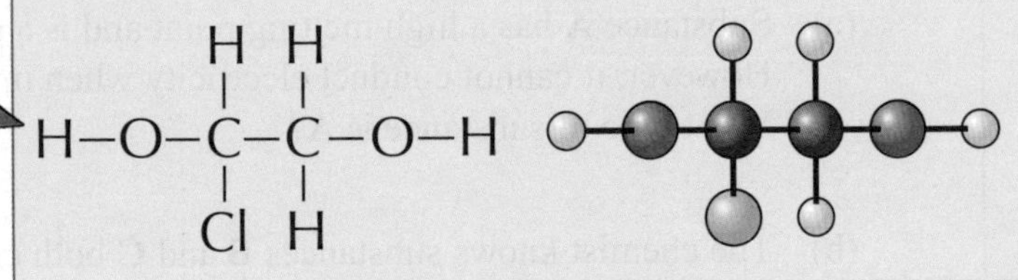

Supplement

You Can Work Out the **Formula** of an **Ionic Compound**

1) Ionic compounds are made up of a positively charged part and a negatively charged part.
2) The overall charge of any ionic compound is zero. So all the negative charges in the compound must balance all the positive charges.
3) You can use the charges on the individual ions present to work out the formula for the ionic compound. Here's an example:

Example: What is the chemical formula of calcium nitrate?

1) Write out the formulas of the calcium and nitrate ions: Ca^{2+}, NO_3^-
2) Work out the ratio of Ca : NO_3 that gives an overall neutral charge. You'd need 2 lots of NO_3^- to balance out the 2+ charge on Ca^{2+}. So the chemical formula of calcium nitrate would be $Ca(NO_3)_2$.

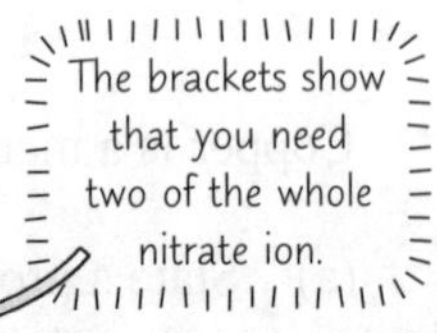

The brackets show that you need two of the whole nitrate ion.

Supplement

REVISION TIP

Every chemical compound has its own formula

There'll be a lot of different molecules popping up throughout this book. Have a look through and when you find one you don't know, use its formula to work out what elements it contains.

Balancing Equations

Equations crop up everywhere in chemistry — you can't hide from them. They show you just what's happening in a chemical reaction — what reacts together and what's formed.

Equations Show the Reactants and Products of a Reaction

1) A chemical reaction can be described as the process of going from reactants to products.
2) You can write word equations or symbol equations to show any chemical reaction.

E.g. magnesium reacts with oxygen to produce magnesium oxide:

Word equation: magnesium + oxygen → magnesium oxide

Symbol equation: $2Mg + O_2 \rightarrow 2MgO$

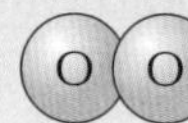

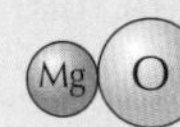

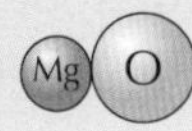

Symbol Equations Need to be Balanced

1) There must always be the same number of atoms of each element on both sides of the equation — atoms can't just disappear.
2) You balance the equation by putting numbers in front of the formulas where needed. Take this equation for reacting sulfuric acid with sodium hydroxide:

$$H_2SO_4 + NaOH \rightarrow Na_2SO_4 + H_2O$$

3) The formulas are all correct but the numbers of some atoms don't match up on both sides.
4) You can't change formulas like H_2SO_4 to H_2SO_5. You can only put numbers in front of them.
5) The more you practise, the quicker you get, but all you do is this:

- Find an element that doesn't balance and pencil in a number to try and sort it out.
- See if all the elements balance now. If they don't, pencil in another number somewhere else and see if that will fix it.
- Carry on chasing unbalanced elements and you'll get it balanced pretty quickly.

In the equation above you'll notice we're short of an H atom on the RHS (right-hand side).

1) The only thing you can do about that is make it $2H_2O$ instead of just H_2O:

$$H_2SO_4 + NaOH \rightarrow Na_2SO_4 + 2H_2O$$

2) But that now gives too many H atoms and O atoms on the RHS, so to balance that up you could try putting a 2 in front of the NaOH on the LHS (left-hand side):

$$H_2SO_4 + 2NaOH \rightarrow Na_2SO_4 + 2H_2O$$

3) And suddenly there it is. Everything balances.

Putting a 2 in front of the NaOH has balanced the Na atoms too.

Balancing Equations

State Symbols Tell You the State of a Substance in an Equation

You saw on the previous page how a chemical reaction can be shown using a word equation or symbol equation. Symbol equations can also include state symbols next to each substance — they tell you what physical state the reactants and products are in:

(s) — solid (l) — liquid (g) — gas (aq) — aqueous

'Aqueous' means 'dissolved in water'.

Here are a couple of examples:

Aqueous hydrogen chloride reacts with solid calcium carbonate to form aqueous calcium chloride, liquid water and carbon dioxide gas:

$$2HCl_{(aq)} + CaCO_{3(s)} \rightarrow CaCl_{2(aq)} + H_2O_{(l)} + CO_{2(g)}$$

Chlorine gas reacts with aqueous potassium iodide to form aqueous potassium chloride and solid iodine:

$$Cl_{2(g)} + 2KI_{(aq)} \rightarrow 2KCl_{(aq)} + I_{2(s)}$$

Supplement

Ionic Equations Show Just the Useful Bits of Reactions

1) You can also write an ionic equation for any reaction involving ions that happens in solution.
2) In an ionic equation, only the reacting particles (and the products they form) are included.
3) To write an ionic equation, all you need to do is look at the balanced symbol equation and take out any aqueous (dissolved) ions that are present on both sides of the equation.

Write the ionic equation for the following reaction:
$$CaCl_{2\,(aq)} + 2NaOH_{(aq)} \rightarrow Ca(OH)_{2\,(s)} + 2NaCl_{(aq)}$$

You should make sure your symbol equation is balanced before you start trying to write the ionic equation (see the previous page for more on how to balance symbol equations).

1) Anything that's ionic (i.e. made of ions — see page 23) and aqueous will break up into its ions in solution. So, write out the equation showing all the aqueous ions separately.

$$Ca^{2+}_{(aq)} + 2Cl^-_{(aq)} + 2Na^+_{(aq)} + 2OH^-_{(aq)} \rightarrow Ca(OH)_{2\,(s)} + 2Na^+_{(aq)} + 2Cl^-_{(aq)}$$

2) To get to the ionic equation, cross out anything that's the same on both sides of the equation — here, that's the Na^+ and Cl^- ions.

$$Ca^{2+}_{(aq)} + \cancel{2Cl^-}_{(aq)} + \cancel{2Na^+}_{(aq)} + 2OH^-_{(aq)} \rightarrow Ca(OH)_{2\,(s)} + \cancel{2Na^+}_{(aq)} + \cancel{2Cl^-}_{(aq)}$$

$$Ca^{2+}_{(aq)} + 2OH^-_{(aq)} \rightarrow Ca(OH)_{2\,(s)}$$

The overall charge should be the same on both sides. Here, charge on RHS = 0 and charge on LHS = (2+) + (2 × 1–) = 0.

Supplement

Getting good at balancing equations takes patience and practice

Remember, a number in front of a formula applies to the entire formula — so $3Na_2SO_4$ means three lots of Na_2SO_4. The little numbers within or at the end of a formula only apply to the atom (or group of atoms in brackets) immediately before. So the 4 in Na_2SO_4 means there are 4 Os, but there's just 1 S, not 4.

Warm-Up & Exam Questions

The best way to practise all that equation balancing is to just have a go. So here are some questions to try.

Warm-Up Questions

1) What's the formula for a compound with 1 magnesium atom, 1 carbon atom and 3 oxygen atoms?
2) Write the word equation and the symbol equation for the reaction of sodium hydroxide with hydrochloric acid to make sodium chloride and water.
3) S A potassium ion has the formula K^+ and a carbonate ion has the formula CO_3^{2-}. What is the formula of potassium carbonate?

Exam Questions

1 Sulfuric acid (H_2SO_4) reacts with ammonia (NH_3) to form ammonium sulfate, $(NH_4)_2SO_4$.

(a) Write a balanced symbol equation for this reaction.

[2]

(b) How many hydrogen atoms are present in the formula for ammonium sulfate?

[1]

[Total 3 marks]

2 Methane (CH_4) burns in oxygen to make carbon dioxide and water.

(a) Which molecule involved in the reaction is composed of only one element?

[1]

(b) Complete and balance the symbol equation for the reaction below.

$$CH_4 \quad + \quad .... \rightarrow CO_2 \quad + \quad ....$$

[2]

(c) This reaction can also be done using ethane (C_2H_6) in place of methane.
How many more carbon and hydrogen atoms are present in ethane than in methane?

[2]

[Total 5 marks]

Supplement

3 The reaction of nitric acid with sodium hydroxide can be described by the following equation:

$$HNO_{3\,(aq)} + NaOH_{(aq)} \rightarrow NaNO_{3\,(aq)} + H_2O_{(l)}$$

(a) Write the ionic equation for the reaction.

[2]

(b) Nitric acid can be produced by reacting nitrogen dioxide gas (NO_2) with water.
This reaction also produces nitrogen monoxide gas (NO).
Write the balanced symbol equation for this reaction.
Include state symbols for the reactants and products.

[3]

[Total 5 marks]

Supplement

Relative Atomic and Molecular Mass

The actual mass of an atom is very, very small — far too small to weigh. So you usually give the mass of an atom by comparing it to the mass of other atoms instead. This is known as its relative mass.

Relative Atomic Mass Takes Isotopes into Account

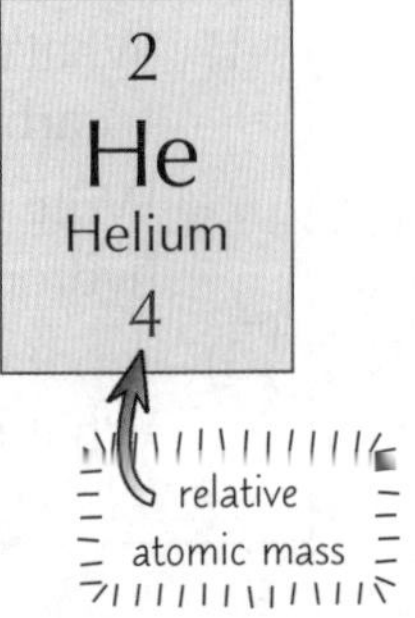

1) In the periodic table, the elements all have two numbers next to them. The bigger one is the relative atomic mass (A_r) of the element.

The relative atomic mass of an element is the average mass of naturally occurring atoms of an element on a scale where the ^{12}C atom has a mass of exactly 12 units.

2) If an element only has one isotope, its A_r will be the same as its mass (nucleon) number (see p.15).
3) If an element has more than one isotope, its A_r is the average of the mass numbers of all the different isotopes, taking into account how much there is of each one. So, it might not be a whole number.

> For example, chlorine has two stable isotopes, chlorine-35 and chlorine-37. There's quite a lot of chlorine-35 around and not so much chlorine-37 — so chlorine's A_r works out as 35.5.

You'll be given the periodic table in your multiple choice and theory exams, so there's no need memorise relative atomic masses.

Relative Molecular Mass, M_r

The relative molecular mass, M_r, of a compound is the relative atomic masses (A_r) of all the atoms in its formula added together.

For example, ammonia (NH_3) contains one nitrogen atom (A_r = 14) and three hydrogen atoms (A_r = 1). So the M_r of ammonia is 14 + (1 × 3) = 17.

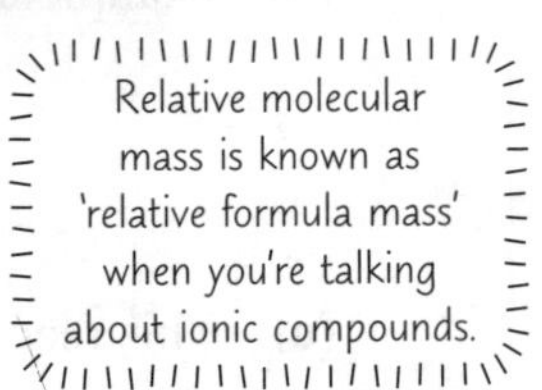

Relative molecular mass is known as 'relative formula mass' when you're talking about ionic compounds.

You Can Use **M_r** to Work Out **Masses** in a **Reaction**

1) The relative molecular masses of the substances in a reaction can tell you the amount in grams of the substances that will react with each other.
2) For example, for the reaction $C + O_2 \rightarrow CO_2$, 12 g of C (A_r = 12) will react with 32 g of O_2 (M_r = 32) to form 44 g of CO_2 (M_r = 44).
3) You can use this ratio to find the masses of reactants and products in a reaction.

> Example: Find the mass of carbon needed to form 11 g of CO_2.
>
> Answer: You know that 12 g of C produces 44 g of CO_2.
>
> 11 g is $11 \div 44 = \frac{1}{4}$ of that amount of product.
>
> So you'll need $\frac{1}{4}$ of the amount of reactant too: $12 \div 4 = 3$ g of carbon.

Relative molecular mass is the sum of all the relative atomic masses

It's really easy to work out relative molecular masses — even for larger molecules. Just work out how many atoms of each element are present, multiply each by its A_r and add them all together.

Moles

The mole might seem a bit confusing. But don't be put off by the funny word, it's not that hard really...

"The Mole" is a Unit for the Amount of a Substance

One mole of a substance contains 6.02×10^{23} particles.

The number 6.02×10^{23} is known as Avogadro's constant.

1) The mole is used to measure the amount of a substance that you have.
2) When you have exactly one mole of atoms or molecules of any element or compound, they will have the same mass in grams as the relative atomic mass, A_r, (or relative formula mass, M_r) of the element or compound.

Examples:

Carbon has an A_r of 12.	So one mole of carbon weighs exactly 12 g.
Nitrogen gas, N_2, has an M_r of 28 (2 × 14).	So one mole of N_2 weighs exactly 28 g.
Carbon dioxide, CO_2, has an M_r of 44.	So one mole of CO_2 weighs exactly 44 g.

3) This means that 12 g of carbon, or 28 g of N_2, or 44 g of CO_2, all contain the same number of particles — one mole, or 6.023×10^{23} atoms or molecules.

You can Calculate the Number of Moles in a Given Mass:

$$\text{Number of Moles} = \frac{\text{Mass in g (of element or compound)}}{M_r \text{ (of element or compound)}}$$

Example: How many moles are there in 66 g of carbon dioxide?
Answer: M_r of CO_2 = 12 + (16 × 2) = 44
No. of moles = Mass (g) ÷ M_r = 66 ÷ 44 = 1.5 moles

1) You may need to rearrange the equation to find the mass of a certain number of moles.
2) Putting an equation into a formula triangle makes rearranging equations straightforward. Here's the formula triangle that links moles, mass and relative formula mass.
3) To use a formula triangle, just cover the thing you want to find, and you're left with the expression you need to calculate it. The line through the triangle stands for division.
4) So to work out mass in grams of an element or compound, you would multiply the number of moles by the M_r.

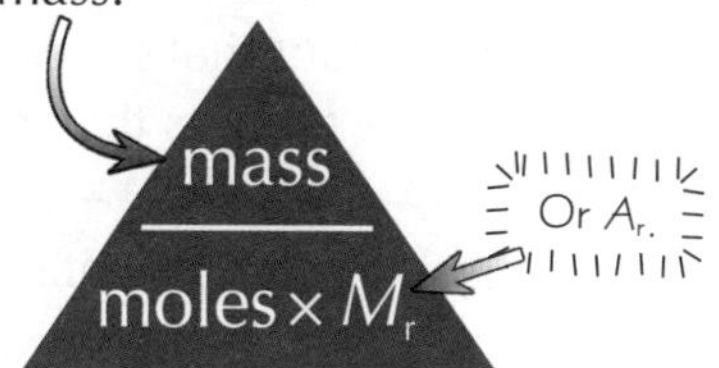

You need to be able to convert between moles and grams

Take some time to get your head round all of this. Write out the formula and the formula triangle on this page until you know them by heart. Then do it again later, to make sure it's really sunk in.

Calculating Masses in Reactions

You've already seen mass calculations on page 36. You can do the same kind of thing, but using moles.

You can Calculate the Amount of **Product** from a **Mass** of **Reactant**

You can use a balanced chemical equation to work out the mass of product formed from a given mass of a reactant. Here's how...

1) Write out the balanced equation.
2) Work out relative formula masses (M_r) of the reactant and product you're interested in.
3) Find out how many moles there are of the substance you know the mass of.
4) Use the balanced equation to work out how many moles there'll be of the other substance (i.e. how many moles of product will be made by this many moles of reactant).
5) Use the number of moles to calculate the mass.

Don't worry — these steps should all make sense when you look at the example below.

EXAMPLE:

What mass of magnesium oxide is made when 60 g of magnesium is burnt in air?

1) Write out the balanced equation. $2Mg + O_2 \rightarrow 2MgO$
2) Work out the relative formula masses of the reactants and products you're interested in. $A_r(Mg)$: 24 $M_r(MgO)$: 24 + 16 = 40
3) Calculate the number of moles of magnesium in 60 g: moles = mass ÷ M_r = 60 ÷ 24 = 2.5
4) Look at the ratio of moles in the equation. 2 moles of Mg react to produce 2 moles of MgO. So 2.5 moles of Mg will produce 2.5 moles of MgO.
5) Calculate the mass of 2.5 moles of magnesium oxide. mass = moles × M_r = 2.5 × 40 = 100 g of MgO

The mass of product (in this case magnesium oxide) is called the yield of a reaction. Masses you calculate in this way are called theoretical yields. In practice you never get 100% of the yield, so the amount of product you get will be less than you calculated.

If the question had said, "find how much magnesium gives 100 g of magnesium oxide", you'd calculate the number of moles of magnesium oxide first, because that's the one you'd have the information about.

Reactions **Stop** When **One** Reactant is **Used Up**

1) A reaction stops when all of one of the reactants is used up. Any other reactants are said to be in excess.
2) The reactant that's used up in a reaction is called the limiting reactant (because it limits the amount of product that's formed).

In the MgO example above, O_2 is in excess in the air. So Mg is the limiting reactant — it's the amount of Mg that determines how much MgO is made.

Example: A scientist burnt hydrogen in pure oxygen to form water: $2H_2 + O_2 \rightarrow 2H_2O$
If she started with 1 mole of H_2 and 0.8 moles of O_2, which reactant was in excess?

Answer:
1) From the equation, you can see that you need 1 mole of O_2 to react with every 2 moles of H_2. So you would need 0.5 moles of O_2 to react with 1 mole of H_2.
2) The scientist had 0.8 – 0.5 = 0.3 moles more O_2 than she needed to react with the amount of H_2 she had. So the O_2 was in excess.

3) The amount of product formed is directly proportional to the amount of the limiting reactant used.

Supplement

Supplement

Percentage Yield and Percentage Purity

Theoretical yields are useful for getting an idea of how much product you'll make, but no reaction is 100% efficient. Chemists use percentage yield calculations to work out how productive their reaction was.

Supplement

Percentage Yield Compares **Actual** and **Theoretical** Yield

1) The theoretical yield of a reaction can be calculated from the balanced equation (see page 33).
2) Percentage yield is given by the formula:

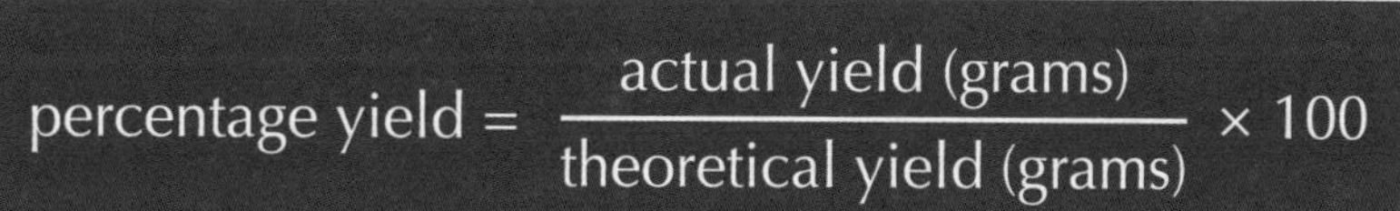

$$\text{percentage yield} = \frac{\text{actual yield (grams)}}{\text{theoretical yield (grams)}} \times 100$$

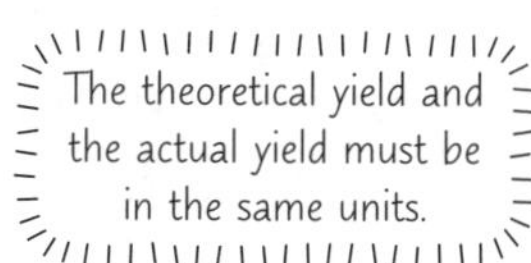

The theoretical yield and
the actual yield must be
in the same units.

3) Percentage yield is always somewhere between 0 and 100%.
4) A 100% yield means that you got all the product you expected to get.
5) A 0% yield means that no reactants were converted into product, i.e. no product at all was made.

Zinc oxide can be reduced using carbon:

$$2ZnO + C \rightarrow 2Zn + CO_2$$

A scientist reduced 121.5 g of zinc oxide using excess carbon and produced 78 g of zinc metal. Calculate the percentage yield of this reaction.

1) Find the relative masses of zinc oxide and zinc.

   $M_r(ZnO) = 65 + 16 = 81$
   $A_r(Zn) = 65$

2) Work out the number of moles of the reactant (zinc oxide) you have.

   moles of ZnO = mass ÷ M_r
   = 121.5 ÷ 81 = 1.5 moles

3) Use the balanced equation to work out how many moles of the desired product (zinc) you should end up with.

   2 moles of zinc oxide react to produce 2 moles of zinc. So 1.5 moles of zinc oxide will produce 1.5 moles of zinc.

4) Find the theoretical yield of the desired product (zinc) by converting moles to mass.

   mass = moles × M_r
   = 1.5 × 65 = 97.5 g

5) Put the numbers into the formula to find the percentage yield.

   $$\text{percentage yield} = \frac{\text{actual yield}}{\text{theoretical yield}} \times 100 = \frac{78}{97.5} \times 100 = 80\%$$

You Can Also Calculate How **Pure** Your Sample Is

You can work out the percentage purity of a sample using a similar calculation:

$$\text{percentage purity} = \frac{\text{pure yield (grams)}}{\text{total impure yield (grams)}} \times 100$$

Example: A reaction used to produce ibuprofen had a yield of 10 g. But the product only contained 8 g of pure ibuprofen. So the percentage purity of the product was (8 ÷ 100) x 100 = 80%

Supplement

Warm-Up & Exam Questions

Relative atomic and molecular masses are going to crop up a lot more as you carry on learning about chemistry. Good job there's some practice questions here for you to have a go at.

Warm-Up Questions

1) Define the relative atomic mass of an element.
2) Calculate the number of moles in 90 g of water. M_r of water = 18.
3) 0.500 moles of substance X has a mass of 87.0 g. What is the relative formula mass of X?
4) Describe what a limiting reactant is.
5) A student's reaction produces 12 g of a product which contains 7.8 g of a pure chemical. Calculate the percentage purity of the product.

Exam Questions

1 Which of the following is the M_r of calcium chloride ($CaCl_2$)?

☐ **A** 54 ☐ **B** 75.5

☐ **C** 111 ☐ **D** 71

[Total 1 mark]

Supplement

2 Nitrogen dioxide is produced by the following reaction:

$$2NO + O_2 \rightarrow 2NO_2$$

Find the number of moles of NO in 15 g and use this to calculate how much NO_2 would be produced if 15 g of NO was used in the reaction.

[Total 2 marks]

3 A pharmacist is synthesising aspirin ($C_9H_8O_4$).
After the experiment, the pharmacist calculates that he has made 12.4 moles of aspirin.
What mass of aspirin has the pharmacist made? Give your answer in grams.
The relative atomic mass, A_r, of C = 12, of H = 1 and of O = 16.

[Total 2 marks]

4 A sample of copper was made by reducing 4.0 g of copper oxide with methane gas.
The sample was then filtered, washed and dried. 2.9 g of copper was obtained.
(A_r values: H = 1, Cu = 64, O = 16.) The equation for this reaction is:

$$CH_4 + 4CuO \rightarrow 4Cu + 2H_2O + CO_2$$

(a) Use the equation to calculate the maximum mass of copper which could be obtained from the reaction (the theoretical yield).

[3]

(b) Calculate the percentage yield of the reaction.

[2]

[Total 5 marks]

Supplement

Empirical and Molecular Formulae

This isn't as complicated as it sounds. Just follow the same method every time and you'll be fine.

Finding the **Empirical Formula**

The empirical formula gives you the smallest whole number ratio of atoms in a compound.
Here's a method for calculating an empirical formula from experimental data:

1) List all the elements in the compound.
2) Underneath them, write their experimental masses.
3) Find the number of moles of each element by dividing each mass by the relative atomic mass (A_r) for that particular element.
4) Turn the numbers you get into a nice simple ratio by dividing by the smallest number of moles.
5) Get the ratio in its simplest whole number form — that's the empirical formula of the compound.

If the amounts of each element are in percentages, just divide each one by the A_r for that element.

EXAMPLE:

In an experiment, some iron powder is burned in air to produce iron oxide. Use the following experimental data to find the empirical formula of the iron oxide made.

Mass of empty container	32.0 g
Mass of container + mass of iron powder	76.8 g
Mass of container + iron oxide	96.0 g

(A_r for iron = 56, A_r for oxygen = 16)

During the experiment, oxygen is gained. The mass of oxygen gained is the difference between the mass of the container and iron powder and the mass of the container and iron oxide: 96.0 g – 76.8 g = 19.2 g.
The mass of iron used is the difference between the mass of the container with the iron powder and the mass of the empty container: 76.8 g – 32.0 g = 44.8 g.

1) List the two elements:	Fe	O
2) Write in the experimental masses:	44.8	19.2
3) Find the number of moles of each element:	44.8 ÷ 56 = 0.8	19.2 ÷ 16 = 1.2
4) Divide by the smallest number of moles:	0.8 ÷ 0.8 = 1	1.2 ÷ 0.8 = 1.5
5) Multiply to get whole numbers:	1 × 2 = 2	1.5 × 2 = 3

You don't have to multiply if you get whole numbers in step 4.

So the simplest formula is 2 atoms of Fe to 3 atoms of O, i.e. Fe_2O_3.

The **Empirical** and **Molecular Formulae** Won't Always **Match**

1) The molecular formula can be different to the empirical formula of a compound. The molecular formula tells you the actual number of atoms of each element in a single molecule.
2) Molecular formulae are whole-number multiples of empirical formulae.

Example: A molecule has an empirical formula of $C_4H_3O_2$, and a relative molecular mass of 166. Work out its molecular formula.

Method:

1) Find the mass of the empirical formula: (4 × 12) + (3 × 1) + (2 × 16) = 48 + 3 + 32 = 83 g
2) The relative molecular mass is 166, so there are 166 ÷ 83 = 2 empirical units in the molecule.
3) The molecular formula must be the empirical formula × 2: $C_4H_3O_2 \times 2 = C_8H_6O_4$.

Supplement

Moles and Concentration

Concentration is all about "how much" of a substance you have in a solution.

Supplement

Concentration is the 'Amount of Stuff' per Unit Volume

1) The concentration of a solution is usually measured in moles per dm^3 (i.e. moles per litre). So 1 mole of stuff in 1 dm^3 of solution has a concentration of 1 mole per dm^3 (or 1 mol/dm^3).

1 dm^3 = 1000 cm^3 = 1 litre

2) You might also sometimes see concentration being measured in grams per dm^3. So 56 grams of stuff dissolved in 1 dm^3 of solution has a concentration of 56 g per dm^3 (or 56 g/dm^3).

Concentration = Number of Moles ÷ Volume

1) To find the concentration of a solution, here's the formula you'll need:

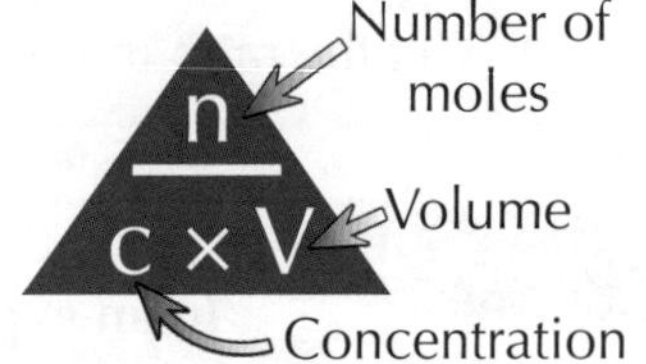

$$\text{Concentration (in mol/dm}^3\text{)} = \frac{\text{Number of moles (in mol)}}{\text{Volume of solution (in dm}^3\text{)}}$$

Example: What's the concentration of a solution with 2 moles of potassium iodide in 500 cm^3?

Answer: You've got 2 moles of potassium iodide and 500 cm^3 = 0.5 dm^3.
Now just stick these numbers in the formula: Concentration = 2 ÷ 0.5 = 4 mol/dm^3

2) You can use the same formula to find the number of moles that are in a solution:

Example: How many moles of sodium chloride are in 250 cm^3 of a 3 mol/dm^3 solution?

Answer: 250 cm^3 = 0.25 dm^3. So, using the formula from the triangle...
Number of moles = concentration × volume = 3 × 0.25 = 0.75 moles

3) You can use it to work out the volume of a solution too:

Example: What volume of 6 mol/dm^3 hydrochloric acid solution would contain 1.2 moles of hydrogen chloride?

Answer: If you've got the moles and the concentration, then just plug them into the formula.
Volume = number of moles ÷ concentration = 1.2 ÷ 6 = 0.2 dm^3

Multiplying this by 1000 would give you the volume in cm^3 — 200 cm^3

You Can Also Calculate Concentration in Grams per dm^3

Calculating concentrations in grams per dm^3 is easy. Divide the mass of the chemical in grams by the volume of solvent you used to dissolve it in dm^3.

Example: Give the concentration in g/dm^3 of a solution made by dissolving 3 g of NaCl in 100 cm^3 of water.

Answer: Concentration = mass (g) ÷ volume (dm^3) = 3 ÷ 0.1 = 30 g/dm^3

Remember to keep everything in the right units. In this case, 100 cm^3 ÷ 1000 = 0.1 dm^3.

Supplement

Moles and Concentration

Converting Moles per dm³ to Grams per dm³

To change your concentration from mol/dm³ to g/dm³, all you need to do is use the formula you met on page 37 to convert the moles per dm³ into mass per dm³.

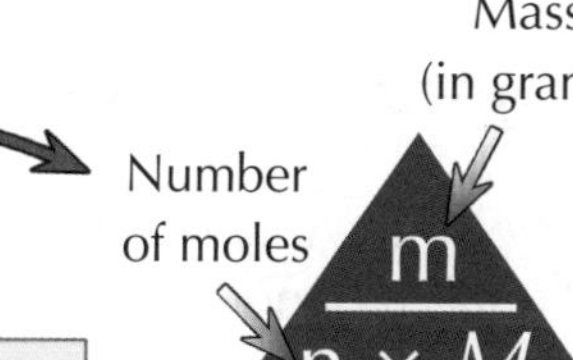

Example: You have a 0.0400 mol/dm³ solution of sulfuric acid. What is the concentration in grams per dm³?

Answer: 1) Work out the relative formula mass of the chemical.
H_2SO_4 = (1 × 2) + 32 + (16 × 4) = 98

2) Convert the concentration from moles/dm³ to grams/dm³.
In 1 dm³: mass in grams = moles × relative formula mass
= 0.0400 × 98 = 3.92 g
So the concentration in g/dm³ = 3.92 g/dm³

You Can Calculate Concentration Using Titration Results

1) Titrations are experiments that let you find the volumes of two solutions that are needed to react together completely.
2) If you know the concentration of one of the solutions, you can use the volumes from the titration experiment, along with the reaction equation, to find the concentration of the other solution.
3) For example, you can use the results of a titration experiment to find the concentration of an alkali when you know the volume and concentration of an acid that reacted with it:

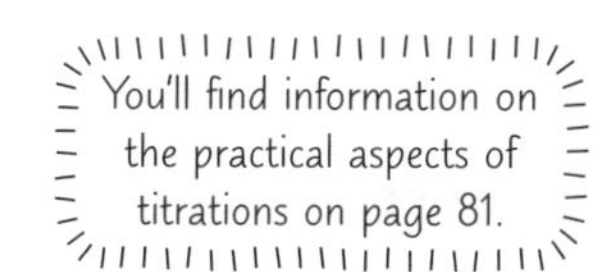

You'll find information on the practical aspects of titrations on page 81.

Supplement

Supplement

EXAMPLE:

It takes 25.0 cm³ of 0.100 mol/dm³ sulfuric acid to neutralise 30.0 cm³ of sodium hydroxide solution in a titration experiment.
The equation for this reaction is: $2NaOH + H_2SO_4 \rightarrow Na_2SO_4 + 2H_2O$
Find the concentration of the alkali in mol/dm³.

1) Work out how many moles of acid you have, using the formula: moles = concentration × volume.

moles = 0.100 × (25.0 ÷ 1000)
= 0.00250 moles of H_2SO_4

Convert the volume into dm³. (1000 cm³ = 1 dm³)

2) Use the equation to work out how many moles of the alkali you must have had, using the ratios in the balanced equation.

1 mole of H_2SO_4 reacts with 2 moles of NaOH
So 0.00250 moles of H_2SO_4 must react with
0.00250 × 2 = 0.00500 moles of NaOH

3) Finally, work out the concentration of the alkali.

concentration = number of moles ÷ volume
= 0.00500 ÷ (30.0 ÷ 1000)
= 0.1666... mol/dm³ = 0.167 mol/dm³

Again, convert the volume into dm³.

Practise, practise, practise...

A lot of numbers to deal with here. The only way to get good at these calculations is by practising them, plain and simple. You can check your answer by doing the calculation in reverse — if you end up with the concentration that you're given in the question, you're on to a winner.

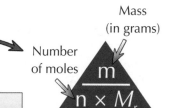

Calculating Gas Volumes

Another formula to learn on this page — this time about the volume of gases.

Avogadro's Law — One Mole of Any Gas Occupies 24 dm^3

1) The space that one mole of a gas takes up is called its molar gas volume. Here's a handy fact about molar volume that you definitely need to learn:

One mole of any gas always occupies 24 dm^3 (= 24 000 cm^3) at room temperature and pressure (RTP: 20 °C and 1 atmosphere).

24 dm^3 is the molar gas volume at RTP.

2) This means you can use the formula below to convert the number of moles of any gas at RTP to a volume:

If you need to work out the moles of gas from its mass, use the formula moles = mass ÷ M_r (see page 37).

Volume (dm^3) = moles of gas × 24

Example: What's the volume of 4.5 moles of chlorine at RTP?
Answer: volume of 1 mole = 24 dm^3, so volume of 4.5 moles = 4.5 × 24 dm^3 = 108 dm^3

Example: How many moles are there in 8280 cm^3 of hydrogen gas at RTP?

Answer: $$\text{Number of moles} = \frac{\text{Volume of gas}}{\text{Volume of 1 mole}} = \frac{8.28}{24} = 0.345 \text{ moles}$$

Don't forget to convert from cm^3 to dm^3.

Supplement

You Can Calculate Volumes in Reactions If You Know the Masses

Find the volume of carbon dioxide produced at RTP when 2.4 g of carbon is completely burned in oxygen. (A_r of carbon = 12, A_r of oxygen = 16)

1) Write out the balanced equation: $C + O_2 \rightarrow CO_2$
2) Work out the relative atomic or formula mass of the substance you know the mass of: A_r of C = 12
3) Calculate the number of moles of carbon in 2.4 g: moles = mass ÷ A_r = 2.4 ÷ 12 = 0.2
4) Look at the ratio of moles in the equation: 1 mole of C reacts to produce 1 mole of CO_2. So 0.2 moles of C will react to produce 0.2 moles of CO_2.
5) Use the formula above to work out the volume: volume = moles × 24 = 0.2 × 24 = 4.8 dm^3

Use the formula to work out the volume of any gas at RTP

All this stuff ties in with what you saw on page 38 — if you're not comfortable working out reacting masses, have a look there to refresh your memory. The only new thing here is molar volume: 1 mole of gas = 24 dm^3. This is the same for all gases at RTP, so you've only got one new formula to learn.

Warm-Up & Exam Questions

You've met quite a few important equations and calculations in that last section. So give these practice questions a go and check how well you've understood them all.

Warm-Up Questions

1) Glucose has the molecular formula $C_6H_{12}O_6$. What is its empirical formula?
2) A molecule has an empirical formula of CH_2 and an M_r of 42. What is its molecular formula?
3) How many moles of hydrochloric acid are there in 25 cm³ of a 0.10 mol/dm³ solution?
4) True or false? Only O_2, N_2 and CO_2 have a molar volume of 24 dm³ at RTP.

Exam Questions

1 A student burns manganese powder in a container to produce manganese oxide. Some of the student's results are shown in the table:

mass of container	36.48 g
mass of container + manganese	84.88 g

(a) Calculate the mass of manganese present in the oxide. Give your answer in grams.

[1]

(b) The mass of oxygen in the oxide produced was 14.08 g.
Calculate the empirical formula of the oxide.
$A_r(Mn) = 55$, $A_r(O) = 16$

[3]

[Total 4 marks]

2 Sodium hydroxide (NaOH) reacts with sulfuric acid to produce sodium sulfate (Na_2SO_4) and water.
$A_r(Na) = 23$, $A_r(O) = 16$, $A_r(S) = 32$, $A_r(H) = 1$

(a) A solution of NaOH has a concentration of 7.4 mol/dm³.
What volume of this solution would contain 2 moles of NaOH?

[1]

(b) What is the concentration, in mol/dm³, of a solution with 3 moles of sodium sulfate in 750 cm³?

[1]

(c) Convert your answer for part (b) into g/dm³.

[2]

[Total 4 marks]

3 Calcium carbonate decomposes under heating to form calcium oxide and carbon dioxide.
The balanced equation for this reaction is shown below:

$$CaCO_{3(s)} \rightarrow CaO_{(s)} + CO_{2(g)}$$

25 g of $CaCO_3$ were heated by a student.
Assuming that all the calcium carbonate decomposed, calculate the volume occupied at RTP by the quantity of CO_2 produced by this reaction. (Relative atomic masses: Ca = 40, O = 16, C = 12)

[Total 4 marks]

Supplement

Revision Summary for Sections 3 & 4

You've made it through Sections 3 and 4. Now make sure you've understood everything you read by having a go at these revision questions. Make sure you can get them all right before moving on.

- Try these questions and tick off each one when you get it right.
- When you've done all the questions for a topic and are completely happy with it, tick off the topic.

Atoms, Isotopes and Electron Shells (p.15-19) ☐

1) Give the relative masses and charges of protons, neutrons and electrons. ☐
2) What does an atom's proton number tell you about the atom? ☐
3) Give one way that a radioactive isotope is used in medicine. ☐
4) What is the electronic structure of phosphorus? ☐

Elements, Ions and Bonding (p.21-30) ☐

5) Describe the difference between a compound and a mixture. ☐
6) Give an example of an alloy. ☐
7) An atom forms an ion by losing 2 electrons. What will the charge on the ion be? ☐
8) Draw the dot and cross diagram for H_2O. ☐
9) True or false? Ionic compounds are usually more volatile than simple molecular compounds. ☐

S
10) Describe the structure of silicon dioxide. ☐
11) Draw a labelled diagram to illustrate metallic bonding. ☐

Formulas of Compounds and Balancing Equations (p.32-34) ☐

12) How many oxygen atoms are in a molecule of $Ca(OH)_2$? ☐

S
13) Does an ionic compound have a positive, negative or neutral overall charge? ☐

14) Is the following equation balanced? $2Mg + O_2 \rightarrow MgO$ ☐

S
15) What are the state symbols for: a) gas b) liquid c) solid d) aqueous ☐
16) Explain how to write an ionic equation using the balanced symbol equation for a reaction. ☐

Relative Atomic and Molecular Masses (p.36) ☐

17) What is the relative atomic mass of ^{12}C? ☐
18) Why is chlorine's A_r not a whole number? ☐
19) How would you calculate the relative molecular mass of a molecule? ☐

Supplement

Moles and Calculations (p.37-44) ☐

20) State Avogadro's constant. ☐
21) Imagine you are given the number of moles present in a sample of a compound and the M_r of the compound. How would you work out the mass of the sample? ☐
22) What would increasing the amount of the limiting reactant do to the amount of product formed in a reaction? ☐
23) What equation would you use to calculate the percentage yield of a reaction? ☐
24) True or false? Empirical formulas show the actual number of atoms of each element in a molecule. ☐
25) How would you convert a concentration from moles/dm^3 to grams/dm^3? ☐
26) Define the molar gas volume and give its value. ☐

Electrolysis

You need to know all about how electrolysis works. So get ready, here we go...

Electrolysis Means 'Splitting Up with Electricity'

Electrolysis is the breakdown of an ionic compound, molten or in aqueous solution, by the passage of electricity.

An electrolyte is just a liquid or solution that can conduct electricity. An electrode is a solid that conducts electricity and is submerged in the electrolyte.

1) During electrolysis, an electric current is passed through an electrolyte. The electrolyte is a molten or dissolved ionic compound (it must be molten or dissolved so that the ions are free to move).
2) The ions move towards the electrodes, where they react, and the compound decomposes.

Supplement

3) The positive ions in the electrolyte will move towards the cathode (–ve electrode) and remove electrons from the circuit.
4) The negative ions in the electrolyte will move towards the anode (+ve electrode) and provide electrons, which then flow along a metallic conductor back towards the cathode.
5) This creates a flow of charge through the electrolyte as ions travel to the electrodes.
6) As ions gain or lose electrons, they form the uncharged element and are discharged from the electrolyte.

Electrolysis of Molten Ionic Solids Forms Elements

1) An ionic solid can't be electrolysed because the ions are in fixed positions and can't move.
2) Molten ionic compounds can be electrolysed because the ions can move freely and conduct electricity.
3) Molten ionic compounds are always broken up into their elements. A good example of this is the electrolysis of molten lead(II) bromide:

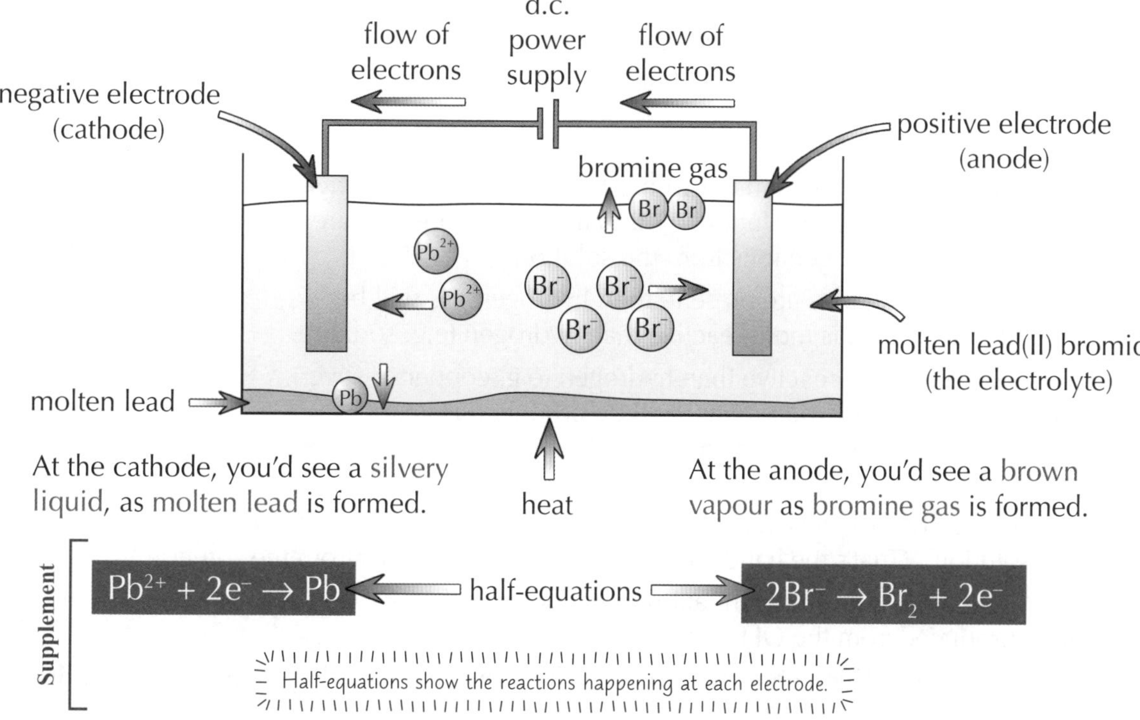

At the cathode, you'd see a silvery liquid, as molten lead is formed.

At the anode, you'd see a brown vapour as bromine gas is formed.

Supplement

$Pb^{2+} + 2e^- \rightarrow Pb$ ← half-equations → $2Br^- \rightarrow Br_2 + 2e^-$

Half-equations show the reactions happening at each electrode.

4) The electrodes are made of an inert material, such as platinum or carbon, so they don't react with the electrolyte.

Electrolysis of Aqueous Solutions

When carrying out electrolysis on an aqueous solution, you have to factor in the ions in water.

Electrolysis of Aqueous Solutions Involves the Ions From Water

1) In aqueous solutions, as well as the ions from the ionic compound, there will be hydrogen ions (H^+) and hydroxide ions (OH^-) from the water.
2) Either a metal (from the metal ions in the salt solution) or hydrogen (from the H^+ ions in the water) will form at the negative electrode (cathode).
3) Meanwhile, a non-metal will form at the positive electrode (anode). This will either be a substance formed from the non-metal ions in the salt solution, or oxygen formed from the OH^- ions in the water.
4) You can predict what products will form at the electrodes when an aqueous solution is electrolysed. Here are three examples that you need to know:

Aqueous Electrolyte	Product at Cathode	Observations	Product at Anode	Observations
concentrated hydrochloric acid, HCl	hydrogen	colourless bubbles	chlorine	green bubbles
dilute sulfuric acid, H_2O/H_2SO_4	hydrogen	colourless bubbles	oxygen	colourless bubbles
concentrated aqueous sodium chloride, NaCl	hydrogen	colourless bubbles	chlorine	green bubbles

Supplement

You Can Predict The Products of Electrolysis

You need to be able to predict what products will form when an aqueous solution that contains halide ions is electrolysed. Here's how you work it out:

Halide ions are the 1– ions formed from Group VII elements. That's F^-, Cl^-, Br^- and I^-.

- At the cathode, the product that is formed depends on the reactivity of the positive ions in the solution. (That's any metal ions that are present, plus the hydrogen ions from the solution.)
- If H^+ ions and metal ions are present, then hydrogen gas will be produced if the metal is more reactive than hydrogen (e.g. sodium).
- But if the metal is less reactive than hydrogen (e.g. copper or silver), then a solid layer of the pure metal will be produced instead.

You can use a reactivity series to compare the reactivity of metals. Hydrogen sits just above copper in the reactivity series on p.97.

- At the anode, the products that are formed depend on the concentration of the negative ions in the solution. (That's the halide ions plus the hydroxide ions from the solution.)
- If the solution has a low concentration of halide ions, then oxygen and water will be produced from the OH^- ions.
- If the solution has a high concentration of halide ions, then a halogen gas will be produced.

Supplement

Electrolysis of Aqueous Solutions

Example: Electrolysis of Sodium Chloride (NaCl) Solution

1) A solution of sodium chloride (NaCl) contains four different ions: Na^+, Cl^-, OH^- and H^+.

2) Sodium metal is more reactive than hydrogen. So at the cathode, hydrogen gas is produced.

$$2H^+ + 2e^- \rightarrow H_2$$

3) In a concentrated solution of sodium chloride, lots of chloride ions are present. So at the anode, chlorine gas is produced.

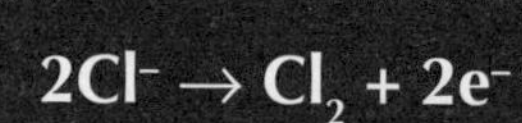

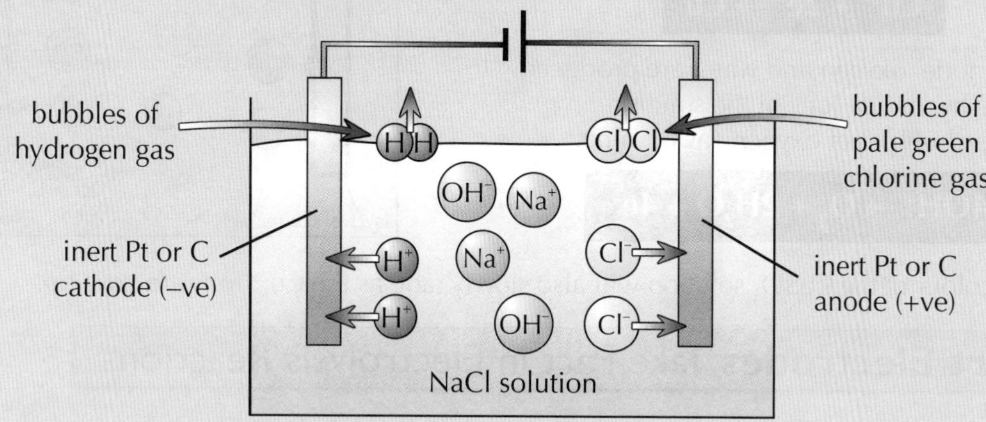

4) In a dilute solution of sodium chloride, the concentration of Cl^- ions is much lower.

5) As a result, oxygen gas (O_2) and water (H_2O) are produced at the anode instead of chlorine.

$$4OH^- \rightarrow O_2 + 2H_2O + 4e^-$$

All **Aqueous Solutions** Follow This Pattern:

Concentrated Hydrochloric Acid (HCl)

In concentrated hydrochloric acid, there are three ions present: H^+, Cl^-, and OH^-.
The reactions that happen at the electrodes are:

Cathode half-equation: $2H^+ + 2e^- \rightarrow H_2$

Anode half-equation: $2Cl^- \rightarrow Cl_2 + 2e^-$

Dilute Sulfuric Acid (H_2SO_4)

In dilute sulfuric acid, there are three ions present: H^+, SO_4^{2-}, and OH^-.
The reactions that happen at the electrodes are:

Cathode half-equation: $2H^+ + 2e^- \rightarrow H_2$

Anode half-equation: $4OH^- \rightarrow O_2 + 4H_2O + 2e^-$

There are lots of ions to think about here...

In the exam, it might be a good idea to write out all of the ions in the solution, and then circle the ones that react at the electrodes. That way, you're less likely to forget any of the ions present.

Electrolysis of Copper Sulfate

Copper sulfate is a classic example of how changing the electrodes can change the products of electrolysis.

Copper Sulfate Electrolysis with Inert Electrodes Produces **Oxygen**

1) A solution of copper sulfate ($CuSO_4$) contains four different ions: Cu^{2+}, SO_4^{2-}, H^+ and OH^-.
2) When you electrolyse copper sulfate solution with inert carbon electrodes:
   - Copper is less reactive than hydrogen, so copper metal is produced at the cathode. You'll see a coating of copper on the electrode.

     $$Cu^{2+} + 2e^- \rightarrow Cu$$

   - At the anode, oxygen and water are produced from the hydroxide ions in the solution. You'll see bubbles of oxygen gas forming.

     $$4OH^- \rightarrow O_2 + 2H_2O + 4e^-$$

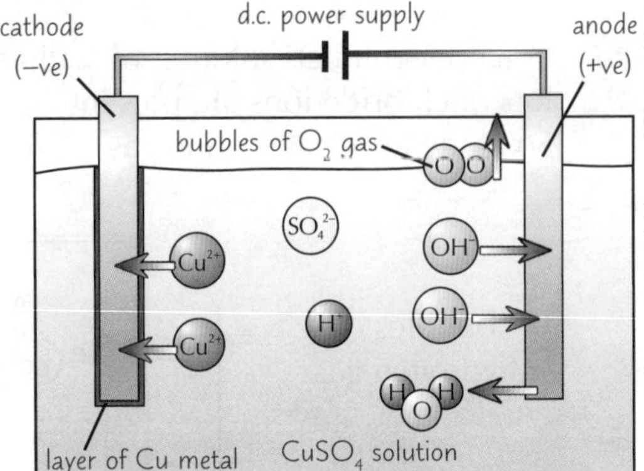

3) The blue colour of the $CuSO_4$ solution will also slowly fade as the Cu^{2+} ions are used up.

Non-Inert Electrodes Take Part in Electrolysis Reactions

1) If you use copper electrodes in a solution of copper sulfate instead of inert electrodes, the result is different. Copper metal is still produced at the cathode, but the anode will now release copper ions into the solution.

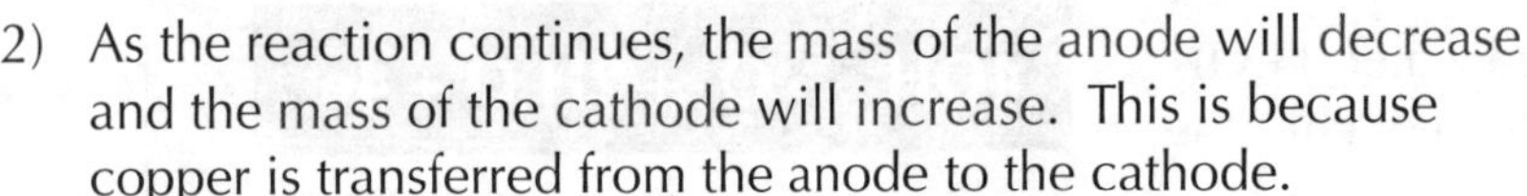

2) As the reaction continues, the mass of the anode will decrease and the mass of the cathode will increase. This is because copper is transferred from the anode to the cathode.
3) If you increase the current (e.g. by adding batteries) you will increase the rate of electrolysis. This means there will be a bigger difference between the mass of the two electrodes after the same amount of time.

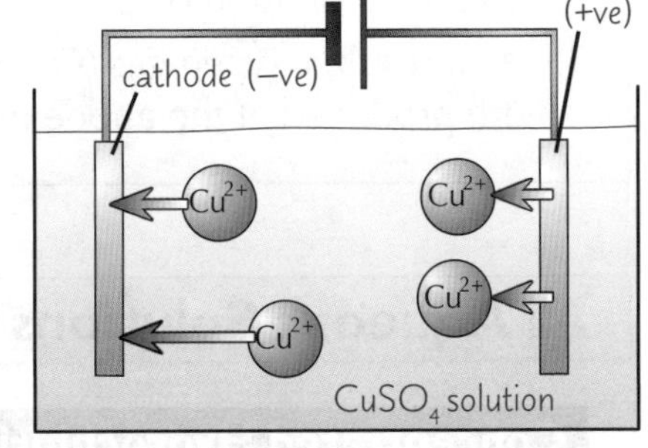

4) The electrical supply acts by:
   - Pulling electrons off copper atoms at the anode:

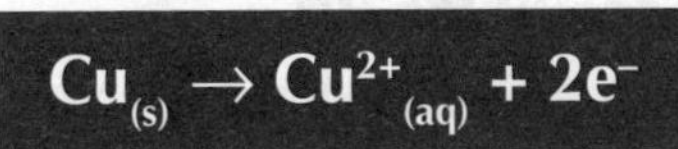

   - Offering electrons at the cathode to nearby Cu^{2+} ions:

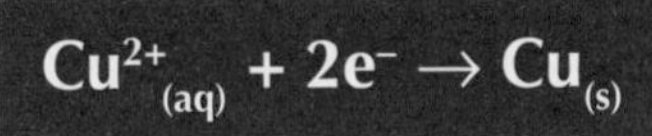

Cu²⁺(aq) + 2e⁻ → Cu(s)

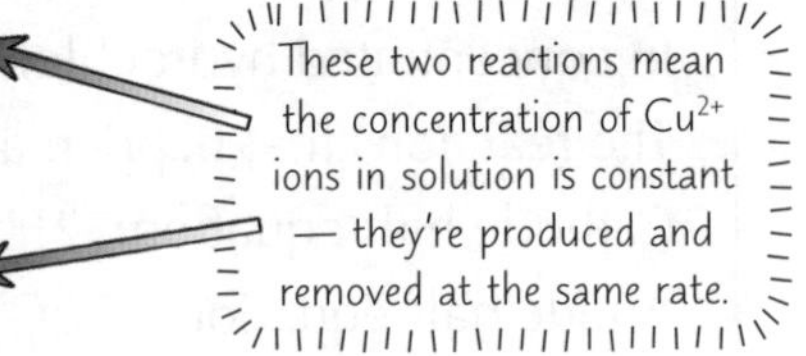

These two reactions mean the concentration of Cu²⁺ ions in solution is constant — they're produced and removed at the same rate.

Electrolysis Can be Used to **Purify Copper**

Copper can be extracted from its ore using carbon (see p.102), but copper made in this way is impure. Electrolysis is used to purify it — this method uses electrolysis with copper electrodes:

When copper is purified using electrolysis, the anode starts off as a big lump of impure copper, the electrolyte is copper(II) sulfate solution (which contains Cu^{2+} ions) and the cathode starts off as a thin piece of pure copper. Here's what happens during the process:

1) The impure copper anode loses electrons, dissolving into the electrolyte to form copper ions.
2) The copper ions gain electrons at the pure copper cathode, and add to it as a layer of pure copper.
3) Any impurities from the impure copper anode sink to the bottom of the cell, forming a sludge.

Supplement

Practical Applications of Electrolysis

Electrolysis isn't just used in laboratories — it's got some really important uses in industry as well.

Electroplating is Applying a **Metal Coating** to an Object

1) Electroplating is coating the surface of a metal with another metal using electrolysis.

2) The cathode is the object you're going to electroplate, the anode is often a bar of the metal you're using for the plating. Your electrolyte is a solution containing the metal ions of the metal you're plating.

3) Electroplating is really useful. Household objects like cutlery and cooking utensils are electroplated with metals to stop them corroding. The metals used for protection are unreactive and don't corrode easily.

4) Jewellery and decorative items are often electroplated with metals like gold or silver. This improves the appearance of the metals — making them look shiny and attractive.

Example: Electroplating silver onto a brass cup.

- The cathode is the brass cup and the anode is a bar of pure silver.
- The electrolyte is silver nitrate solution ($AgNO_3$).
- The positive silver ions from the electrolyte move towards the cathode. At the cathode, they gain an electron each to become neutral silver atoms. So silver metal gets deposited on the brass cup.

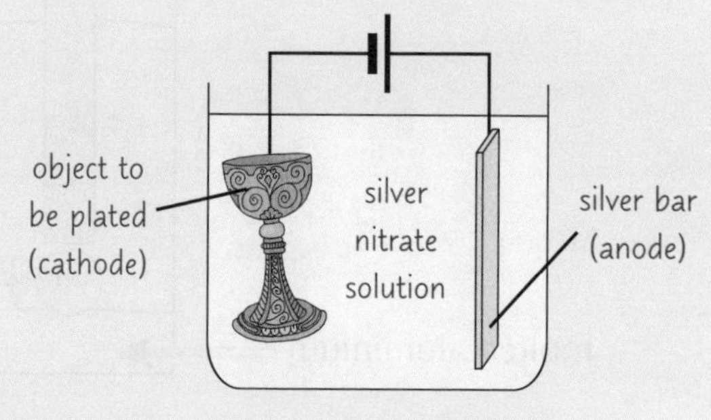

- At the anode, silver atoms lose electrons and move into the solution as silver ions. This replaces the ions from the electrolyte that have been used up at the cathode.

Power Cables are Commonly Made from **Copper** and **Aluminium**

1) Pure copper and aluminium can both be produced using electrolysis.

2) They are both metals and are therefore good conductors of electricity.

3) Both metals are used in power cables and wires.

Aluminium is cheaper and lighter than copper. Aluminium cables also contain a steel core to make them stronger.

4) It is important to protect wires from factors such as corrosion. Plastics and ceramics are commonly used to protect wires as they are both electrical insulators — they cannot conduct an electrical charge.

Practical Applications of Electrolysis

Metals can be Extracted From Their Ores Using Electrolysis

1) Aluminium is extracted from bauxite ore by electrolysis. Bauxite contains aluminium oxide, Al_2O_3.
2) Aluminium oxide melts at a very high temperature so it's mixed with cryolite to lower the melting point.
3) Adding cryolite increases the electrical conductivity of the mixture, as cryolite is more conductive than aluminium oxide.
4) The molten mixture conducts electricity because it contains free ions.
5) Carbon electrodes are used.
6) The positive Al^{3+} ions are attracted to the negative electrode where they each pick up three electrons and turn into neutral aluminium atoms. These then sink to the bottom of the electrolysis tank.
7) The negative O^{2-} ions are attracted to the positive electrode where they each lose two electrons. The neutral oxygen atoms will then combine to form O_2 molecules.

Cryolite is an aluminium based compound with a lower melting point than aluminium oxide.

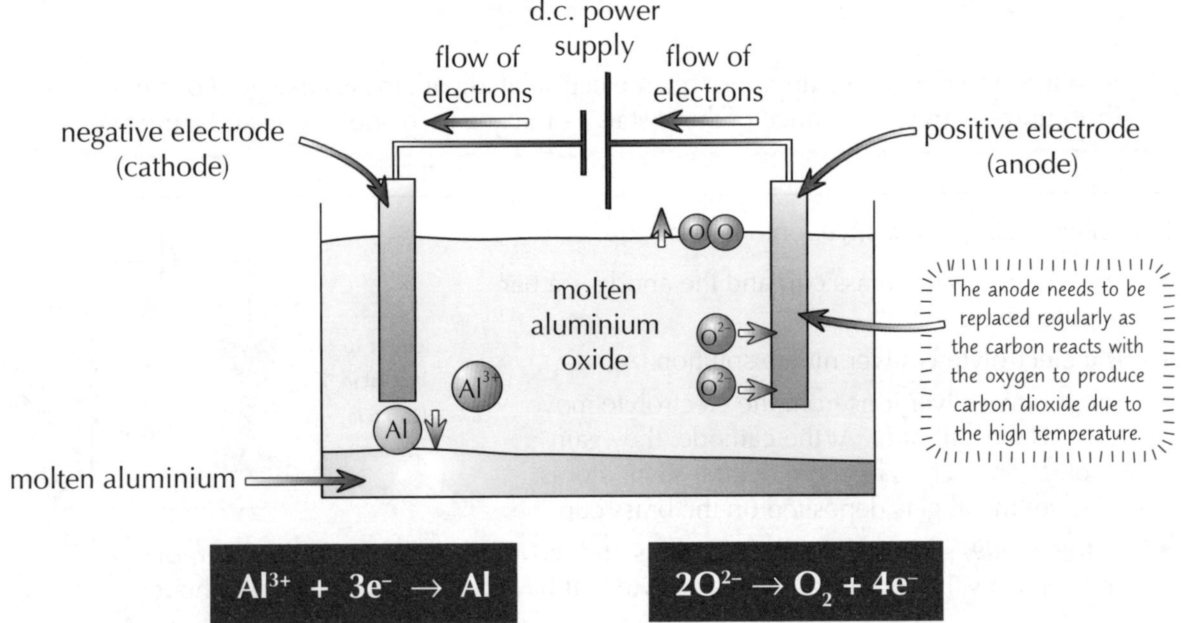

$Al^{3+} + 3e^- \rightarrow Al$

$2O^{2-} \rightarrow O_2 + 4e^-$

Electrolysis of Concentrated NaCl Produces H_2, Cl_2 and NaOH

1) You've already seen the electrolysis of concentrated sodium chloride (NaCl) on page 49.
2) The electrolyte contains four ions — Na^+, Cl^-, H^+ and OH^-.
3) Na^+ is more reactive than H^+, so H_2 gas is formed at the cathode.
4) As a halide ion (Cl^-) is present at a high concentration, Cl_2 gas is formed at the anode.
5) The Na^+ and OH^- ions are left behind in the electrolyte, so a solution of NaOH is formed.
6) All three products of this electrolysis process are industrially useful chemicals.

Extracting metals by electrolysis requires a lot of energy

Aluminium oxide is an ionic compound. As you know from page 28, ionic compounds have high melting points due to the extremely strong bonds between the ions. As a result, a lot of energy is needed to break these bonds and melt the ore. This makes electrolysis a very expensive process.

Cells

Electrochemical cells are really useful. They can be used to produce electricity which can power a huge variety of things. In fact, batteries are just groups of electrochemical cells connected together.

Chemical Reactions in a Cell Produce Electricity

An electrochemical cell is a basic system made up of two different electrodes in contact with an electrolyte. An example of a simple electrochemical cell is shown in the diagram below.

1) The two electrodes must be able to conduct electricity and so are usually metals.
2) The electrolyte is a liquid that contains ions which react with the electrodes.
3) The chemical reactions between the electrodes and the electrolyte set up a charge difference between the electrodes.
4) If the electrodes are then connected by a wire, the charge is able to flow and electricity is produced.
5) A voltmeter can also be connected to the circuit to measure the voltage of the cell.

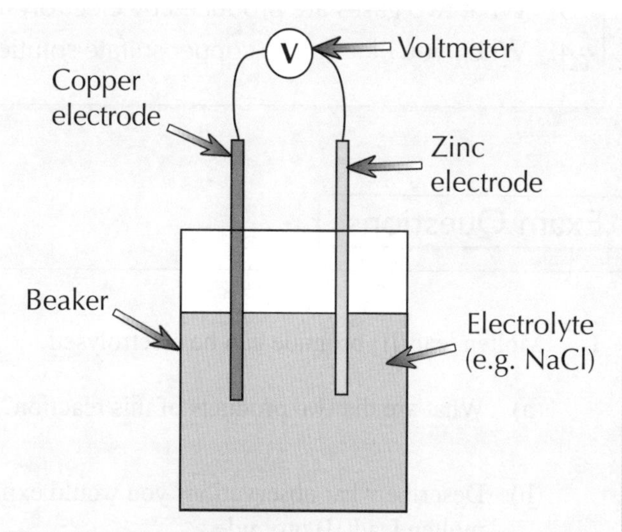

Supplement

The Voltage of a Cell Depends on Many Factors

1) Different metals will react differently with the same electrolyte — this is what causes the charge difference, or the voltage, of the cell. So the type of electrodes used will affect the voltage of the cell.
2) The bigger the difference in reactivity of the electrodes, the bigger the voltage of the cell.

EXAMPLE:

A student wants to make a cell with the greatest possible voltage. He has a choice of three metals to make the two electrodes from, which are shown with their relative reactivities in the table. What metals should he choose?

Metal	Reactivity
zinc	most reactive
iron	↓
copper	least reactive

To create the biggest difference in voltage, you need to pick the two metals with the biggest difference in reactivity. So the student should use zinc and copper in his cell.

3) Oxidation (loss of electrons) occurs at the most reactive electrode. Reduction (gain of electrons) occurs at the least reactive electrode.

There's more about redox on page 72.

4) The electrolyte used in a cell will also affect the size of the voltage since different ions in solution will react differently with the metal electrodes used.

Supplement

The two electrodes need to be connected for charge to flow

This stuff can be a bit tricky. Make sure you learn all the parts of a simple cell and what function they have. You could even draw out a chemical cell for yourself to make sure you've learnt it all.

Warm-Up & Exam Questions

You've reached the end of Section 5 — congratulations. Now, in a shocking turn of events, there's some exam questions to do. I know, I wasn't expecting this level of excitement either.

Warm-Up Questions

1) Define electrolysis.
2) Which electrode are positive ions attracted to during electrolysis? [S]
3) What two gases are produced by electrolysing dilute sulfuric acid?
4) When you electrolyse copper sulfate solution with inert electrodes, what forms at the cathode? [S]

Exam Questions

1 Molten lead(II) bromide can be electrolysed.

(a) What are the two products of this reaction?

[2]

(b) Describe what observations you would expect to make during the electrolysis of molten lead(II) bromide.

[2]

[Total 4 marks]

2 Electroplating is useful for protecting objects against corrosion.

(a) What is used as the cathode in an electroplating process?

[1]

(b) Suggest why it is sometimes necessary to replace the anode during electroplating.

[2]

[Total 3 marks]

3 When concentrated sodium chloride solution is electrolysed, a gas is produced at each electrode.

(a) Name the gas produced at the negative electrode.

[1]

(b) Name the gas produced at the positive electrode.

[1]

(c) Why are inert electrodes used in this process?

[1]

Supplement

(d) Give the half-equation for the reaction at the negative electrode.

[1]

(e) If concentrated copper chloride solution is electrolysed, copper metal is produced at the negative electrode, instead of the gas named in part (a). Explain why.

[1]

[Total 5 marks]

Exam Questions

4 Aluminium is extracted by electrolysis of molten aluminium oxide (Al_2O_3).

(a) Complete the half-equation below for the reaction that occurs at the negative electrode.

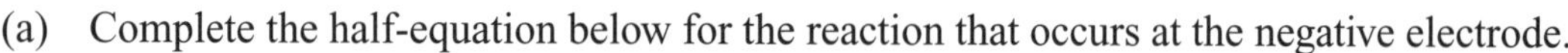

.... + $3e^-$ → ....

[1]

(b) What is the name of the main Al_2O_3-containing ore used to produce aluminium?

[1]

(c) The positive electrode is made of carbon.
Suggest why the positive electrode will need to be replaced over time.

[1]

[Total 3 marks]

5 A student investigated the effect of changing one electrode on the voltage produced by a cell. The other electrode was made of zinc, which is less reactive than all of the other metals tested. Her results are shown in the table below.

Metal used (alongside zinc)	**1**	**2**	**3**
Voltage produced	4 V	2.5 V	3 V

(a) Write the order of reactivity of the metals used from **lowest** to **highest**.
Explain your answer.

[3]

(b) In the cell using zinc and metal **1**, which metal would be oxidised?

[1]

[Total 4 marks]

6 A student investigated the products of electrolysis of a variety of aqueous solutions.

(a) An aqueous solution of copper sulfate ($CuSO_4$) undergoes electrolysis with inert electrodes.

(i) State the **four** ions that this solution contains.

[1]

(ii) Suggest what substance the inert electrodes could be made from.

[1]

(b) The student repeats the electrolysis using copper electrodes and observes that the anode and cathode change mass over time.
Explain this observation.

[3]

(c) When dilute potassium bromide solution is electrolysed with inert electrodes, neither potassium nor bromine are discharged. Explain why and state what is produced instead.

[4]

[Total 9 marks]

Supplement

Endothermic and Exothermic Reactions

Chemical reactions may take energy in from the surroundings or release it to the surroundings.

Reactions are **Exothermic** or **Endothermic**

An EXOTHERMIC reaction is one which gives out energy to the surroundings, usually in the form of heat and usually shown by a rise in temperature of the surroundings.

Combustion reactions (where something burns in oxygen — see page 58) are always exothermic.

An ENDOTHERMIC reaction is one which takes in energy from the surroundings, usually in the form of heat and usually shown by a fall in temperature of the surroundings.

Energy Level Diagrams Show the **Change** in **Energy**

Energy level diagrams show the energy levels of the reactants and the products in a reaction. You can use them to work out if energy is released (exothermic) or taken in (endothermic).

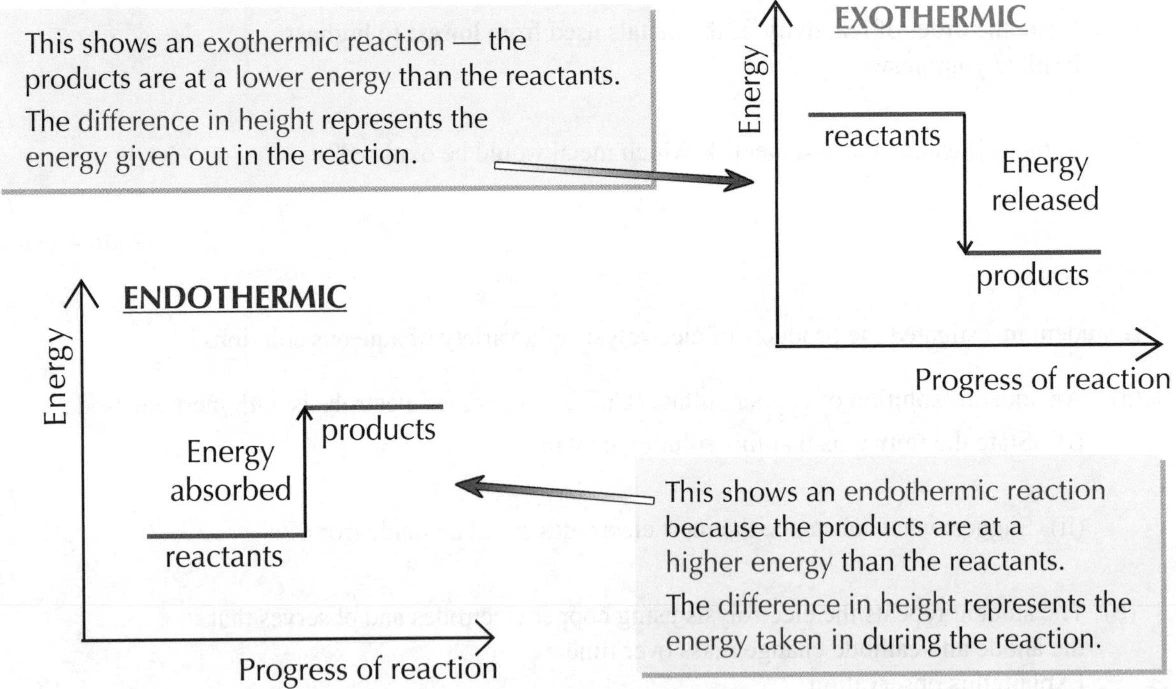

This shows an exothermic reaction — the products are at a lower energy than the reactants. The difference in height represents the energy given out in the reaction.

This shows an endothermic reaction because the products are at a higher energy than the reactants. The difference in height represents the energy taken in during the reaction.

An energy level diagram shows energy change during a reaction

REVISION TIP

Remember, "exo-" = exit, so an exothermic reaction is one that gives out energy — and endothermic just means the opposite. The diagrams above might seem a bit confusing — remember, it's the energy in the chemicals themselves, not in their surroundings, which is being shown. To help you remember them, why not draw them out and label them for yourself.

Bond Energies

Energy transfer in chemical reactions is all to do with making and breaking bonds.

Energy Must Always be **Supplied** to **Break Bonds**

1) During a chemical reaction, old bonds are broken and new bonds are formed.
2) Energy must be supplied to break existing bonds — so bond breaking is an endothermic process.
3) Energy is released when new bonds are formed — so bond formation is an exothermic process.

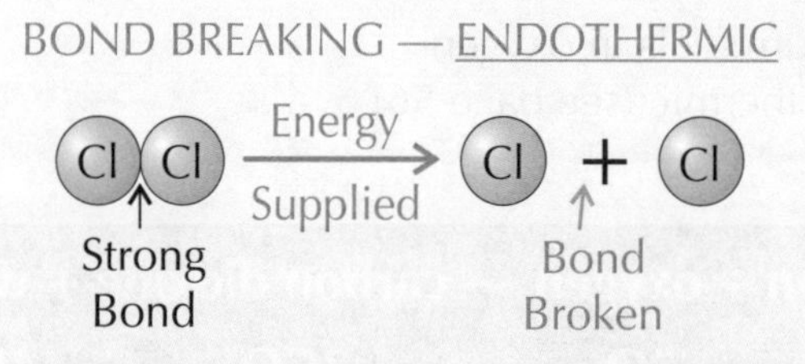

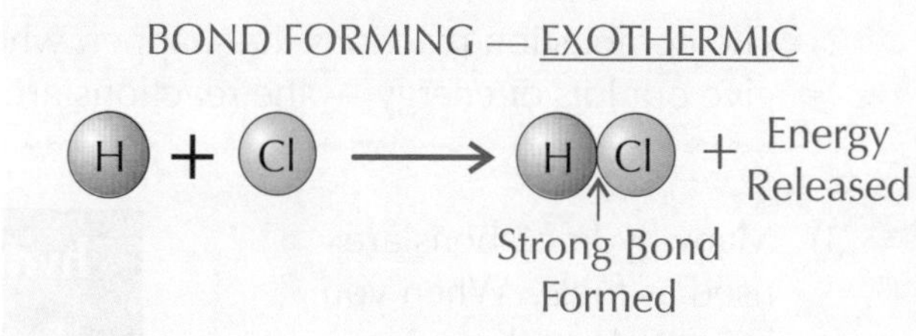

4) In endothermic reactions, the energy used to break bonds is greater than the energy released by forming them.
5) In exothermic reactions, the energy released by forming bonds is greater than the energy used to break them.

Bond Energy Calculations — Need to be Practised

1) Every chemical bond has a particular bond energy associated with it. This bond energy varies slightly depending on the compound the bond occurs in.
2) You can use these known bond energies to calculate the overall energy change for a reaction.

Overall Energy Change = Energy required to break bonds – Energy released by forming bonds

3) A positive energy change means an endothermic reaction and a negative energy change means an exothermic reaction.

EXAMPLE:

Using the bond energy values below, calculate the energy change for the following reaction, where hydrogen and chlorine react to produce hydrogen chloride:

H—H + Cl—Cl → 2H—Cl

H—H: 436 kJ/mol Cl—Cl: 242 kJ/mol H—Cl: 431 kJ/mol

1) Work out the energy required to break the original bonds. (1 × H—H) + (1 × Cl—Cl) = 436 + 242 = 678 kJ/mol
2) Work out the energy released by forming the new bonds. (2 × H—Cl) = 2 × 431 = –862 kJ/mol
3) Work out the overall change. overall energy change = energy required to break bonds – energy released by forming bonds = 678 – 862 = –184 kJ/mol

You should write values for energy released as negative numbers to show the process is exothermic (but you don't need to use this minus sign in the calculation).

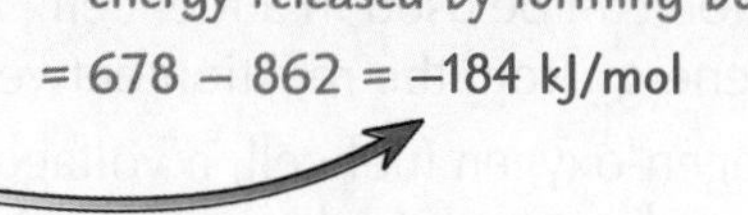

The negative energy change shows the reaction is exothermic. If you draw the energy level diagram for this reaction, the line for the products should be lower than the line for the reactants and the arrow between them should point down.

Supplement

It's useful to draw out the molecules in full for these calculations...

...then you can count all the different types of bonds more easily. This might look hard now, but with a bit of practice you'll find it much easier, and it'll win you easy marks if you understand all the theory behind it.

Energy from Fuels

There are a wide variety of fuels that can be used as a source of energy.

Fuels Release Energy in Combustion Reactions

1) Fuels are substances which can be used as a source of energy. This energy is usually released by combustion (burning).

2) The combustion reactions that happen when you burn fuels in oxygen give out lots of energy — the reactions are very exothermic (see page 56).

3) Many hydrocarbons are used as fuels. When you burn hydrocarbons in plenty of oxygen, the only products are carbon dioxide and water — this is called complete combustion.

hydrocarbon + oxygen → carbon dioxide + water

E.g. $C_3H_8 + 5O_2 \rightarrow 3CO_2 + 4H_2O$

There's more about hydrocarbons on page 128.

Radioactive Isotopes Can be Used as a Source of Energy

See page 16 for more on isotopes.

1) Isotopes of certain radioactive elements, such as plutonium and uranium, may also be used as a source of energy.
2) Radioactive nuclei are large and unstable, causing them to decay (break down) and release energy.
3) Uranium-235 (^{235}U) is a radioactive isotope often used in nuclear power stations.
4) Neutrons are fired at ^{235}U atoms, causing them to break apart and release energy, more neutrons and 'daughter' nuclei.
5) The energy released by ^{235}U is used to heat water into steam. This steam drives huge turbines connected to generators, which produce electricity.

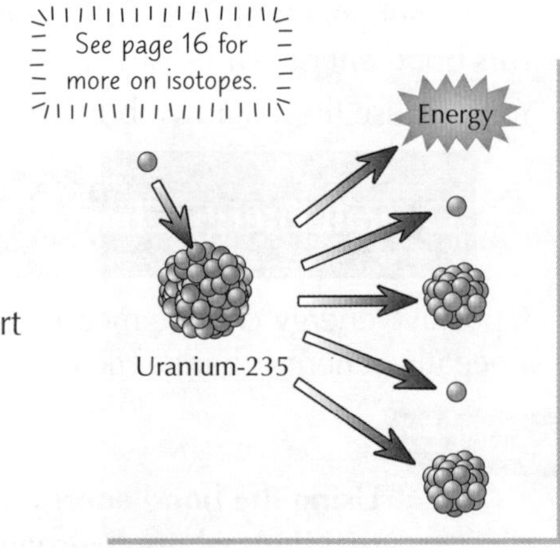

Reacting Hydrogen with Oxygen Releases Energy

1) The reaction between hydrogen and oxygen releases energy, so hydrogen can be used as a fuel.
2) The overall reaction is:

hydrogen + oxygen → water

$2H_2 + O_2 \rightarrow 2H_2O$

This reaction only produces water, so there are no harmful products such as carbon dioxide (see p.116).

Supplement

3) This reaction can be used in a fuel cell. A fuel cell is a type of electrochemical cell (p.53) that uses energy from the reaction between a fuel and oxygen to produce electricity.
4) In a hydrogen-oxygen fuel cell, a voltage (i.e. electrical energy) is produced by reacting hydrogen and oxygen. In the reaction, hydrogen is oxidised and oxygen is reduced (see page 72 for more on oxidation and reduction).

Combustion is a textbook example of an exothermic reaction

There are a couple of key equations on this page, for complete combustion and hydrogen-oxygen fuel cells. Try reading them, covering them up and seeing how well you can remember them.

Warm-Up & Exam Questions

Well, that was a fun section, I'm sure you'll agree. Here are some equally fun questions to test how much you remember from the last three pages. Bet you weren't expecting that...

Warm-Up Questions

1) What is an exothermic reaction?
2) What is an endothermic reaction?
3) Is bond breaking an exothermic or endothermic reaction? [S]

Exam Questions

1 The diagrams below represent the energy changes in four different chemical reactions.

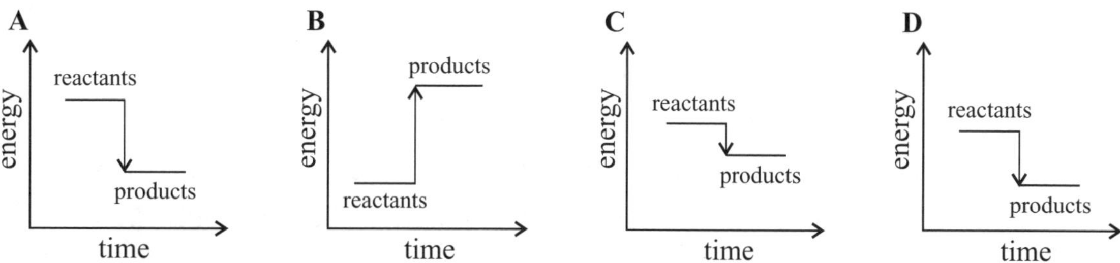

Write the letter of **one** diagram, **A**, **B**, **C** or **D**, which illustrates an endothermic reaction.

[Total 1 mark]

2 Hydrocarbons are commonly used as fuels. Burning hydrocarbons in an oxygen-rich environment produces water and carbon dioxide.

(a) What is the purpose of burning fuels?

[1]

Carbon dioxide is not considered to be a desirable product as it contributes to climate change.

(b) Name a fuel that is not a source of carbon dioxide.

[1]
[Total 2 marks]

Supplement

3 When methane burns in air it produces carbon dioxide and water, as shown below. The bond energies for each bond in the molecules involved are shown in the table.

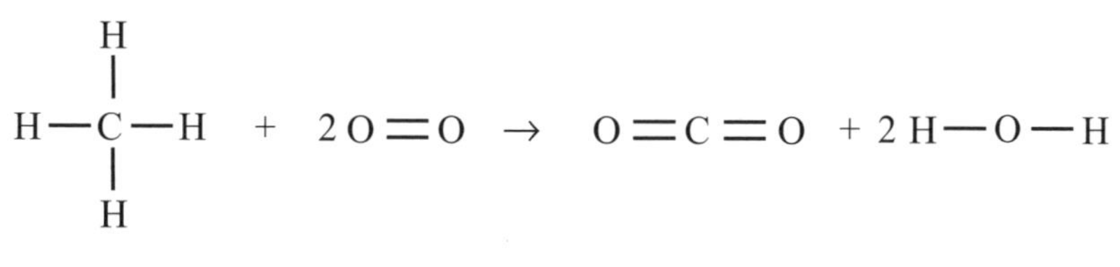

	Bond energies / kJ per mol
C – H	414
O = O	494
C = O	800
O – H	459

(a) Which **two** types of bond are broken during the reaction?

[1]

(b) Calculate the overall energy change for the reaction.

[4]
[Total 5 marks]

Supplement

Revision Summary for Sections 5 & 6

So there we are — the end of Sections 5 and 6. Now there's just this page of questions left to go. Use these questions to test your knowledge of all the important facts you've just learned.

- Try these questions and tick off each one when you get it right.
- When you've done all the questions for a topic and are completely happy with it, tick off the topic.

Electrolysis and Electrochemical Cells (p.47-53) ☐

1) What is an electrolyte? ☐
2) Why can molten ionic compounds be electrolysed but ionic solids can't? ☐
3) Which electrode are negative ions attracted to during electrolysis? ☐
4) At which electrode can hydrogen gas be produced when electrolysing an aqueous solution? ☐
5) What is produced at the anode if halide ions are present in a concentrated aqueous solution? ☐
6) What forms at the anode when you electrolyse aqueous copper sulfate using inert electrodes? ☐
7) What is electroplating used for? ☐
8) Name two metals commonly used to produce cables and wires. ☐
9) Why is aluminium oxide mixed with cryolite in electrolysis? ☐
10) Write the anode and cathode half-equations for the electrolysis of aluminium oxide. ☐
11) True or false? The more reactive electrode in an electrochemical cell is oxidised. ☐

Endothermic & Exothermic Reactions and Bond Energies (p.56-57) ☐

12) What temperature change would you expect to occur in an endothermic reaction? ☐
13) If the products of a reaction have less energy than the reactants, is the reaction endothermic or exothermic? ☐
14) Draw an energy level diagram for an exothermic reaction. ☐
15) True or false? Energy is released when bonds are broken. ☐
16) How would you calculate the overall energy change of a reaction using bond energies? ☐

Energy from Fuels (p.58) ☐

17) Is the combustion of fuels an endothermic or exothermic reaction? ☐
18) Give one example of a radioactive isotope that may be used as a source of energy. ☐
19) What is the equation for the reaction inside hydrogen-oxygen fuel cells? ☐

Rate of Reaction

The rate of a reaction depends on: temperature, concentration (or pressure for gases) and the size of the particles (for solids). This is because these factors affect how particles in a reaction collide with each other.

A Reaction is a **Chemical Change**

A physical change can be reversed by changing the conditions. E.g. lowering the temperature can stop ice melting.

1) If a substance changes from one state of matter to another (for example when it boils or melts), or gets added to a mixture, what happens is a physical change — no new substances are made. Chemical reactions are different...

2) During a chemical reaction, bonds between atoms break and the atoms change places. The atoms from the substances you start with (the reactants) rearrange themselves to form different chemicals (the products).

Particles **Must Collide** in Order to React

1) A reaction can only happen between particles if they collide.
2) The rate of a chemical reaction depends on the collision rate of reacting particles (how often they collide).

The rate of reaction is how fast the reactants are changed into products.

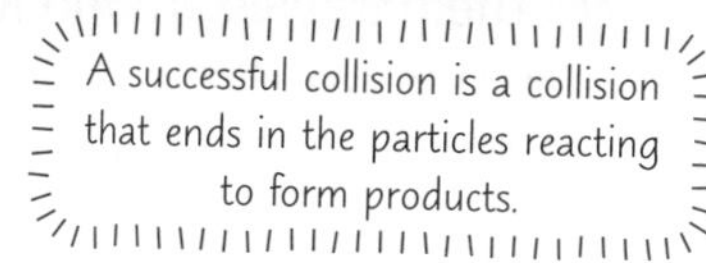

A successful collision is a collision that ends in the particles reacting to form products.

3) The more successful collisions there are, the faster the reaction is.
4) This means that if you increase the number of collisions the reaction happens more quickly (i.e. the rate increases).
5) Temperature, concentration (or pressure) and particle size all affect the rate of a reaction.

Increasing the **Temperature** Increases **Rate**

1) When the temperature is increased the particles move faster. If they move faster, they're going to have more frequent collisions. So increasing the temperature increases the rate of reaction.

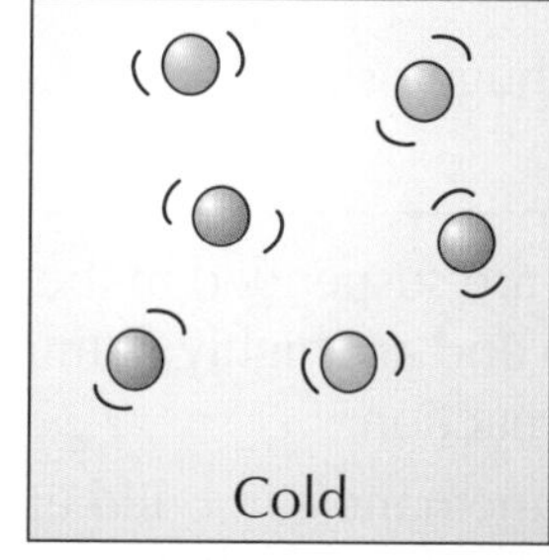

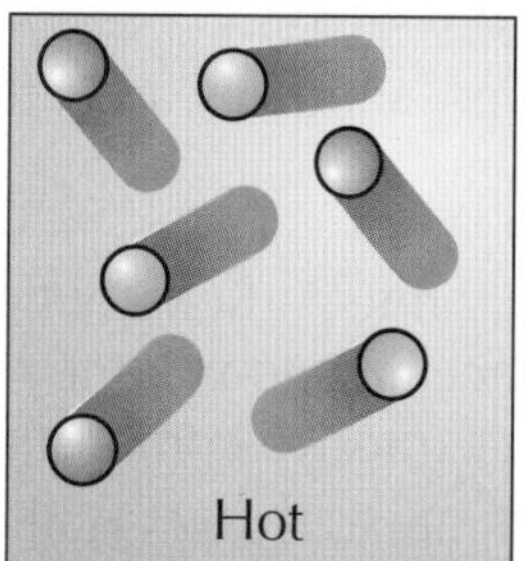

Supplement

2) Reactions only happen if the particles collide with enough energy (called the activation energy).

The activation energy is the minimum amount of energy needed to break the bonds in the reactants and start the reaction.

3) Higher temperatures increase the energy of the collisions, since the particles are moving faster.
4) This means that at higher temperatures there will be more successful collisions (more particles will collide with enough energy to react).

Rate of Reaction

Increasing **Concentration** (or **Pressure**) Increases **Rate**

1) If a solution is made more concentrated it means there are more particles of reactant in the same volume. This makes collisions more likely, so the reaction rate increases.
2) In a gas, increasing the pressure means that the particles are more crowded. This means that the frequency of collisions between particles will increase — so the rate of reaction will also increase.

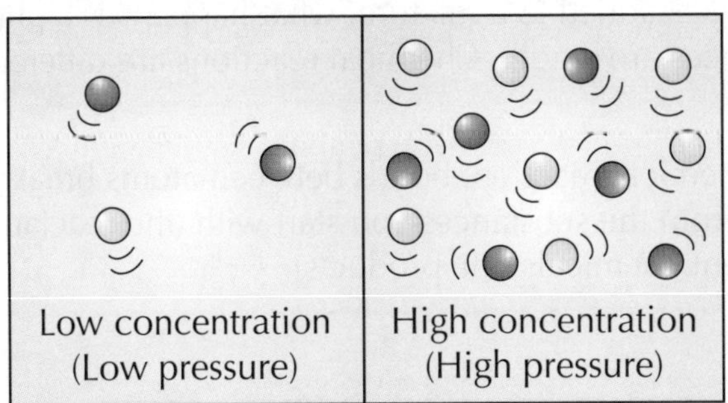

Smaller Solid Particles (or **More Surface Area**) Means a Higher **Rate**

1) If one reactant is a solid, breaking it into smaller pieces will increase its surface area to volume ratio (i.e. more of the solid will be exposed, compared to its overall volume).
2) The particles around it will have more surface to collide with, so the frequency of collisions will increase.
3) This means that the rate of reaction is faster for solids with a larger surface area to volume ratio.

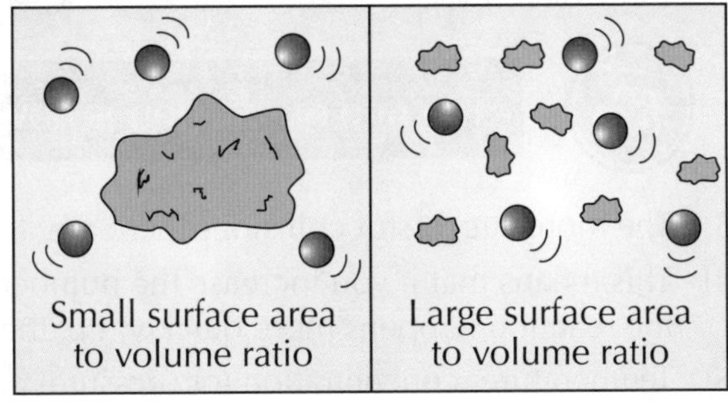

Explosions are **Very Fast** Reactions

1) When you have a high reaction rate for a combustion reaction, you can end up with an explosion (a rapid release of gas and energy).
2) Explosions can occur very suddenly and are a huge risk in certain industries. For example:

- In flour mills, very fine particles of flour are suspended in the air. These dust particles have a high surface area to volume ratio and are highly flammable, so a small spark could lead to an explosive combustion reaction.
- In coal mines, flammable gases such as methane can build up. A high concentration of methane could ignite with a very high rate of combustion, causing a major explosion.

REVISION TIP

It's easier to learn stuff when you know the reasons for it

Once you've learnt everything on these pages, rates of reaction should start making a lot more sense to you. The concept's fairly simple — the more often particles bump into each other, the more likely they are to react, so the faster the reaction happens. (If you're doing the Extended course, don't forget that the amount of energy the particles have is important too.)

More on the Rate of Reaction

Catalysts are very important for commercial reasons — they increase reaction rate and reduce energy costs in industrial reactions. They're also important in living things — read on to find out more...

A **Catalyst Increases** the **Rate** of a Reaction

1) A catalyst is a substance which increases the rate of a reaction, without being chemically changed or used up in the reaction.
2) Using a catalyst won't change the products of the reaction — so the reaction equation will stay the same.
3) Because it isn't used up, you only need a tiny bit to catalyse large amounts of reactants.
4) Catalysts tend to be very fussy about which reactions they catalyse though — you can't just use any catalyst in a reaction and expect it to work.

Supplement

Catalysts **Lower** the Activation Energy

1) Catalysts work by decreasing the activation energy (see page 61) needed for a reaction to occur.
2) They do this by providing an alternative reaction pathway that has a lower activation energy.
3) As a result, more of the particles have at least the minimum amount of energy needed for a reaction to occur when the particles collide.
4) You can show the effect of a catalyst on an energy level diagram.

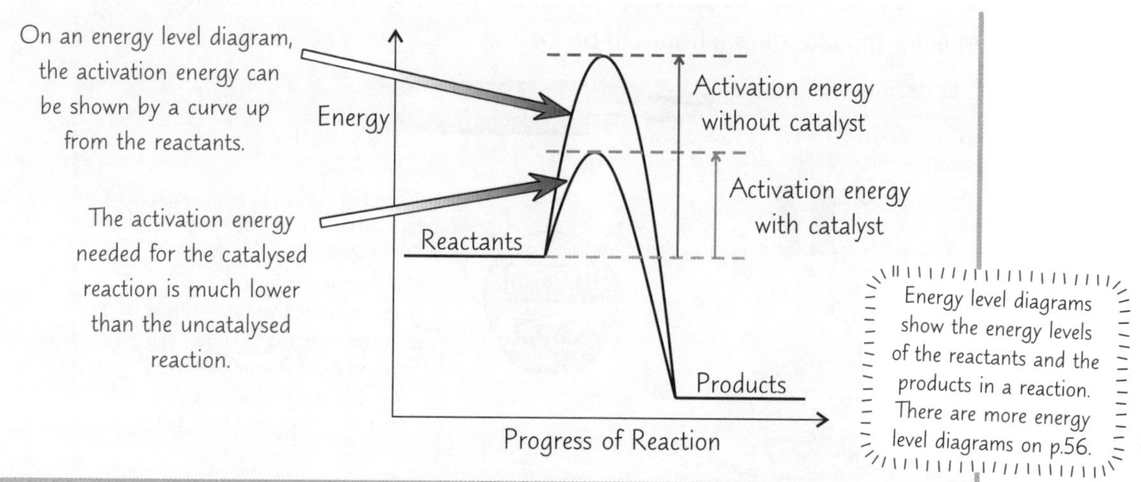
On an energy level diagram, the activation energy can be shown by a curve up from the reactants.
The activation energy needed for the catalysed reaction is much lower than the uncatalysed reaction.
Energy
Activation energy without catalyst
Activation energy with catalyst
Reactants
Products
Progress of Reaction

Energy level diagrams show the energy levels of the reactants and the products in a reaction. There are more energy level diagrams on p.56.

Supplement

Enzymes Control **Cell Reactions**

1) Enzymes are biological catalysts.
2) This means that they catalyse (speed up) the chemical reactions in living cells.

- Enzymes from yeast cells are used in the fermentation process which is used to make alcoholic drinks.
- They catalyse the reaction that converts sugars (such as glucose) into ethanol and carbon dioxide.

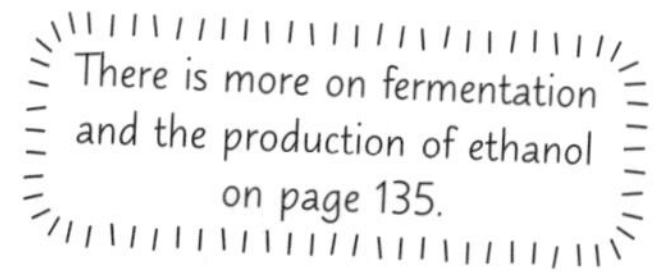

There is more on fermentation and the production of ethanol on page 135.

3) Every enzyme works best at a specific temperature and pH. High temperatures and extreme pH values can denature (destroy) the enzyme, meaning it is no longer able to catalyse the reaction.

Enzymes make sure reactions happen fast enough for us to stay alive

Some reactions take a very long time to happen by themselves, which isn't good for industrial reactions. Catalysts help to produce an acceptable amount of product in an acceptable length of time.

Investigating Reaction Rates

All this talk about the rate of reaction is just fine, but it's no good if you can't measure it.

The **Rate** of a Reaction Can be **Measured**

1) The rate of a reaction can be observed either by how quickly the reactants are used up or how quickly the products are formed. It's usually a lot easier to measure products forming.
2) The rate can be calculated using the following equation:

$$\text{Rate of Reaction} = \frac{\text{Amount of reactant used or amount of product formed}}{\text{Time}}$$

If a reaction produces a gas, there are different ways that the rate of reaction can be measured...

You Can Measure the **Volume** of Gas Given Off

1) This involves the use of a gas syringe to measure the volume of gas given off.
2) The more gas given off during a set time interval, the faster the reaction.
3) You can tell the reaction has finished when no more gas is produced.
4) You can use your results to plot a graph of gas volume against time taken.
5) The units for the rate of reaction will be cm^3/s.

You can also measure the volume of gas produced using an upside down measuring cylinder or burette. This is covered on page 7.

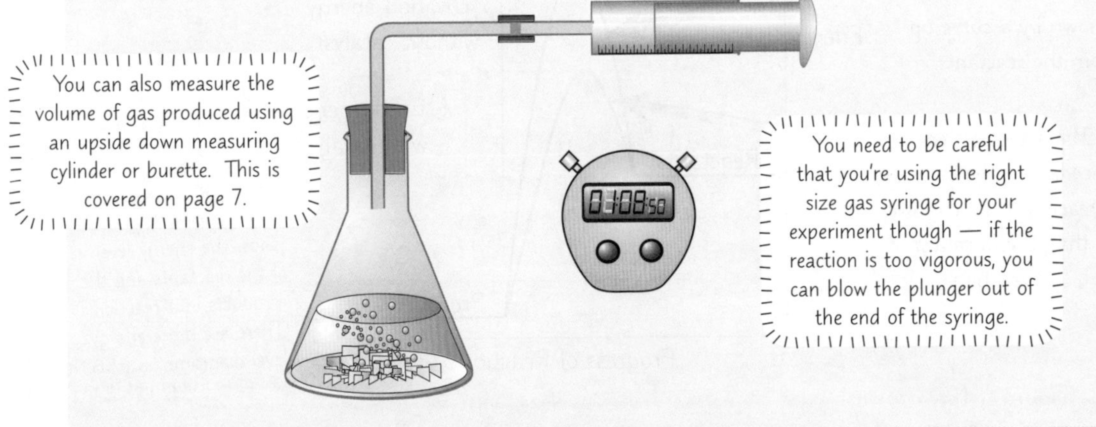

You need to be careful that you're using the right size gas syringe for your experiment though — if the reaction is too vigorous, you can blow the plunger out of the end of the syringe.

You Can Measure the **Change in Mass**

1) You can measure the rate of a reaction that produces a gas using a mass balance.
2) As the gas is released, the lost mass is easily measured on the balance. The quicker the reading on the balance drops, the faster the reaction.
3) You know the reaction has finished when the reading on the balance stops changing.
4) You can use your results to plot a graph of change in mass against time.
5) For this type of experiment, the rate of reaction will be in units of g/s.

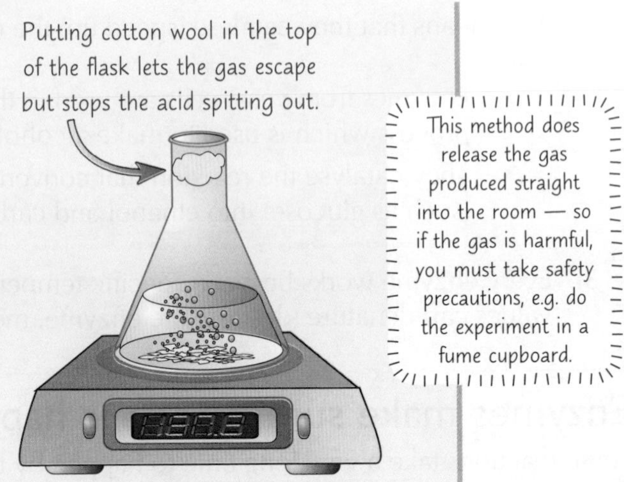

Putting cotton wool in the top of the flask lets the gas escape but stops the acid spitting out.

This method does release the gas produced straight into the room — so if the gas is harmful, you must take safety precautions, e.g. do the experiment in a fume cupboard.

Investigating Reaction Rates

The methods on the previous page can be used to investigate the effect of a variable on the rate of a reaction.

Supplement

You Can Measure how a **Variable** Affects **Rate**

You can use the volume of gas produced by a reaction to investigate the effect of a variable on the rate of that reaction.

For example, if you want to measure the effect of particle size on rate using marble chips and hydrochloric acid:

1) Set up the experiment so that you are measuring the volume of gas produced (or the mass lost).
2) Take readings at regular time intervals and record the results in a table.
3) Repeat the experiment with exactly the same volume and concentration of acid, and exactly the same mass of marble chips, but with the marble more crunched up. Then repeat with the same mass of powdered marble.

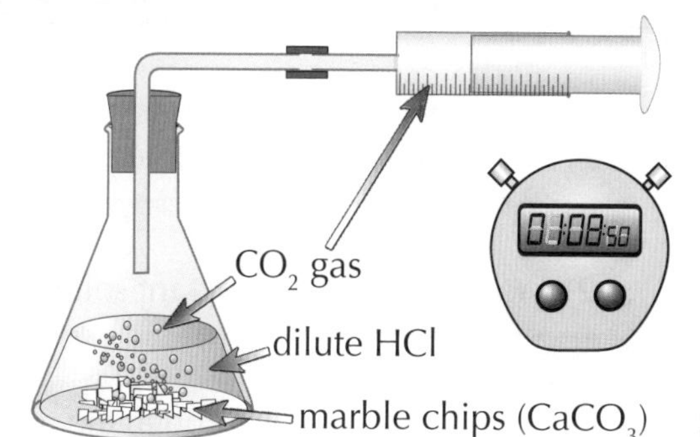

You should only change one variable at a time and keep the rest the same.

To measure the effect of concentration on rate, you could follow the same method described above. But this time repeat the experiment with exactly the same mass and surface area of marble chips and exactly the same volume of acid, but using different concentrations of acid.

To investigate the effect of different catalysts on a reaction, you should repeat the experiment with the same volume and concentration of reactants using different catalysts. The amount of catalyst used must be kept the same each time.

Supplement

You Need to Understand **Graphs** for the **Rate of Reaction**

1) A graph showing the results of a reaction rate investigation will usually have time on the *x*-axis and the variable being measured on the *y*-axis.
2) The steeper the line on the graph, the faster the rate of reaction. Over time the line becomes less steep as the reactants are used up.
3) A flat line on the graph shows that the reaction has finished as there is no more change in the variable.
4) The quickest reactions have the steepest lines and become flat in the least time.
5) The graph below show how the rate of the reaction between marble chips and excess hydrochloric acid varies with the size of the particles of marble.

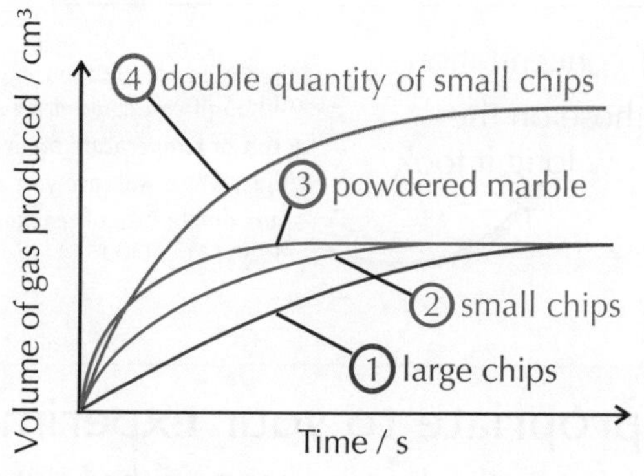

- Using finer particles means that the marble has a larger surface area.
- Lines 1 to 3 on the graph on the left show that the finer the particles are (and the greater the surface area of the solid reactants), the sooner the reaction finishes and so the faster the reaction.
- Line 4 shows the reaction if a greater mass of small marble chips is added. The extra surface area gives a faster reaction and there is also more gas evolved overall.

Investigating Reaction Rates

Here's how to use precipitation to measure the rate of reaction It's less accurate than using a mass balance or a gas syringe, but it's handy because it lets you investigate a reaction that doesn't produce a gas.

Supplement

A **Precipitate** Makes the Solution **Cloudy**

1) This method works for any reaction where mixing two see-through solutions produces a precipitate, which clouds the solution.

2) You mix the two reactant solutions and put the flask on a piece of paper that has a mark on it.

3) Observe the mark through the mixture and measure how long it takes for the mark to be obscured. The faster it disappears, the faster the reaction.

E.g. Sodium thiosulfate and hydrochloric acid are both clear solutions. They react together to form a yellow precipitate of sulfur.

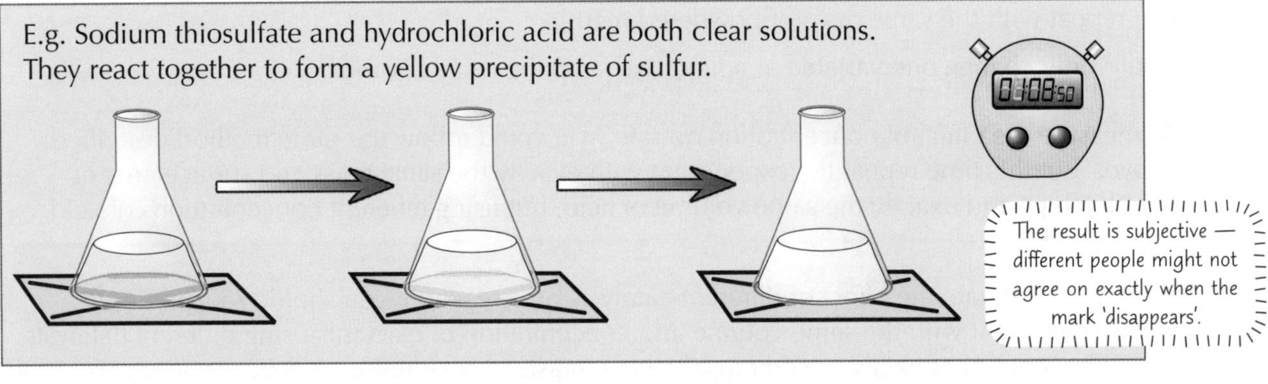

The result is subjective — different people might not agree on exactly when the mark 'disappears'.

You can Investigate the Effect of **Temperature** on **Rate**

The reaction between sodium thiosulfate and hydrochloric acid can be repeated at different temperatures.

1) Use a water bath to heat both solutions to the right temperature before you mix them.
2) The depth of liquid must be kept the same each time.
3) The results will show that the higher the temperature, the quicker the reaction and therefore the less time it takes for the mark to disappear. These are typical results:

independent variable →	**Temperature / °C**	20	25	30	35	40
dependent variable →	**Time taken for mark to disappear / s**	193	151	112	87	52

4) This reaction can also be used to test the effects of concentration.
5) This reaction doesn't give you a set of graphs like those on the previous page. All you get is a set of readings of how long it took for the mark to disappear at each temperature.

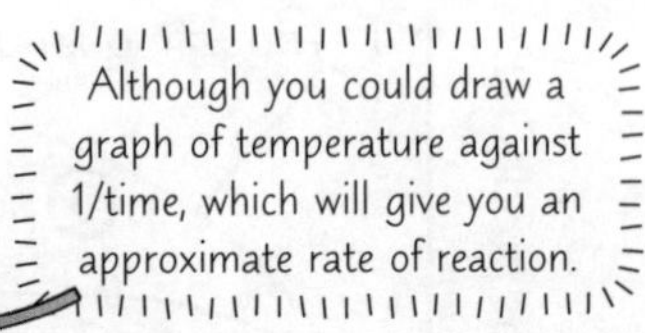

Although you could draw a graph of temperature against 1/time, which will give you an approximate rate of reaction.

Make sure you use a method appropriate to your experiment

The method shown on this page only works if there's a really obvious change in the solution. If there's only a small change in colour, it might not be possible to observe and time the change.

Photochemical Reactions

Some reactions need light in order to get going, and the amount of light can affect the reaction rate...

Photochemical Reactions Need Light

1) All reactions need energy to be supplied in order for the reaction to start (the activation energy).

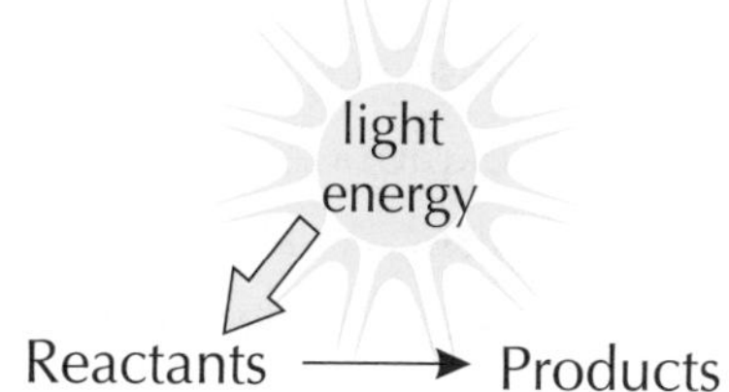

2) A photochemical reaction is a reaction that is started by energy in the form of light.

3) You need to know about these photochemical reactions...

Substitution Reactions with Chlorine

1) Alkanes, such as methane (CH_4), are generally unreactive compounds made up of carbon and hydrogen.
2) Alkanes can react with chlorine to form chloroalkanes.
3) A mixture of alkane and chlorine molecules will not react on its own, but it will react when exposed to ultraviolet (UV) light.
4) This is because the UV light breaks the bonds in the chlorine molecules, creating highly reactive atoms.
5) A greater intensity of UV light means more bonds are broken per unit of time, which leads to a faster reaction rate.

There's more about this reaction on page 129.

$$CH_4 + Cl_2 \xrightarrow{UV} CH_3Cl + HCl$$

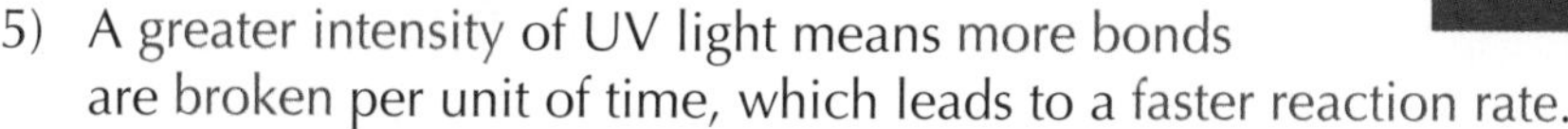

Producing Photographic Negatives

1) Black-and-white photographic film is covered in silver salts, such as silver chloride.
2) When a photograph is taken, areas of the paper are exposed to light. The silver salts break down where the paper is exposed. This reaction produces silver metal, which appears black.
3) The reaction creates a negative image. The brighter the light that shines on the paper, the faster the silver salt breaks down and so the darker the film turns.

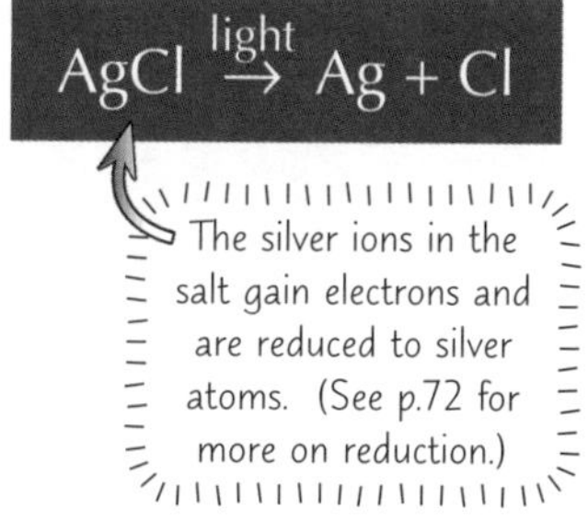

$$AgCl \xrightarrow{light} Ag + Cl$$

The silver ions in the salt gain electrons and are reduced to silver atoms. (See p.72 for more on reduction.)

Photosynthesis In Plants

1) Photosynthesis is a reaction that green plants use to make their own food.
2) It converts carbon dioxide and water into glucose (a sugar) and oxygen.

$$6CO_2 + 6H_2O \xrightarrow{light} C_6H_{12}O_6 + 6O_2$$

3) The reaction happens in the presence of sunlight.
4) The light (energy) is absorbed by a green pigment called chlorophyll.
5) As long as there are enough reactants available, more light means a higher rate of photosynthesis.

Supplement

Supplement

Brighter light means a faster rate for photochemical reactions

Try reading this page outside — you never know, it might help speed up your revision....

Warm-Up & Exam Questions

It's easy to think you've understood something when you've just read through it. These questions should test whether you really understand the previous lot of pages.

Warm-Up Questions

1) A salt is dissolved in a solvent — is this a physical change or a chemical change?
2) Why are explosions a serious hazard in flour mills?
3) True or False? A catalyst is unchanged chemically during a reaction.
4) Explain why enzymes are known as 'biological catalysts'.

Exam Questions

1 Oxygen and water can be produced by the decomposition of hydrogen peroxide (H_2O_2).

Samples of three catalysts with the same surface area were added to hydrogen peroxide solution. The same volume and concentration of hydrogen peroxide was used each time. The volume of oxygen produced over time was measured and recorded, and is shown in the graph.

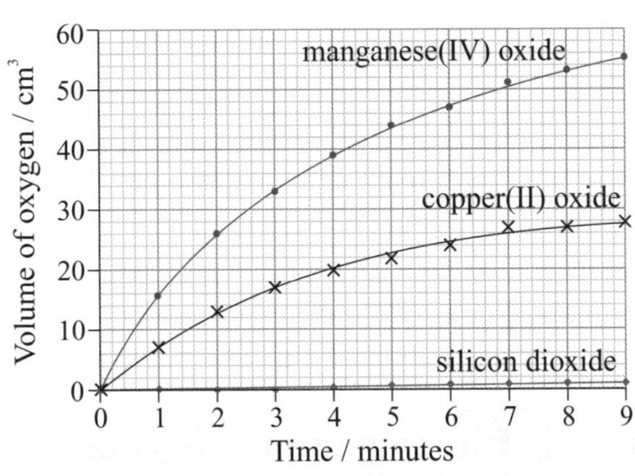

(a) How much oxygen was produced after 3 minutes with copper(II) oxide?

[1]

(b) State, with a reason, the most effective catalyst.

[2]

[Total 3 marks]

2 The rate of a reaction can be measured using different methods.

(a) If one of the products is a gas, the rate of reaction can be measured by recording the change in mass of the reaction vessel using a mass balance.

(i) Suggest **one** disadvantage of this method.

[1]

(ii) Describe a method, other than measuring a change in mass, that could be used to measure the rate of a reaction when one of the products is a gas.

[1]

Supplement

(b) (i) A student wants to investigate how temperature affects the rate of a reaction that produces a precipitate. Outline a suitable method for this investigation.

[4]

(ii) Predict the result of the student's investigation. Explain your prediction.

[3]

[Total 9 marks]

Exam Questions

Supplement

3 Plants produce glucose using energy from light.

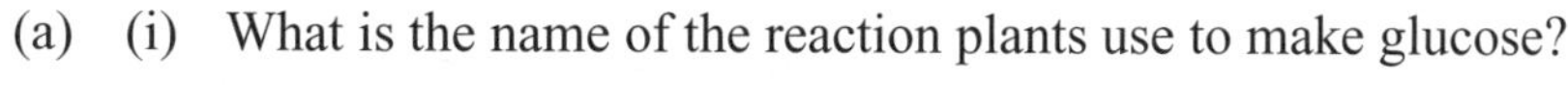

(a) (i) What is the name of the reaction plants use to make glucose?

[1]

(ii) Name the gas produced by this reaction.

[1]

(b) Describe and explain the difference in the rate of glucose production in dim light compared to bright sunlight.

[2]

[Total 4 marks]

4 This question is about the rate of reaction between magnesium and hydrochloric acid. The chemical equation for the reaction is:

$$Mg_{(s)} + 2HCl_{(aq)} \rightarrow MgCl_{2(aq)} + H_{2(g)}$$

(a) The graph below shows how the volume of hydrogen produced changes over the course of the reaction when a small lump of magnesium is added to excess hydrochloric acid.

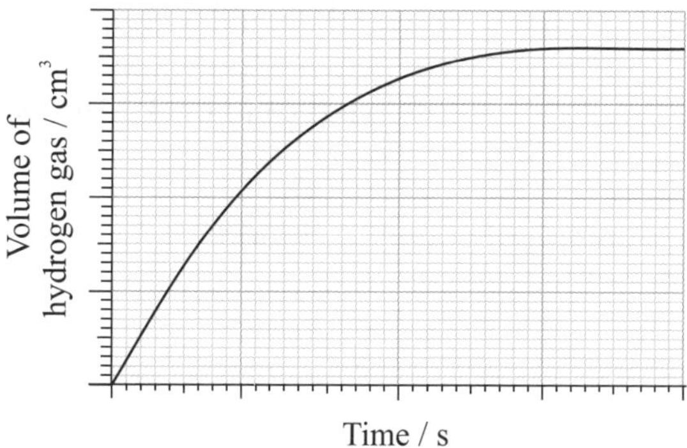

On the same axes, sketch a curve to show how the volume of hydrogen produced over time would change if an identical piece of magnesium was added to excess hydrochloric acid with a higher concentration.

[2]

(b) Explain why increasing the concentration of a reactant increases the rate of the reaction.

[2]

(c) How would you expect the reaction rate to change if the magnesium was cut into smaller pieces?

[1]

(d) Explain why cutting the magnesium into smaller pieces affects the rate of this reaction.

[2]

(e) State **one** change that could be made to alter the rate of reaction, other than changing the concentration of the acid and the size of the magnesium pieces.

[1]

[Total 8 marks]

Reversible Reactions

Some reactions can go backwards. Honestly, that's all you need...

Reversible Reactions Can Go In Either Direction

This equation shows a reversible reaction — the products (C and D) can react to form the reactants (A and B) again:

The '$\rightleftharpoons$' shows the reaction goes both ways.

1) In reversible reactions, if the reaction is endothermic in one direction, it will be exothermic in the other.
2) The direction of the reaction depends on the reaction conditions — changing the reaction conditions, for example by heating or adding water, can change the direction of the reaction.
3) A good example of this is the dehydration of hydrated copper(II) sulfate:

See page 56 for more on endothermic and exothermic reactions.

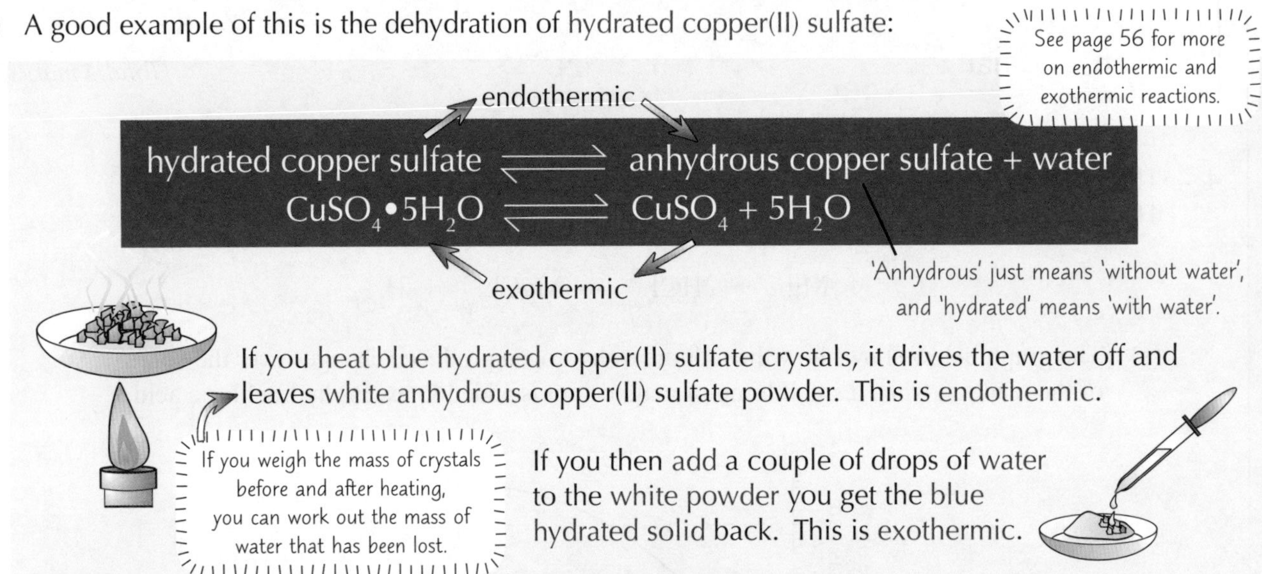

'Anhydrous' just means 'without water', and 'hydrated' means 'with water'.

If you heat blue hydrated copper(II) sulfate crystals, it drives the water off and leaves white anhydrous copper(II) sulfate powder. This is endothermic.

If you weigh the mass of crystals before and after heating, you can work out the mass of water that has been lost.

If you then add a couple of drops of water to the white powder you get the blue hydrated solid back. This is exothermic.

4) A similar example is the dehydration of cobalt(II) chloride — hydrated cobalt(II) chloride is pink, but when heated gently it forms blue anhydrous cobalt(II) chloride crystals.

Supplement

Reversible Reactions Can Reach Equilibrium

1) In a reversible reaction, both the forward and the reverse reactions are happening at the same time.
2) As the reactants react, their concentrations fall — so the forward reaction will slow down (see page 62). But as more and more products are made and their concentrations rise, the backward reaction will speed up.
3) After a while the forward reaction will be going at exactly the same rate as the backward one — the system is at equilibrium.
4) At equilibrium, both reactions are still happening, but there's no overall effect. (This is known as a dynamic equilibrium.) This means the concentrations of reactants and products have reached a balance and won't change.
5) Equilibrium is only reached if the reversible reaction takes place in a 'closed system'. A closed system just means that none of the reactants or products can escape and nothing else can get in.

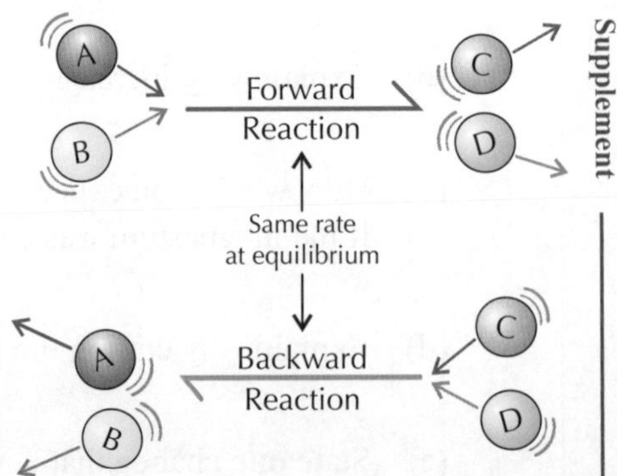

Chemical equilibrium — lots of activity, but not to any great effect

The idea of equilibrium is something that you need to understand if you're taking the Extended course. Have another read and make sure you've got the basics sorted before turning the page...

Equilibrium

Reversible reactions don't like change — so if you alter something in a reversible system, the system will respond to try and undo the change.

Supplement

Reversible Reactions Try to Counteract Changes...

If you change the conditions of a reversible reaction at equilibrium, the system will try to counteract that change. This rule can be used to predict the effect of any changes you make to a reaction system.

...Such as Changes to the Temperature...

1) All reactions are exothermic in one direction and endothermic in the other (see previous page).
2) If you decrease the temperature, the equilibrium will move in the exothermic direction to produce more heat. This means you'll get more products for the exothermic reaction and fewer products for the endothermic reaction.
3) If you raise the temperature, the equilibrium will move in the endothermic direction to try and decrease it. You'll now get more products for the endothermic reaction and fewer products for the exothermic reaction.

$N_2 + 3H_2 \rightleftharpoons 2NH_3$

Here the forward reaction is exothermic — a decrease in temperature moves the equilibrium to the right (making more NH_3).

...Pressure...

1) Changing the pressure only affects an equilibrium involving gases.
2) If you increase the pressure, the equilibrium tries to reduce it — it moves in the direction where there are fewer molecules of gas.
3) If you decrease the pressure, the equilibrium tries to increase it — it moves in the direction where there are more molecules of gas.
4) You can use the balanced symbol equation for a reaction to see which side has more molecules of gas.

$N_2 + 3H_2 \rightleftharpoons 2NH_3$

There are 4 moles on the left (1 of N_2 and 3 of H_2) but only 2 on the right. So, if you increase the pressure, the equilibrium shifts to the right (making more NH_3).

You can talk about the amount of gas on each side of the equilibrium in terms of molecules or moles.

...or Concentration

1) If you change the concentration of either the reactants or the products, the system will no longer be at equilibrium.
2) So the system responds to bring itself back to equilibrium again.
3) If you increase the concentration of a reactant, the system tries to decrease it favouring the forward reaction.
4) If you decrease the concentration of a reactant, the system tries to increase it again by favouring the reverse reaction.
5) Increasing or decreasing the concentration of the products will affect the system in the opposite way.

$N_2 + 3H_2 \rightleftharpoons 2NH_3$

If more N_2 or H_2 is added, the forward reaction increases to produce more NH_3.

So, you do one thing, and the reaction does the other...

The best way to get your head around all this is to practise it. So find a reversible reaction, and then think about how changing each condition will affect the position of the equilibrium.

Oxidation and Reduction

Now for something a bit different — oxidation and reduction. When REDuction and OXidation happen during a reaction at the same time, it's known as a redox reaction. You'll learn all about it here.

If Something **Gains Oxygen** it's **Oxidised**

Oxidation can mean the addition of oxygen and reduction can mean the removal of oxygen.

Oxidation is the gain of oxygen.
Reduction is the loss of oxygen.

E.g. $Fe_2O_3 + 3CO \rightarrow 2Fe + 3CO_2$
Iron(III) oxide is reduced to iron (as oxygen is removed).
Carbon monoxide is oxidised to carbon dioxide (as oxygen is added).

If you see Roman numerals in a chemical name, it's called an oxidation state. It's the same as the positive charge on a metal ion. E.g. iron has an oxidation state of +3 in iron(III) oxide.

If **Electrons** are **Transferred**, it's a **Redox Reaction**

You can also define oxidation and reduction in terms of electrons:

A handy way to remember this is OIL RIG: Oxidation Is Loss, Reduction Is Gain (of electrons).

A loss of electrons is called oxidation.
A gain of electrons is called reduction.

The substances being oxidised and reduced can be called oxidising or reducing agents:

An oxidising agent oxidises another substance during a redox reaction.
A reducing agent reduces another substance during a redox reaction.

Supplement

The substance that is oxidised is the reducing agent. The substance that is reduced is the oxidising agent.

For example, in the reaction between sodium metal and chlorine gas:
Sodium is oxidised to sodium ions (each atom loses an electron) — it's the reducing agent:
$$2Na \rightarrow 2Na^+ + 2e^-$$
Chlorine is reduced to chloride ions (each atom gains an electron) — it's the oxidising agent:
$$Cl_2 + 2e^- \rightarrow 2Cl^-$$
The sodium ions and chloride ions attract together to form the ionic compound sodium chloride:
So overall: $2Na + Cl_2 \rightarrow 2NaCl$

You can describe this type of reaction as a redox reaction:

In terms of electron transfer, a redox reaction is a reaction in which electrons move from the oxidised species to the reduced species.

If you're taking the Extended course, remember — OIL RIG

Oxidation is loss, reduction is gain — of electrons that is. It is slightly confusingly the other way round for oxygen, but OIG RIL doesn't really have the same ring to it.

Oxidation States

You met oxidation states briefly on the previous page. Here they are in more detail.

Every **Atom** and **Ion** has an **Oxidation State**

1) The oxidation state of an element tells you the total number of electrons it has donated or accepted.
2) For example, in the redox reaction between sodium and chlorine on the previous page, each sodium ion has donated one electron, so it has an oxidation state of +1. Each chloride ion has accepted one electron, so it has an oxidation state of –1.
3) The change in oxidation state can show whether something is oxidised or reduced. If a substance is oxidised, its oxidation state increases. If it's reduced, its oxidation state decreases.
4) There's a set of rules that you can use to work out the oxidation state of an atom when it's in a compound, in an ion, or just on its own. Take a deep breath, here we go...

1) Uncombined elements, like He and Ar, have an oxidation state of 0.

2) Elements just bonded to identical atoms, like O_2 and H_2, also have an oxidation state of 0.

3) The oxidation state of a simple ion, like Na^+, is the same as its charge.

In this case, that's +1.

4) Combined oxygen is nearly always –2.

5) Combined hydrogen is +1.

6) The sum of the oxidation states for a neutral compound is 0.

Fe_2O_3 — Total of all oxidation states = 0
Oxidation state of O = –2 (total = 3 × –2 = –6),
so the total oxidation state of Fe = (0 – (–6)) = +6.
There are two iron atoms so each one must have an oxidation state of +6 ÷ 2 = +3.

Supplement

You Need to Know About These **Redox Reactions**:

Acidified potassium manganate(VII), $KMnO_4$, is an oxidising agent.
In a redox reaction, the MnO_4^- ion is reduced to Mn^{2+}. During the reaction:

- The colour of the solution changes from purple to colourless.
- The oxidation state of manganese changes from +7 to +2.

The total oxidation state of MnO_4^- is –1. The total oxidation state of O in the ion is (4 × –2 =) –8, so the oxidation state of Mn in MnO_4^- = –1 – (–8) = +7.

Potassium iodide is a reducing agent. In a redox reaction, iodide ions (I^-) are oxidised to iodine molecules (I_2).

- The colour of the solution changes from colourless to brown.
- The oxidation state of iodine changes from –1 to 0.

Supplement

Oxidation state changes can be used to spot redox reactions

If an atom's oxidation state increases in a reaction, it's being oxidised. If it decreases, it's being reduced.

Warm-Up & Exam Questions

Try your hand at these questions — it's the best way to see what you've learnt so far.

Warm-Up Questions

1) Explain what is meant by the term 'reversible reaction'.
2) Anhydrous copper(II) sulfate can be formed by heating hydrated copper(II) sulfate. State how hydrated copper(II) sulfate can be reformed.
3) What does it mean to say that a reaction is at 'equilibrium'?
4) This equation shows how zinc ions react with copper ions: $Zn_{(s)} + Cu^{2+}_{(aq)} \rightarrow Zn^{2+}_{(aq)} + Cu_{(s)}$
   Is this a redox reaction? Explain your answer.

S

Exam Questions

1 In the reaction below, hydrated cobalt(II) chloride forms anhydrous cobalt(II) chloride and substance X on heating.

$$\text{hydrated cobalt(II) chloride} \rightleftharpoons \text{anhydrous cobalt(II) chloride} + \text{X}$$

(a) What can you deduce about this reaction from the symbol $\rightleftharpoons$?

[1]

(b) Name substance **X**.

[1]

[Total 2 marks]

2 Iron can be extracted by heating iron(III) oxide (Fe_2O_3) with carbon (C), to produce iron and carbon dioxide.

$$2Fe_2O_3 + 3C \rightarrow 4Fe + 3CO_2$$

(a) Explain why the iron(III) oxide is described as being reduced during this reaction.

[1]

(b) Name the reducing agent in this reaction.

S

[1]

[Total 2 marks]

Supplement

3 When ammonium chloride is heated, it breaks down into ammonia and hydrogen chloride. The reaction is reversible.

$$NH_4Cl_{(s)} \rightleftharpoons NH_{3(g)} + HCl_{(g)}$$

Two students are trying to deduce the optimum conditions to favour the forward reaction.

The first student suggests a temperature of 375 °C and a pressure of 1 atmosphere.
The second student suggests a temperature of 250 °C and a pressure of 5 atmospheres.

Using your knowledge of equilibrium reactions, deduce which conditions are more favourable for the forward reaction. Explain your answer.

[Total 5 marks]

Supplement

Acids and Alkalis

To test the pH of a solution, you can use an indicator — and that means pretty colours...

The **pH Scale** Goes from **0 to 14**

1) The pH scale is a measure of how acidic or alkaline a solution is. A neutral substance has pH 7.
2) An acid is a substance that has a pH of less than 7. The strongest acid has pH 0.
3) An alkali is a substance that has a pH greater than 7. The strongest alkali has pH 14.

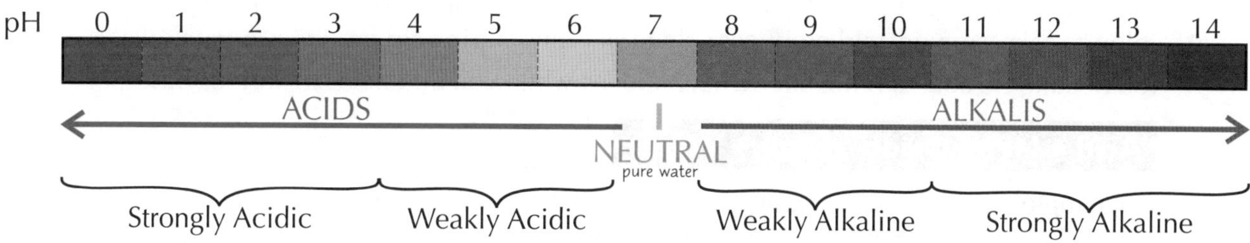

An **Indicator** is Just a **Dye** That Changes **Colour**

The dye in an indicator changes colour depending on whether it's above or below a certain pH. Indicators are very useful for estimating the pH of a solution. There are several different types:

1) Universal indicator is a very useful combination of dyes which gives the colours shown above. To find the pH of an aqueous solution, dip Universal indicator paper into the test solution and compare the resulting colour to a chart.

You can also use Universal indicator solution — just add a few drops to the test solution.

2) Litmus indicator tests whether a solution is acidic or alkaline because it changes colour at about pH 7. It's red in acidic solutions, purple in neutral solutions and blue in alkaline solutions.

Acidic	Neutral	Alkaline

3) Litmus paper comes in two forms — red and blue. Red litmus paper turns blue in alkaline solutions and blue litmus paper turns red in acidic solutions.
4) Methyl orange changes from red in acidic solutions to yellow in alkaline solutions.

Acidic Alkaline

Acids can be **Neutralised** by **Bases** (or **Alkalis**)

An alkali is a base that is soluble in water.

1) A base is a substance that reacts with an acid to produce a salt and water.
2) The reaction between an acid and a base (or an acid and an alkali) is called neutralisation.
3) When an acid neutralises a base (or vice versa), the products are neutral, i.e. they have a pH of 7.
4) Acids are a source of H^+ ions and alkalis are a source of OH^- ions.
5) Neutralisation can be seen in terms of H^+ and OH^- ions like this:

$$H^+ + OH^- \rightarrow H_2O$$

Supplement

6) Neutralisation reactions can also be seen in terms of proton transfer. The acid donates protons (hydrogen ions) which are then accepted by the base.

An acid is a source of hydrogen ions (H^+). They are proton donors.
A base is a substance that can neutralise an acid. They are proton acceptors.

Supplement

Interesting fact — your skin is slightly acidic (around pH 5)

You'll need to know all this stuff later in the section so make sure you've understood it before moving on.

Reactions of Acids and Bases

Acids and bases are an enthusiastic lot — they get involved in loads of reactions.

Salts Form When Acids React with Bases...

1) A salt, an ionic compound, is formed during a neutralisation reaction (a reaction between an acid and a base). This is a general equation for a neutralisation reaction:

   acid + base → salt + water

2) The type of salt depends on the acid used. In general, hydrochloric acid produces chloride salts, sulfuric acid produces sulfate salts and nitric acid produces nitrate salts.
3) You need to be able to remember what happens when you add acids to various bases...

Acid + Metal Oxide → Salt + Water

Example: $2HCl + CuO \rightarrow CuCl_2 + H_2O$ (copper chloride)

These are the same as the acid/alkali neutralisation reaction you met on the previous page.

Acid + Metal Hydroxide → Salt + Water

Example: $HNO_3 + KOH \rightarrow KNO_3 + H_2O$ (potassium nitrate)

4) Ammonia is a base too, but when you add ammonia to an acid, you just make an ammonium salt.

Acid + Ammonia → Ammonium Salt

Examples: $HNO_3 + NH_3 \rightarrow NH_4NO_3$ (ammonium nitrate)
$H_2SO_4 + 2NH_3 \rightarrow (NH_4)_2SO_4$ (ammonium sulfate)

...And When Acids React With Metals or Metal Carbonates

You also need to know what happens when you react an acid with a metal or a metal carbonate. The reaction of acids and metals is covered on page 96 in more detail.

Acid + Metal → Salt + Hydrogen

Example: $2HCl + Mg \rightarrow MgCl_2 + H_2$ (magnesium chloride)

Acid + Metal Carbonate → Salt + Water + Carbon Dioxide

Example: $HCl + Na_2CO_3 \rightarrow 2NaCl + H_2O + H_2$ (sodium chloride)

Ammonium Salt + Base Gives Off Ammonia

If you add a base to a solution containing ammonium ions (NH_4^+), ammonia gas is released.

Base + Ammonium Salt → Salt + Water + Ammonia

Example: sodium hydroxide + ammonium sulfate → sodium sulfate + water + ammonia
$2NaOH + (NH_4)_2SO_4 \rightarrow Na_2SO_4 + H_2O + 2NH_3$

You can use this reaction to test a substance for ammonium ions (NH_4^+) — see p.84.

Quite a few reactions to learn here...

...but learning the general equations for each reaction can help, e.g. acid + base → salt + water.

More on Acids and Bases

Right then. More on acids and bases. Prepare yourself...

Neutralisation Reactions are Used to Control Soil Acidity

1) Plants, including crops (food plants), need the soil to have a specific pH range in order to get the nutrients they need.
2) This means soil pH needs be carefully controlled by farmers and gardeners, as it can affect plant growth.
3) Lime (calcium oxide) is a base that's often used to increase the pH of acidic soil.

Supplement

Acids and Bases Ionise in Water

All acids can ionise in solution — that means splitting up to produce a hydrogen ion, H^+, and another ion. For example,

$HCl \rightarrow H^+ + Cl^-$

$HNO_3 \rightarrow H^+ + NO_3^-$

A hydrogen ion is the same as a proton.

When bases are in solution, they produce hydroxide ions (OH^-).

E.g. $NaOH \rightarrow Na^+ + OH^-$

Acids and Bases Can be Strong or Weak

1) Strong acids (e.g. sulfuric, hydrochloric and nitric acids) ionise almost completely in water — a large proportion of the acid molecules break apart to release H^+ ions. They tend to have low pHs (pH 0-2).
2) Strong bases (like sodium hydroxide) ionise almost completely in water too. They have high pHs.
3) Weak acids (e.g. ethanoic, citric and carbonic acids) do not fully ionise in solution — only a small proportion of the acid molecules break apart to release H^+ ions. Their pHs tend to be around 2-6.
4) Weak bases (like ammonia) don't fully ionise either. Ammonia has a pH of around 11.
5) The ionisation of a weak acid or base is a reversible reaction, which sets up an equilibrium (p.70). Since only a few of the particles ionise, the equilibrium lies well to the left.

Strong acid: $HCl \rightarrow H^+ + Cl^-$

Weak acid: $CH_3COOH \rightleftharpoons H^+ + CH_3COO^-$

Strong base: $NaOH \rightarrow Na^+ + OH^-$

Weak base: $NH_3 + H_2O \rightleftharpoons NH_4^+ + OH^-$

Don't Confuse Strength with Concentration

1) Acid and base strength (i.e. strong or weak) tells you what proportion of the molecules ionise in water.
2) The concentration of an acid or base is different. Concentration measures how much acid or base there is in a volume of water (e.g. in grams per dm^3).
3) So you can have, for example, a dilute strong acid, or a concentrated weak base.

Concentration describes the total number of dissolved molecules — not the number of molecules that ionise.

See page 42 for more information on concentration.

Supplement

Strong and weak are different to concentrated and dilute

Don't ever forget — for acids, strong and weak are to do with how much the acid ionises, while concentrated and dilute are to do with the acid concentration. And it works the same way with bases too.

Types of Oxides

Oxides are chemical compounds that contain oxygen. They might seem quite boring, but they have hidden depths... You need to be able to spot different types of oxides based on their acidic or basic properties.

Oxides can be **Acidic** or **Basic**

1) Many oxides can be classified as either acidic or basic.

Acidic oxides will react with a base to form a salt and water.
Basic oxides will react with an acid to form a salt and water.

2) Whether an oxide is acidic or basic depends on its metallic character.

3) Metals (from the left side of the periodic table) form basic oxides. E.g. Na_2O, K_2O, CaO.

4) Non-metals (from the right side of the periodic table) form acidic oxides. E.g. CO_2, NO_2, SO_3.

Supplement

Other Oxides can be **Amphoteric** or **Neutral**

1) Some oxides are classified as amphoteric. Amphoteric oxides have both acidic and basic properties.

Amphoteric oxides will react with both acids and bases to form a salt and water.

2) Amphoteric oxides tend to be formed from elements that are close to the divide between metals and non-metals in the periodic table.

Example: Aluminium oxide (Al_2O_3) + acid: $Al_2O_3 + 6HCl \rightarrow 2AlCl_3 + 3H_2O$
Aluminium oxide (Al_2O_3) + base: $Al_2O_3 + 2NaOH \rightarrow 2NaAlO_2 + H_2O$

Other amphoteric oxides include zinc oxide (ZnO) and lead oxide (PbO).

3) Neutral oxides are neither acidic or basic — they don't show acidic or basic properties.

Neutral oxides don't react with either acids or bases.

Examples of neutral oxides include carbon monoxide (CO) and nitric oxide (NO).

Supplement

Make sure you know your oxides...

The general trend in oxides is that they change from basic to acidic as you move across the periodic table from left to right. If you're taking the Extended course, things get a little trickier, so make sure you can spot each type of oxide from how they react with acids and bases using the definitions above.

Making Insoluble Salts

Some salts are soluble but insoluble salts aren't. Try saying that fast three times...

Preparing **Salts** Depends on **Solubility**

1) Soluble things dissolve in water. Insoluble things don't dissolve.
2) How you make a salt depends on whether it's soluble or insoluble.
3) Before you make a salt from two reactants, you need to know whether the salt will form as a precipitate (i.e. it's an insoluble salt), or whether it will just form in solution (i.e. it's a soluble salt).

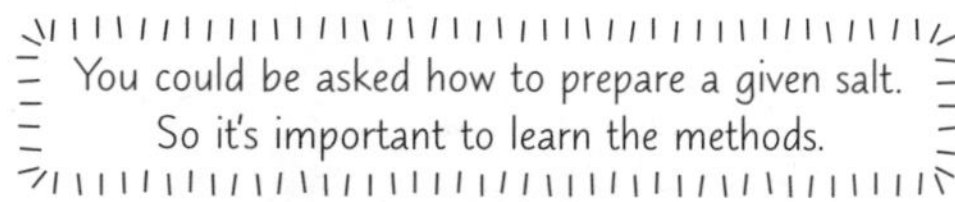

You could be asked how to prepare a given salt.
So it's important to learn the methods.

Supplement

Making **Insoluble** Salts — **Precipitation** Reactions

1) To make a pure, dry sample of an insoluble salt, you can use a precipitation reaction. You just need to pick the right two soluble salts and react them together to get your insoluble salt.
2) E.g. to make lead sulfate (insoluble), you can mix lead nitrate and magnesium sulfate (both soluble).

lead nitrate + magnesium sulfate → lead sulfate + magnesium nitrate

$$Pb(NO_3)_{2\,(aq)} + MgSO_{4(aq)} \rightarrow PbSO_{4\,(s)} + Mg(NO_3)_{2\,(aq)}$$

$$Pb^{2+}_{(aq)} + SO_4{}^{2-}_{(aq)} \rightarrow PbSO_{4\,(s)}$$

Example: Making **Lead Sulfate**

1) Add 1 spatula of lead nitrate to a test tube. Add water to dissolve it. You should use deionised water to make sure there are no other ions about. Shake it thoroughly to ensure that all the lead nitrate has dissolved. Then, in a separate test tube, do the same with 1 spatula of magnesium sulfate.
2) Tip the two solutions into a small beaker, and give it a good stir to make sure it's all mixed together. The lead sulfate will precipitate out.

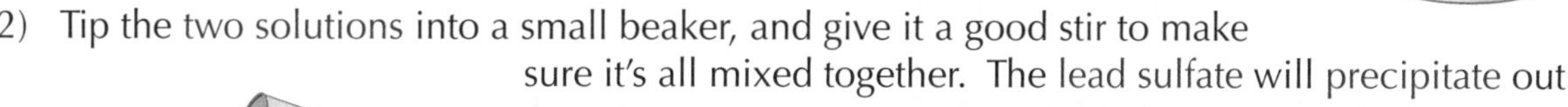

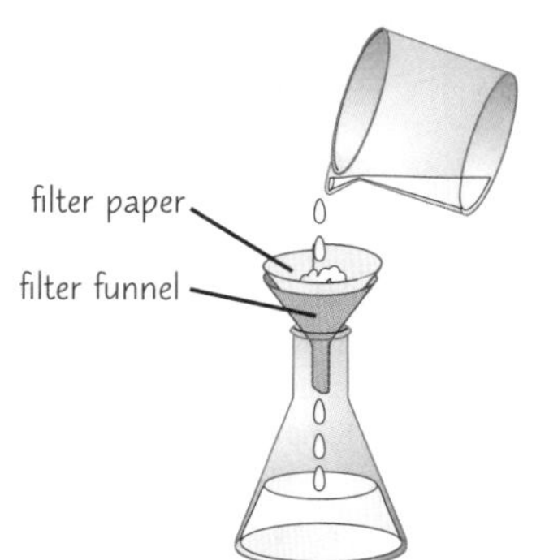

3) Put a folded piece of filter paper into a filter funnel, and stick the funnel into a conical flask.
4) Pour the contents of the beaker into the middle of the filter paper. Make sure that the solution doesn't go above the filter paper — otherwise some of the solid could dribble down the side.
5) Rinse the beaker with more deionised water, and tip this into the filter paper — to make sure you get all the precipitate from the beaker.
6) Rinse the contents of the filter paper with deionised water to make sure that all the soluble magnesium nitrate has been washed away.
7) Then just scrape the lead sulfate onto fresh filter paper and leave it to dry in an oven or a desiccator.

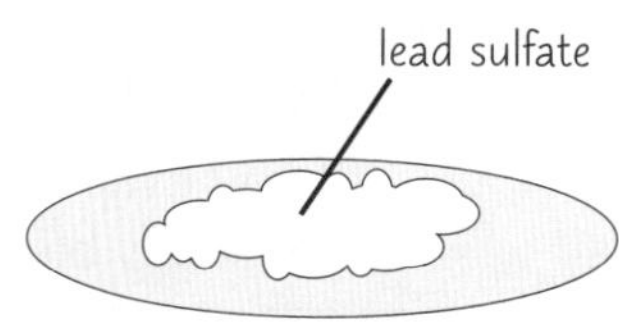

Supplement

The method above can be used to make any insoluble salt...

... as long as you start with two soluble salts (or you won't be able to separate the precipitate and reactants).

Making Soluble Salts

When making a soluble salt (a salt that dissolves in water), you need to be able to separate it from the reaction mixture. How you do that depends on whether the reactants are soluble or insoluble...

Making **Soluble Salts** Using an **Acid** and an **Insoluble Base**

You can make a soluble salt by reacting an acid that contains one of the ions you want in the salt with an insoluble base that contains the other ion you need (often a metal oxide or metal hydroxide).

For some salts, you can use a metal instead of the base.

Method

1) Start by heating the acid in a water bath — this speeds up the reaction between the acid and the insoluble base. Do this in a fume cupboard to avoid releasing acid fumes into the room.

2) Then slowly add the base to the acid — the base and acid will react to produce a soluble salt (and water). You will know when the base is in excess and all the acid has been neutralised because the excess solid will just sink to the bottom of the flask.

It's important that the base is in excess so that you don't have any leftover acid in your product.

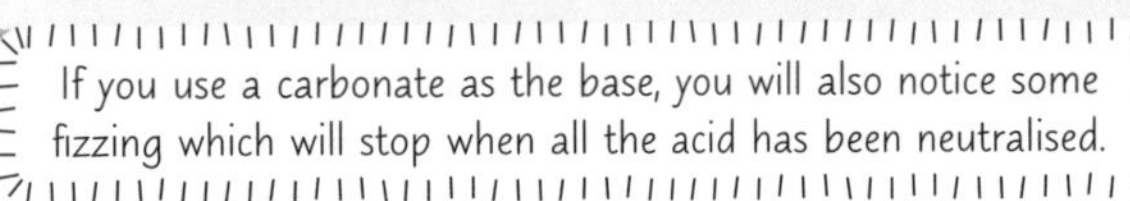

If you use a carbonate as the base, you will also notice some fizzing which will stop when all the acid has been neutralised.

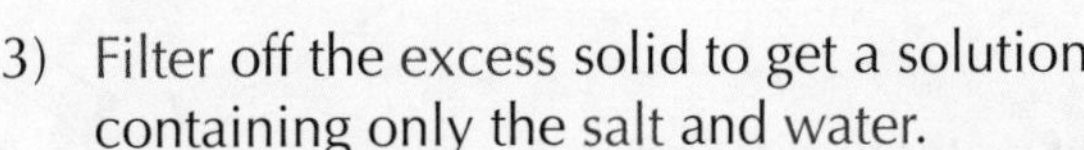

3) Filter off the excess solid to get a solution containing only the salt and water.

filter paper

excess solid

filter funnel

salt and water

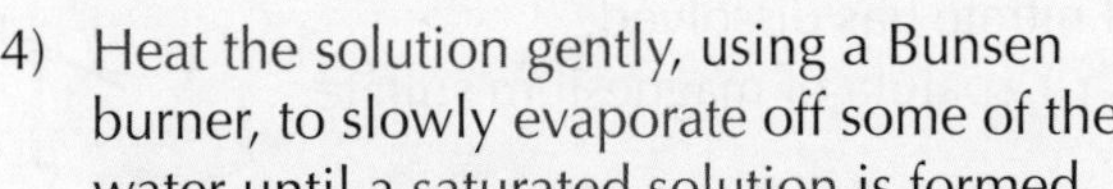

4) Heat the solution gently, using a Bunsen burner, to slowly evaporate off some of the water until a saturated solution is formed.

A saturated solution is a solution in which no more solute will dissolve at that temperature.

5) Leave the solution to cool and allow the salt to crystallise (see p.12).

The salt will begin to crystallise as the solution cools because the solubility of most salts decreases as the temperature decreases.

6) Filter off the solid salt and leave it to dry.

Example: You can add solid copper oxide to warm sulfuric acid to make a solution of copper sulfate:

$$CuO + H_2SO_4 \rightarrow CuSO_4 + H_2O$$

If you evaporate off some of the water and leave this solution to crystallise, you should get lovely blue crystals of hydrated copper sulfate, which you can filter off and dry.

Acid + insoluble base → soluble salt + water

Remember to make sure the base is in excess in this experiment, so that you don't have any leftover acid in your product. That way, the final solution is simply a soluble salt and water.

Making Soluble Salts

Making **Soluble Salts** Using **Acid/Alkali Reactions**

1) Soluble salts can also be made by reacting an acid with an alkali.
2) But you can't tell when the reaction has finished — there's no signal that all the acid has been neutralised. You also can't just add an excess of alkali to the acid, because the salt is soluble and would be contaminated with the excess alkali.
3) Instead, you need to work out exactly the right amount of alkali to neutralise the acid. For this, you need to do a titration using an indicator first. Here's what you do...

Method

1) Measure out a set amount of acid into a conical flask using a pipette.
2) Add a few drops of indicator to the acid. For a titration, you should use an indicator with a single, clear colour change (like methyl orange). Universal indicator is no good as its colour change is too gradual.
3) Slowly add alkali to the acid, using a burette, until you reach the end-point — this is when the acid's been exactly neutralised and the indicator changes colour.

Add the alkali to the acid a bit at a time — giving the conical flask a regular swirl. Go especially slowly when you think the end-point is about to be reached.

4) Note down the initial and final volumes of alkali in the burette and use these to calculate the amount added. Repeat the titration a few times, making sure you get (roughly) the same volume each time.
5) Then, carry out the reaction using exactly the same volumes of alkali and acid but with no indicator, so the salt won't be contaminated with indicator.

You can also use titrations to work out the concentration of an acid or alkali — see page 43.

Supplement

6) The solution that remains when the reaction is complete contains only the salt and water.
7) Slowly evaporate off some of the water and then leave the solution to crystallise (see page 12 for more on crystallisation). Filter off the solid and dry it — you'll be left with a pure, dry salt.

Example: You can make sodium sulfate by titrating sulfuric acid with sodium hydroxide and crystallising the resulting solution.

Titrations can be used to make sure the alkali isn't in excess

Alkalis are soluble in water, so it's hard to stop them from contaminating the soluble salt produced in the reaction. Fortunately, titrations can help you out — they allow you to calculate the exact amount of acid and alkali you need to add to complete the reaction without either of them being in excess.

Warm-Up & Exam Questions

Mmm, salt. There were a lot of experimental methods crammed into the last few pages, so make sure you can remember each of the steps and why they're important before tackling these questions.

Warm-Up Questions

1) What term is used to describe a substance with a pH of 7?
2) What is a base?
3) Write the word equation for the reaction between sulfuric acid and magnesium oxide.
4) What's the difference between a strong acid and a weak acid?
5) What is meant by the term 'amphoteric oxide'?
6) Outline how you could purify a soluble salt produced from the reaction between an insoluble base and an acid.

Exam Questions

1 A student has a test tube containing some acid. They then gradually add some alkali to the test tube.

(a) What ions do all acids produce when in solution?

[1]

(b) What type of reaction takes place between the acid and the alkali?

[1]

[Total 2 marks]

2 Barium oxide is a soluble metal oxide.
What is the likely pH of the solution formed when barium oxide is added to water?

☐ **A** pH 0 ☐ **B** pH 5 ☐ **C** pH 7 ☐ **D** pH 13

[Total 1 mark]

3 A student is preparing samples of salts.

(a) Describe how the student could use a titration to make a solution containing just a salt and water from an acid and an alkali.

[3]

Supplement

(b) The student makes a sample of lead sulfate, an insoluble salt, by mixing two salt solutions. To separate the salt from the reaction mixture, the student pours the whole solid and salt solution into a filter funnel, as shown in the diagram below.

What has the student done wrong? Explain how this could affect the mass of solid salt collected from the solution.

[2]

[Total 5 marks]

Tests for Cations

So, tests for identifying ions in mystery compounds probably don't get your heart racing with excitement. But this section includes lots of different colours so just think of all the pretty revision notes you could make.

You Can Use **Flame Tests** to Identify **Metal Ions**

1) Compounds of some metals produce a characteristic colour when heated in a flame.
2) You can test for various metal ions by putting your substance in a flame and seeing what colour the flame goes.

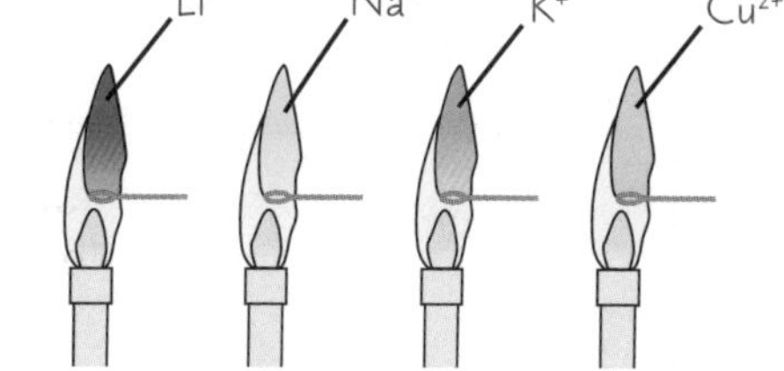

Lithium ions, Li^+, give a (crimson) red flame.
Sodium ions, Na^+, give a yellow flame.
Potassium ions, K^+, give a lilac flame.
Copper(II) ions, Cu^{2+}, give a blue-green flame.

3) To carry out a flame test in the lab, first clean a nichrome wire loop by dipping it into hydrochloric acid and then rinsing it in distilled water.
4) Then dip the wire loop into a sample of the metal compound and put the loop in the clear blue part of a Bunsen flame (the hottest bit). Record what colour the flame goes.

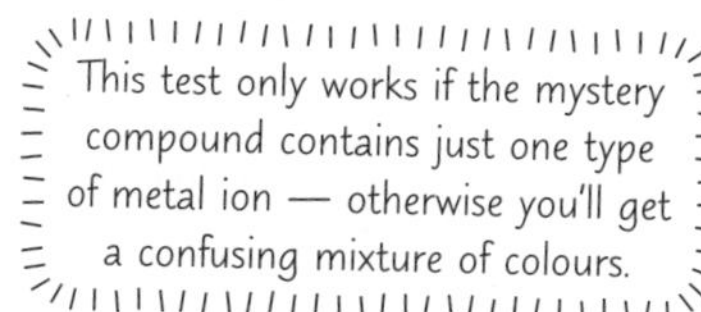
This test only works if the mystery compound contains just one type of metal ion — otherwise you'll get a confusing mixture of colours.

Some **Metal Ions** Form a **Coloured Precipitate** with **NaOH**

This is also a test for metal ions, but it's slightly more complicated:

1) Many metal hydroxides are insoluble and precipitate out of solution when formed. Some of these hydroxides have a characteristic colour.
2) For this test, you add a few drops of sodium hydroxide solution to a solution of your mystery compound.
3) If a hydroxide precipitate forms, you can use its colour to tell which metal ion was in the compound.

Metal Ion	Colour of Precipitate after Few Drops of NaOH Solution	After Excess NaOH Solution Added
Aluminium, Al^{3+}	White	Redissolves to form a colourless solution.
Calcium, Ca^{2+}	White	No change
Chromium(III), Cr^{3+}	Green	Redissolves to form a green solution.
Copper(II), Cu^{2+}	Light blue	No change
Iron(II), Fe^{2+}	Green	No change
Iron(III), Fe^{3+}	Red-brown	No change
Zinc(II), Zn^{2+}	White	Redissolves to form a colourless solution.

'No change' means that the precipitate remains insoluble in excess NaOH.

Tests for Cations

You Can Also Test for **Metal Cations** Using **Ammonia**

Adding aqueous ammonia (NH_3) to solutions of metal ions can also cause precipitates to form. You can use this test to check which metal ion is present.

Metal Ion	Colour of Precipitate after Few Drops of NH_3 Solution	After Excess NH_3 Solution Added
Aluminium, Al^{3+}	White	No change
Calcium, Ca^{2+}	No visible reaction	No precipitate or slight white precipitate
Chromium(II), Cr^{3+}	Grey-green	No change
Copper(II), Cu^{2+}	Light blue	Redissolves to form a dark blue solution
Iron(II), Fe^{2+}	Green	No change
Iron(III), Fe^{3+}	Red-brown	No change
Zinc(II), Zn^{2+}	White	Redissolves to form a colourless solution

Adding **NaOH** to **Ammonium Ions** Produces **Ammonia**

1) To work out whether a substance contains ammonium ions (NH_4^+), all you need to do is add some sodium hydroxide solution to a solution of your mystery substance and gently heat it.

2) If ammonia gas is given off, it means that there are ammonium ions in your mystery substance.

3) You can test for ammonia gas by holding a piece of damp red litmus paper over it. If the mystery gas is ammonia, the litmus paper will turn blue.

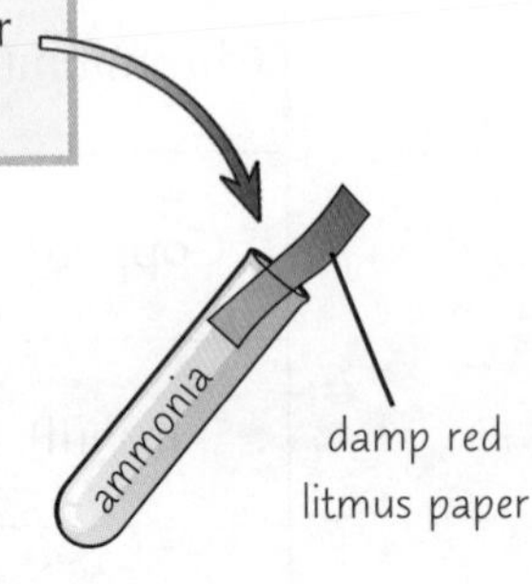

4) Ammonia also has a very distinctive strong smell, but it's not a good idea to go sniffing a mystery gas to figure out what it is — for example, at high concentrations, ammonia is an irritant and toxic.

Flame tests are only useful for testing one type of ion at a time

Lots of ions and colours to learn here, so just take your time. It might help to come up with little ways of remembering the colours — like Li⁺ttle Red Riding Hood. Or Yellow BaNa⁺Na⁺s.

Tests for Anions

The tests for aqueous anions aren't quite as colourful as the aqueous cation tests, but they're still very useful.

Test for **Halide Ions** Using **Silver Nitrate Solution**

To test for chloride ions (Cl^-), bromide ions (Br^-) or iodide ions (I^-), add some dilute nitric acid (HNO_3), followed by a few drops of silver nitrate solution ($AgNO_3$).

Nitric acid needs to be added first to get rid of any carbonate ions — they give a pale precipitate with silver nitrate too, which would confuse the results. You can't use hydrochloric acid, because you'd be adding chloride ions.

$Ag^+_{(aq)} + Cl^-_{(aq)} \longrightarrow AgCl_{(s)}$ A chloride gives a white precipitate of silver chloride.

$Ag^+_{(aq)} + Br^-_{(aq)} \longrightarrow AgBr_{(s)}$ A bromide gives a cream precipitate of silver bromide.

$Ag^+_{(aq)} + I^-_{(aq)} \longrightarrow AgI_{(s)}$ An iodide gives a yellow precipitate of silver iodide.

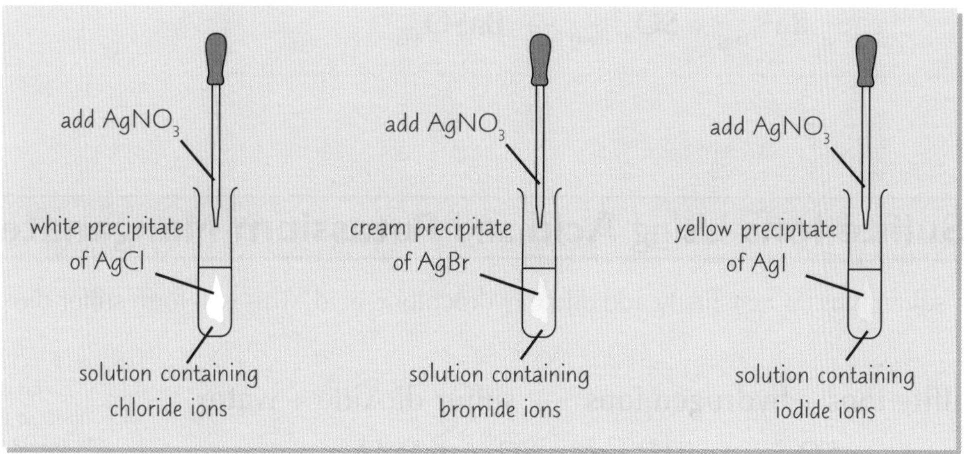

Test for **Carbonates** Using **Dilute Acid**

1) To test for carbonate ions (CO_3^{2-}) in solution, add some dilute acid.

2) If there are carbonate ions present, the mixture will fizz — this is because the carbonate will react with the acid to produce carbon dioxide gas:

carbonate ions + acid → carbon dioxide + water

$$CO_3^{2-} + 2H^+ \rightarrow CO_2 + H_2O$$

3) You can check to see if a gas is carbon dioxide by collecting it and bubbling it through limewater. If it is carbon dioxide, the limewater turns milky.

You can see more tests for gases on page 87.

Tests for Anions

Test for **Nitrates** Using **Aluminium**

1) To test for nitrate ions (NO_3^-) in solution, heat the sample with aluminium foil and sodium hydroxide.
2) Any nitrate ions present will be reduced (see page 72) by the aluminium, forming ammonia (NH_3).
3) Ammonia will turn damp red litmus paper blue.

Test for **Sulfate Ions** Using **Barium Nitrate Solution**

1) To test for sulfate ions (SO_4^{2-}) in solution, first add some dilute hydrochloric acid to the test sample — this stops any precipitation reactions not involving sulfate ions from taking place.
2) Then add some barium nitrate solution. If there are sulfate ions in the solution, a white precipitate of barium sulfate will form:

barium ions + sulfate ions → barium sulfate

$$Ba^{2+}_{(aq)} + SO_{4\,(aq)}^{2-} \rightarrow BaSO_{4\,(s)}$$

Test for **Sulfite Ions** Using **Acid** and **Potassium Manganate(VII)**

1) To test for sulfite ions (SO_3^{2-}), firstly add dilute hydrochloric acid. This will form sulfur dioxide gas (SO_2).

sulfite ions + hydrogen ions → sulfur dioxide + water

$$SO_{3\,(aq)}^{2-} + 2H^+_{(aq)} \rightarrow SO_{2(g)} + H_2O_{(l)}$$

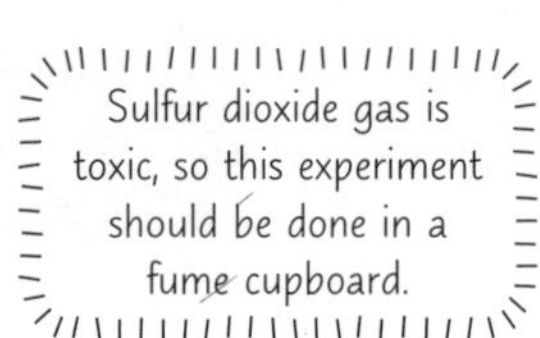

Sulfur dioxide gas is toxic, so this experiment should be done in a fume cupboard.

2) If you collect the sulfur dioxide made, you can bubble it through potassium manganate(VII) solution. The sulfur dioxide will reduce the manganate ions, causing the solution to turn from purple to colourless.

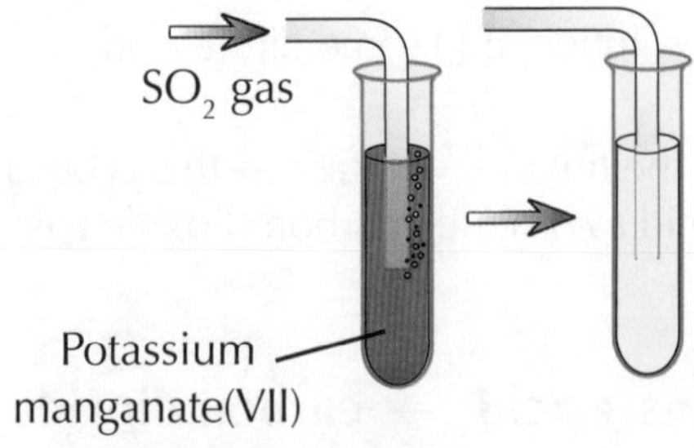

Make sure you know these anion tests

There are a few tests to learn here, along with their results. That's quite a bit of information to take in, so don't just stare at the whole lot till your eyes are swimming and you never ever want to see the word 'precipitate' again. Just learn the tests one by one and you'll be absolutely fine.

Tests for Gases

There are lots of clever ways of testing for different gases, so get learning the ones below.

You Can **Collect Gases** in a **Test Tube**

You can collect gases inside a test tube full of air. This works because the gas you're collecting displaces the air in the tube. There are two ways that this can be done: upward delivery and downward delivery.

This all depends on the density of the gas relative to the density of air.

1) The delivery tube is fed into a test tube either upwards or downwards.
2) Use upward delivery to collect 'lighter than air' gases (e.g. H_2).
3) Use downward delivery to collect 'heavier than air' gases (e.g. CO_2, Cl_2).

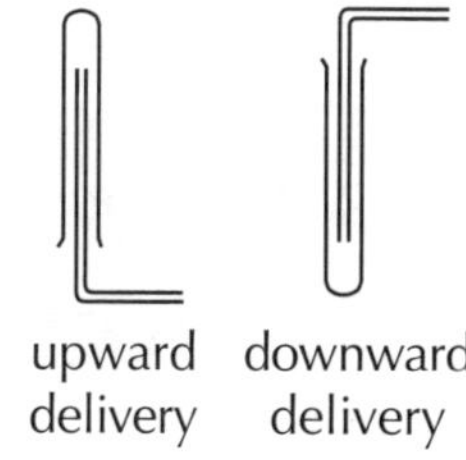

There are **Tests** for **5 Common Gases**

1) Chlorine

Chlorine bleaches damp blue litmus paper, turning it white. (It may turn red for a moment first though — that's because a solution of chlorine is acidic.)

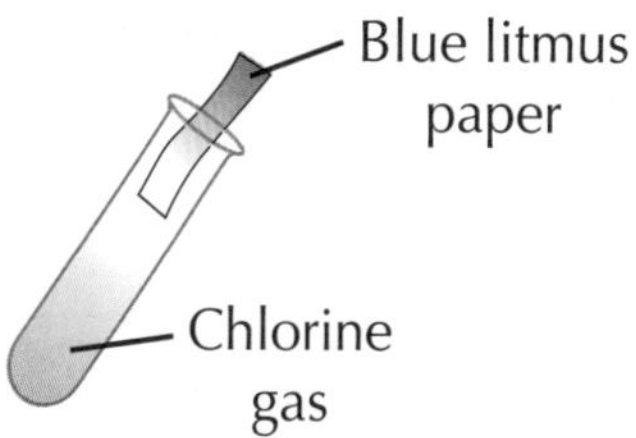

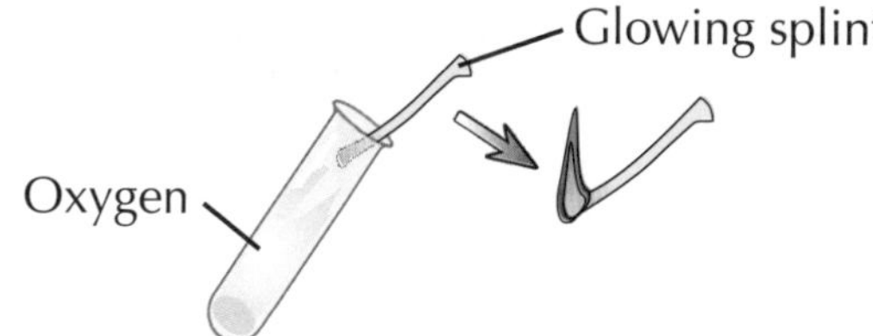

2) Oxygen

Oxygen relights a glowing splint.

3) Carbon Dioxide

Carbon dioxide turns limewater milky — just bubble the gas through a test tube of limewater and watch what happens.

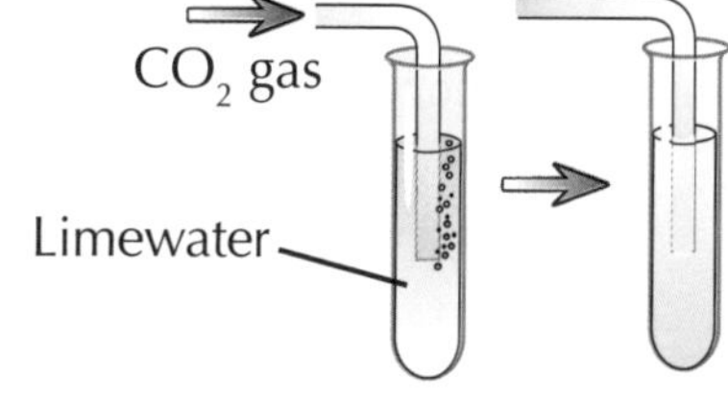

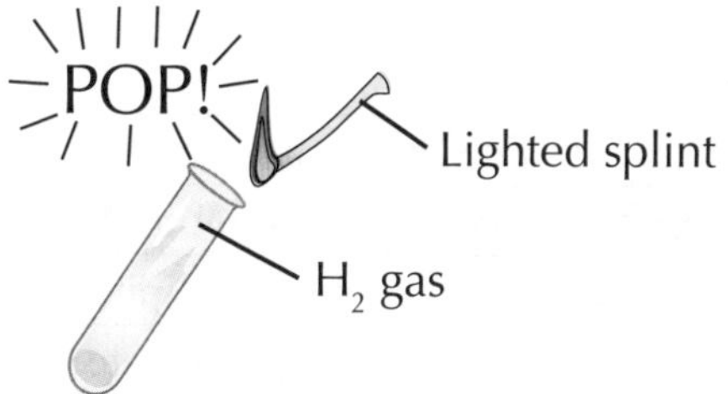

4) Hydrogen

Hydrogen makes a "squeaky pop" with a lighted splint. (The noise comes from the hydrogen burning with the oxygen in the air to form H_2O.)

5) Ammonia

Ammonia turns damp red litmus paper blue.

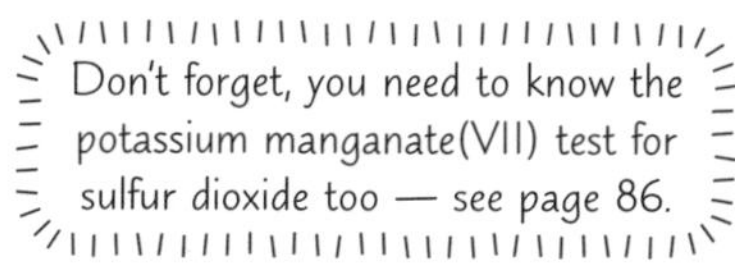

Don't forget, you need to know the potassium manganate(VII) test for sulfur dioxide too — see page 86.

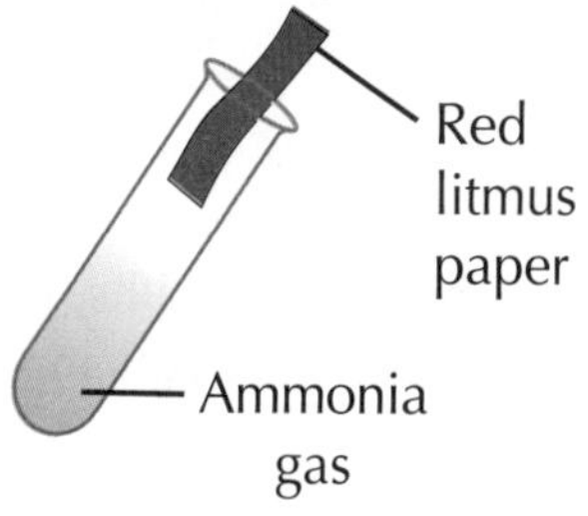

Warm-Up & Exam Questions

Now some questions to test your skills. There are quite a few little details to learn for all those ion and gas tests, so make sure you've got it all before you move on.

Warm-Up Questions

1) What metal ions would produce a lilac flame in a flame test?
2) What colour precipitate forms when you add a few drops of sodium hydroxide to a solution containing copper(II) ions?
3) What happens when you add excess ammonia to a solution containing Fe(II) ions?
4) Describe the test for ammonia gas.

Exam Questions

1 A student carried out flame tests on compounds of four different metal ions. Complete the table below which shows her results.

Flame colour	Metal ion
blue-green	
	Li^+
yellow	

[Total 3 marks]

2 Electrolysis of water produces hydrogen gas and oxygen gas.

(a) Describe a simple laboratory test that you could use to identify hydrogen gas.

[2]

(b) Describe a simple laboratory test that you could use to identify oxygen gas.

[2]

[Total 4 marks]

3 The table below shows the results of a series of chemical tests conducted on two solutions of unknown compounds, **X** and **Y**.

Test	Observation	
	Compound X	**Compound Y**
add a few drops of sodium hydroxide solution	white precipitate	green precipitate
add hydrochloric acid and barium nitrate solution	white precipitate	no precipitate
add nitric acid and silver nitrate solution	no precipitate	yellow precipitate

(a) What is the chemical name of compound **Y**?

[2]

(b) A student says "From these results, I can be certain that compound **X** is calcium sulfate." State whether he is correct. Explain your answer.

[3]

[Total 5 marks]

Revision Summary for Sections 7 & 8

That's Sections 7 and 8 finished with — now it's time for you to test your knowledge before moving on.

- Try these questions and tick off each one when you get it right.
- When you've done all the questions for a topic and are completely happy with it, tick off the topic.

Rates of Reaction, Reversible Reactions and Equilibrium (p.61-71)

1) Describe the difference between a physical change and a chemical change.
2) How does the rate of a reaction change with concentration of reactants?
3) A student carries out a reaction which produces carbon dioxide gas. He collects the carbon dioxide in a gas syringe. How will he know when the reaction has finished?
4) Describe how you could investigate how particle size affects the rate of reaction between solid calcium carbonate and hydrochloric acid.
5) On a rate of reaction graph, what does: a) a steep line show? b) a flat line show?
6) Describe the colour change observed when hydrated cobalt(II) chloride is heated.
7) True or false? In a reaction at equilibrium, both the forward and backward reactions are happening at exactly the same rate.
8) In a reversible reaction, what effect will decreasing the concentration of the reactants have on the equilibrium position?

Oxidation and Reduction (p.72-73)

9) True or false? The loss of oxygen is called oxidation.
10) Define the term 'reducing agent'.
11) State the colour change observed when:
    a) MnO_4^- ions are reduced to Mn^{2+} ions, b) I^- ions are oxidised to I_2 molecules.

Acids, Bases and Salts (p.75-81)

12) What number represents neutral on the pH scale?
13) True or false? Bases are proton acceptors.
14) What are the products of a reaction between an acid and a carbonate?
15) What are the three products of a reaction between a base and an ammonium salt?
16) Define a weak base.
17) Explain how you would make insoluble lead sulfate from soluble lead nitrate and soluble magnesium sulfate.
18) How would you make a soluble salt from an acid and an insoluble base?

Tests for Cations, Anions and Gases (p.83-87)

19) In a flame test, what colour is the flame given by heating sodium ions?
20) What colour precipitate forms when you mix Cr^{3+} ions with a few drops of sodium hydroxide?
21) Which halide ions form a cream precipitate when combined with acidified silver nitrate?
22) Give a way to test for the presence of carbonate ions.
23) Give a way to test for the presence of sulfate ions.
24) What do you observe when sulfur dioxide reacts with acidified potassium manganate(VII)?
25) Which gas would turn damp blue litmus paper white?

The Periodic Table

There are about 100 elements that all materials are made of. They're arranged in the periodic table.

The **Periodic Table** Helps You to **See Patterns** in **Properties**

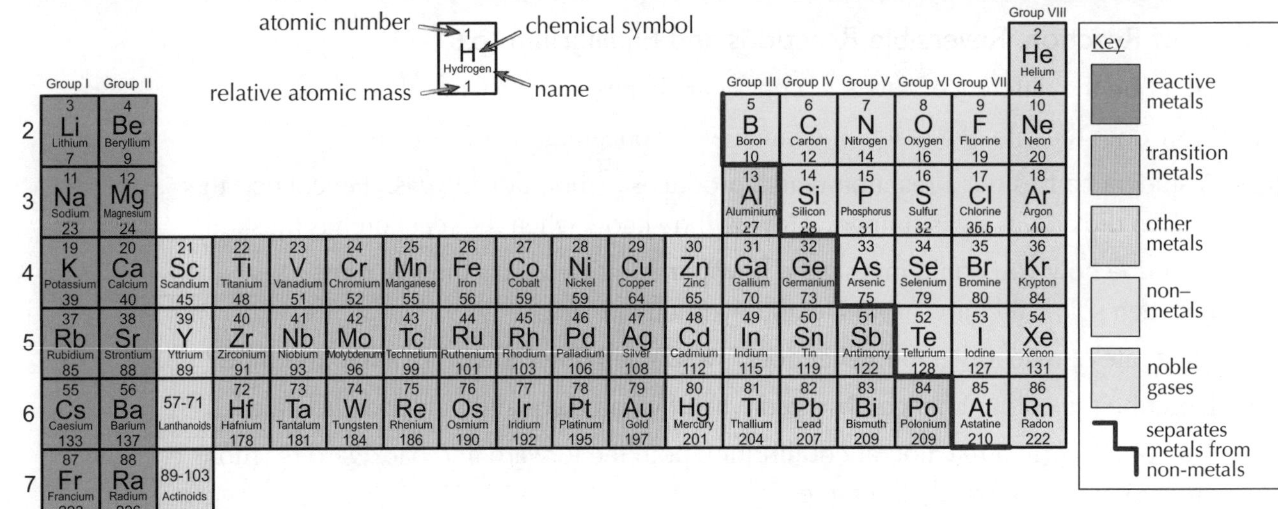

1) The modern periodic table shows the elements in order of increasing atomic number.
2) It's laid out so that elements with similar properties form columns called groups. This means if you know the properties of one element, you can predict the properties of the other elements in the same group.
3) Some of the groups have special names. E.g. Group VII elements are called halogens, and Group VIII are called the noble gases.

> You might sometimes see the groups numbered 1-8 instead of in Roman numerals. Group VIII (or 8) is also sometimes known as Group O.

4) The rows are called periods. The properties of elements change as you go along a period.
5) Most elements in the periodic table are metals.

Metals are towards the bottom and to the left of the periodic table. Metals form positive ions when they react.

Non-metals are at the far right and top of the periodic table. They don't generally form positive ions when they react.

The metallic character of the elements decreases as you move across each period. (See p.96 for more about the characteristics of metals.)

Supplement

Elements in a **Group** Have the **Same Number** of **Outer Electrons**

1) The group to which an element belongs corresponds to the number of electrons in its outer shell. E.g. Group I elements have 1 outer shell electron, Group II elements have 2 outer shell electrons, etc.

> Helium (in Group VIII) is the exception — it only has 2 electrons in its outer shell.

2) That's why elements in the same group have similar properties.
3) The number of outer electrons also explains the transition from metallic to non-metallic character across the table. As the number of outer electrons increases across a period, it becomes more difficult for the elements to lose those electrons to form positive ions with a full outer shell. So elements with fewer outer electrons have stronger metallic character.

Supplement

The periodic table is vital for understanding chemistry

The position of an element in the periodic table gives you information about its properties. Clever stuff.

Group I Elements

Group I elements are sometimes known as the alkali metals. They're pretty reactive.

The **Group I** Elements are **Reactive, Soft Metals**

You might see Group I written as Group 1.

The Group I metals are lithium, sodium, potassium, rubidium, caesium and francium. They all have the following physical properties:

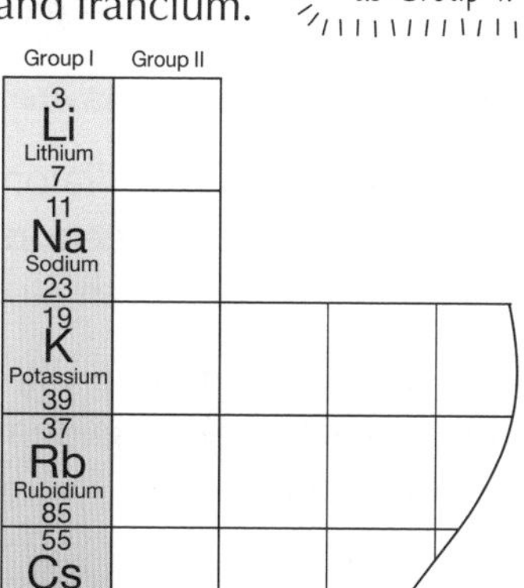

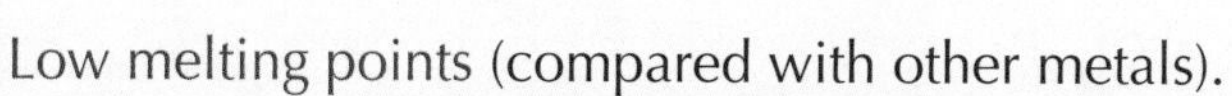

Very soft — they can be cut with a knife.

Low density — lithium, sodium and potassium are less dense than water.

As you go down the group, the melting points decrease and the metals get generally more dense (with the exception of potassium, which is less dense than sodium).

Reactivity with **Water Increases** Down the Group

1) The reaction of a Group I metal with water produces a metal hydroxide solution and hydrogen gas.
2) These reactions can be written as chemical equations — e.g. for sodium the equation is...

Word equation:	sodium + water $\rightarrow$ sodium hydroxide + hydrogen
Symbol equation:	$2Na_{(s)} + 2H_2O_{(l)} \rightarrow 2NaOH_{(aq)} + H_{2(g)}$

3) The reactivity of Group I metals with water increases down the group. This results in the reaction becoming more violent and exothermic:

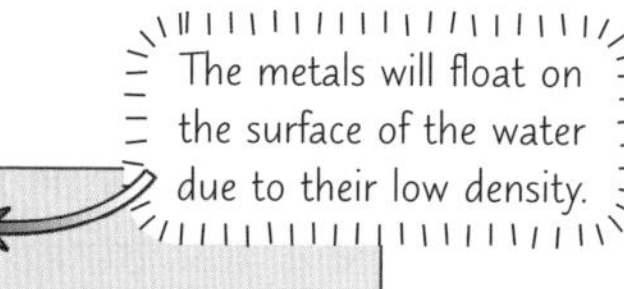

The metals will float on the surface of the water due to their low density.

Lithium will move around the surface, fizzing furiously.
Sodium and potassium do the same, but they also melt in the heat of the reaction. Potassium even gets hot enough to ignite the hydrogen gas being produced.

You Can Make **Predictions** About the **Properties** of Group I Metals

1) You can use what you know about the trends in the physical properties and reactions of Group I to make predictions about the properties of elements in the group and how they will react.

Example: You may predict that the reactions of rubidium and caesium with water will be more violent than the reaction of potassium with water. And sure enough, rubidium and caesium react violently with water and tend to explode when they get wet...

Supplement

2) In the exam, you might be given some properties of elements in a group and asked to identify trends in the group. To identify a trend, you just need to look at the information you're given about the elements and where they sit in the group.

Example: The boiling point of lithium is 1330 °C, the boiling point of sodium is 883 °C and the boiling point of potassium is 759 °C. The order of the elements down Group I is lithium then sodium then potassium, so you can tell that boiling point decreases down the group.

Supplement

Group VII Elements

Here's a page on another periodic table group that you need to be familiar with — the halogens.

Group VII Elements are Known as the 'Halogens'

You might see Group VII written as Group 7.

Group VII is made up of the elements fluorine, chlorine, bromine, iodine and astatine.

Group VI	Group VII	Group VIII
		He
O	9 F Fluorine 19	Ne
S	17 Cl Chlorine 35.5	Ar
Se	35 Br Bromine 80	Kr
	53 I Iodine 127	Xe
	85 At Astatine 210	Rn

1) The Group VII elements are non-metals. They all have similar chemical properties.
2) The halogens exist as diatomic molecules (e.g. Cl_2, Br_2, I_2). Sharing one pair of electrons in a covalent bond (see page 24) gives both atoms a full outer shell.
3) As you go down Group VII, the melting points and boiling points of the halogens increase. The density also increases and they get darker in colour. At room temperature:

Chlorine (Cl_2) is a fairly reactive, poisonous, green gas.

Bromine (Br_2) is a poisonous, red-brown liquid which gives off an orange vapour.

Iodine (I_2) is a dark grey crystalline solid which gives off a purple vapour when heated.

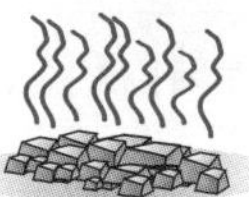

4) The higher up Group VII an element is, the more reactive it is.

You Can Make **Predictions** About the **Properties** of Halogens

You can use the trends in the physical properties of the halogens to predict the properties of elements in the group.

Example: Chlorine melts at –102 °C and iodine melts at 114 °C. Bromine is between chlorine and iodine in the group, so you can predict that its melting point will be roughly halfway between theirs: (–102 + 114) ÷ 2 = 12 ÷ 2 = 6 °C ⟸ The actual melting point of bromine is –7 °C, so this is pretty close.

A More Reactive Halogen Will **Displace** a Less Reactive One

1) The elements in Group VII take part in displacement reactions.
2) A displacement reaction is where a more reactive element 'pushes out' (displaces) a less reactive element from a compound.

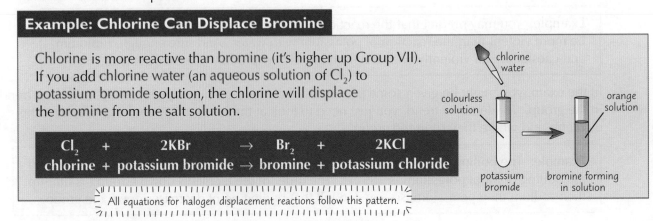

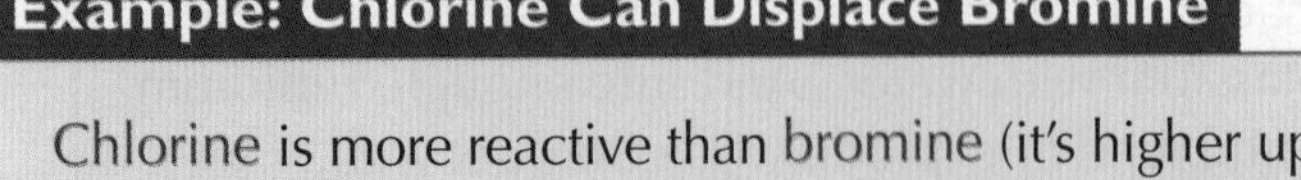

Chlorine is more reactive than bromine (it's higher up Group VII). If you add chlorine water (an aqueous solution of Cl_2) to potassium bromide solution, the chlorine will displace the bromine from the salt solution.

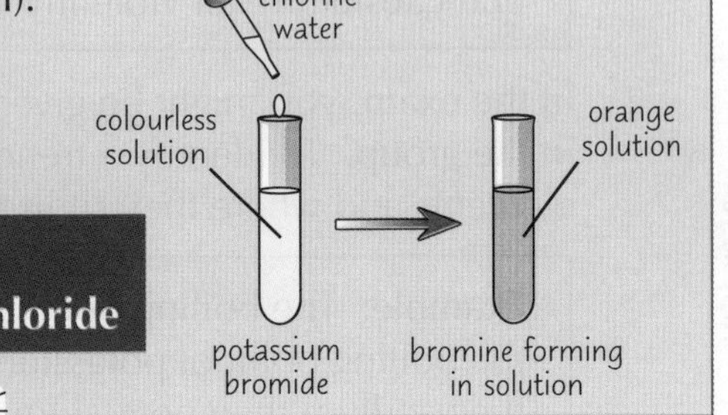

$$Cl_2 + 2KBr \rightarrow Br_2 + 2KCl$$

chlorine + potassium bromide → bromine + potassium chloride

All equations for halogen displacement reactions follow this pattern.

More Group VII and The Noble Gases

Next up, Group VIII. But first, here's a bit more about the halogens...

Halogen Displacement Reactions Show **Reactivity Trends**

The table below shows what should happen when you mix different combinations of chlorine, bromine and iodine water with solutions of the salts potassium chloride, potassium bromide and potassium iodide.

Start with:	**Potassium chloride solution $KCl_{(aq)}$ — colourless**	**Potassium bromide solution $KBr_{(aq)}$ — colourless**	**Potassium iodide solution $KI_{(aq)}$ — colourless**
Add chlorine water $Cl_{2\,(aq)}$ — colourless	no reaction	orange solution (Br_2) formed	brown solution (I_2) formed
Add bromine water $Br_{2\,(aq)}$ — orange	no reaction	no reaction	brown solution (I_2) formed
Add iodine water $I_{2\,(aq)}$ — brown	no reaction	no reaction	no reaction

1) Chlorine displaces both bromine and iodine from salt solutions. Bromine can't displace chlorine, but it does displace iodine. Iodine can't displace chlorine or bromine.
2) This shows the reactivity trend — the halogens get less reactive as you go down the group.
3) You can use this trend to predict how astatine might react. Since astatine is the least reactive halogen, you'd predict it wouldn't displace any other halogens from their salt solutions.

Group VIII Elements are All **Inert, Colourless Gases**

Group VIII is sometimes referred to as Group 8 or Group O.

Group VIII elements are called the noble gases. Group VIII is made up of the elements helium, neon, argon, krypton, xenon and radon.

1) All of the Group VIII elements are colourless gases at room temperature.
2) The noble gases are all monatomic — that just means that their gases are made up of single atoms (not molecules).
3) They're also more or less inert — this means they don't react with much at all. The reason for this is that they have a full outer shell of electrons. This means they don't easily give up or gain electrons.
4) As the noble gases are inert, they're non-flammable — they won't set on fire.

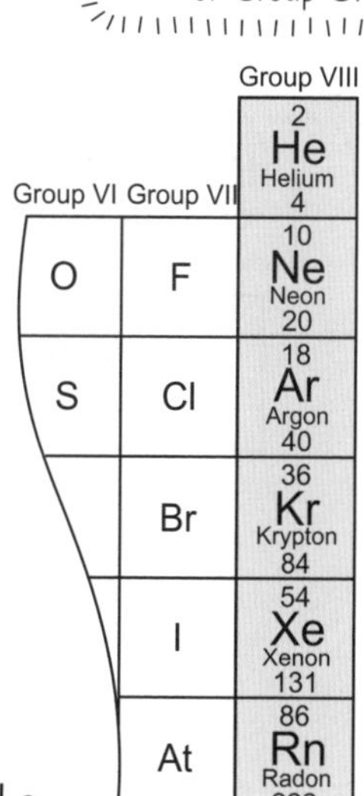

The Noble Gases have **Many Everyday Uses...**

1) Noble gases can be used to provide an inert atmosphere.
2) Argon does this in filament lamps (light bulbs that contain a coil of wire called a filament). Since it's non-flammable, it stops the very hot filament from burning away. Flash photography uses the same principle — argon, krypton and xenon are used to stop the flash filament from burning up during the high temperature flashes.
3) Helium is used in airships and party balloons. Helium has a lower density than air — so it makes balloons float. It is also non-flammable, which makes it safer to use than hydrogen gas.

EXAM TIP

Make sure you know the characteristics of these groups

You'll be given a periodic table in your exam, so you don't have to remember all the names of the Group I metals, halogens and noble gases. However, you might get asked about their properties.

Transition Elements

The transition elements make up the big section in the middle of the periodic table.

Transition Elements Sit Between **Group II** and **Group III**

1) The transition elements (or transition metals) are metals in the centre of the periodic table.

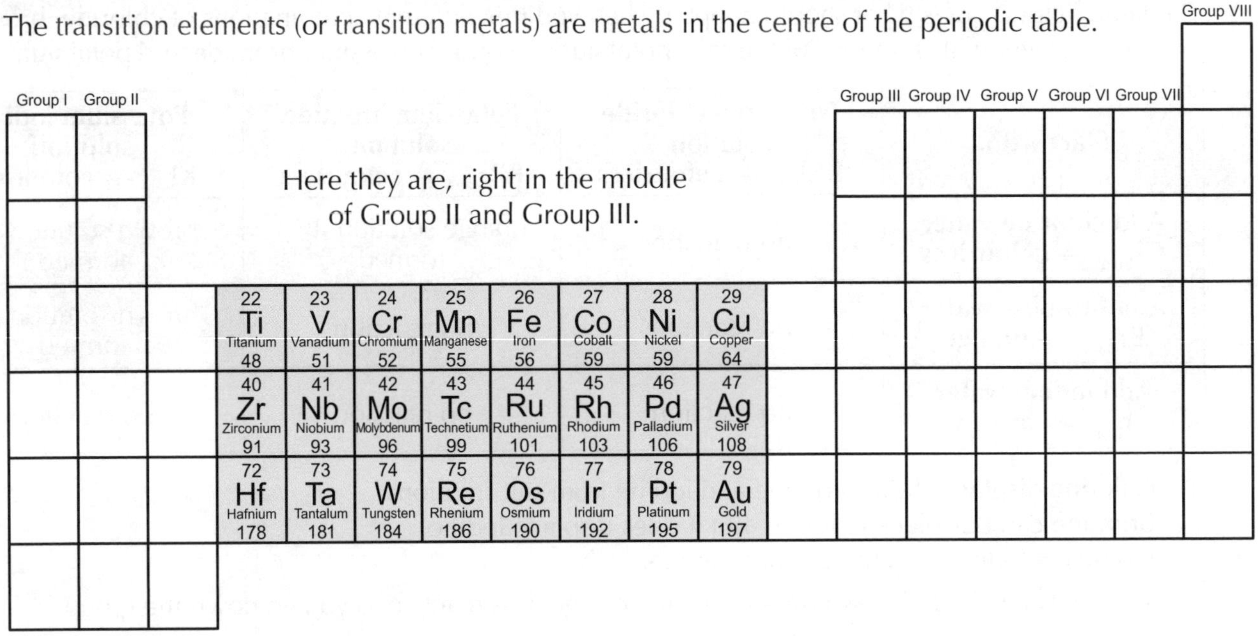

Group I Group II

Group III Group IV Group V Group VI Group VII Group VIII

Here they are, right in the middle of Group II and Group III.

22 Ti Titanium 48	23 V Vanadium 51	24 Cr Chromium 52	25 Mn Manganese 55	26 Fe Iron 56	27 Co Cobalt 59	28 Ni Nickel 59	29 Cu Copper 64
40 Zr Zirconium 91	41 Nb Niobium 93	42 Mo Molybdenum 96	43 Tc Technetium 99	44 Ru Ruthenium 101	45 Rh Rhodium 103	46 Pd Palladium 106	47 Ag Silver 108
72 Hf Hafnium 178	73 Ta Tantalum 181	74 W Tungsten 184	75 Re Rhenium 186	76 Os Osmium 190	77 Ir Iridium 192	78 Pt Platinum 195	79 Au Gold 197

2) The transition metals have all the typical properties of metals (see page 96) — they're relatively hard, strong and shiny materials that conduct heat and electricity well.
3) They have high melting points.
4) They also have high densities. For example, at room temperature, potassium (a Group I metal) has a density of 0.9 g/cm^3, while copper has a density of 9.0 g/cm^3, and iron has a density of 7.9 g/cm^3.
5) Transition metals also have some pretty special properties...

Transition metal ions are often coloured, and so compounds that contain them are colourful.

For example, potassium chromate(VI) is yellow and potassium manganate(VII) is purple.

Roman numerals in the names of transition metal compounds refer to the oxidation state of the metal — see p.73 for more on oxidation states if you're taking the Extended course.

Transition metals and their compounds often make good catalysts (things that speed up the rate of a reaction — see p.63).

Supplement

Transition metals have variable oxidation states. This means they can have more than one ion.

E.g. copper can exist in the 1+ oxidation state as Cu^+ ions and the 2+ oxidation state as Cu^{2+} ions. Iron can exist in the 2+ oxidation state as Fe^{2+} ions and in the 3+ oxidation state as Fe^{3+} ions.

Supplement

Transition metals are pretty useful elements

Transition metals have similar properties to 'typical metals' but also have a few more unusual characteristics. These include forming coloured compounds and having the ability to act as catalysts.

Warm-Up & Exam Questions

Treat these exam questions like the real thing — don't look back through the book until you've finished.

Warm-Up Questions

1) Based on its position in the periodic table, would you expect the chemical properties of potassium to be more similar to those of sodium or calcium?
2) How many electrons do Group I metals have in their outer shell?
3) Do Group I metals get more or less reactive as you go down the group?
4) What happens to the density of the halogens as you go down Group VII?
5) What colour is chlorine gas?
6) In which group of the periodic table are the noble gases?
7) Why are noble gases unreactive?
8) Give two typical properties of transition metals.

Exam Questions

1 The table below shows some of the physical properties of four of the halogens.

Halogen	Properties			
	Atomic number	**Physical state at room temperature**	**Boiling point / °C**	**Reactivity**
Fluorine	9	gas	–188	....
Chlorine	17	gas	?	....
Bromine	35	liquid	58.8	....
Iodine	53	solid	184	....

(a) The table above has a column for reactivity. Write an **X** in the row of the halogen with the **highest** reactivity and a **Y** in the row of the halogen with the **lowest** reactivity.

[2]

(b) Predict the boiling point of chlorine in °C.

[1]

[Total 3 marks]

2 The diagram on the right shows the periodic table.

(a) Element **X** is found in the centre of the periodic table. What name is given to the elements found in this part of the table?

[1]

(b) Element **Y** does not conduct electricity. Predict whether element **Y** will be found to the left or the right of line **A**. Explain your answer.

[2]

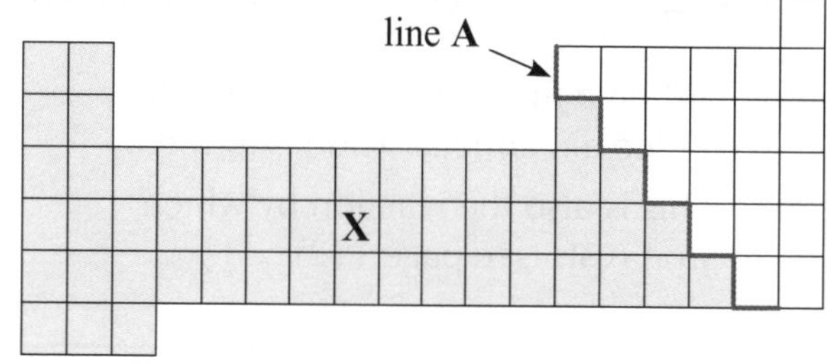

[Total 3 marks]

Metals

Metals are a big group of elements and compounds with unique chemistry. Let's get right into it.

All Metals are **Shiny, Malleable Conductors**

All metals have similar general physical properties:

- They're malleable (they can be rolled or hammered into flat sheets) and ductile (they can be drawn into wires).
- They're great at conducting heat and electricity.
- They're generally shiny solids at room temperature.
- They aren't soluble in water.
- Most have high boiling and melting points.

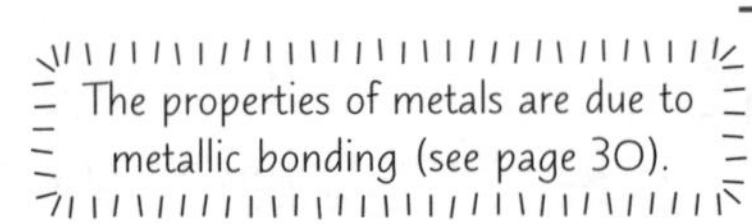

The properties of metals are due to metallic bonding (see page 30).

Supplement

Alloys are Harder Than **Pure Metals**

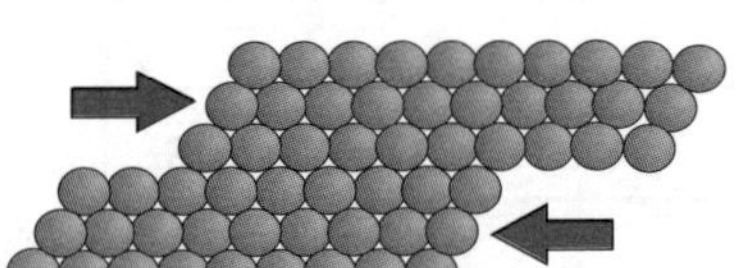

1) Pure metals are malleable because they have a regular arrangement of identical atoms. The layers of atoms can slide over each other.
2) This means some metals aren't strong enough for certain uses, so alloys are used instead. Alloys are made by adding another element to a metal — that could be a non-metal or another metal.
3) Different elements have different sized atoms. So, for example, when an element such as carbon is added to pure iron, the smaller carbon atoms will upset the layers of pure iron atoms, making it more difficult for them to slide over each other. So alloys are stronger.
4) Many metals in use today are actually alloys. We can use our knowledge of metals to design alloys for specific uses.

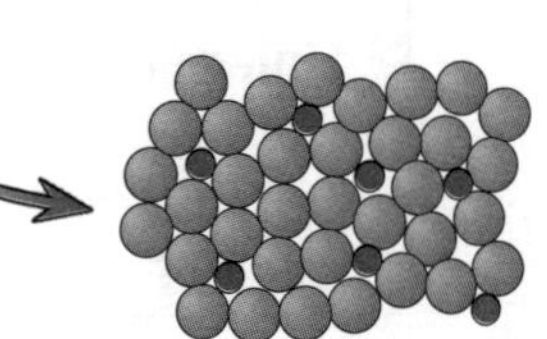

Metals React with **Acids** and **Oxygen**

Metal + Acid → Salt + Hydrogen

1) When a metal reacts with a dilute acid, a salt and hydrogen are produced.

Examples: $2HCl + Mg \rightarrow MgCl_2 + H_2$ (Magnesium chloride)
$H_2SO_4 + Mg \rightarrow MgSO_4 + H_2$ (Magnesium sulfate)

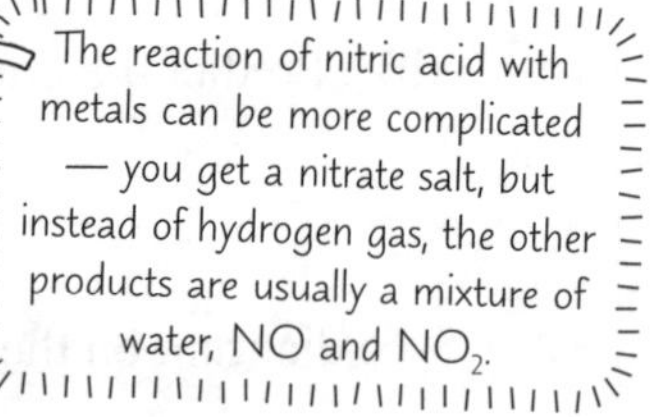

The reaction of nitric acid with metals can be more complicated — you get a nitrate salt, but instead of hydrogen gas, the other products are usually a mixture of water, NO and NO2.

2) You can test for hydrogen using a lighted splint (see page 87).

Metal + Oxygen → Metal Oxide

1) When a metal reacts with oxygen in the air, a metal oxide is formed.
2) This is also the reaction by which iron rusts (see page 112).

Examples:
$2Mg + O_2 \rightarrow 2MgO$ (Magnesium oxide)
$2Fe + O_2 \rightarrow 2FeO$ (Iron oxide)

Metals all behave in similar ways

As you'll see, some metals are more reactive than others. But those that are reactive will react in similar ways. Metals also have certain unique properties which set them apart from the other elements.

The Reactivity Series

Reactivity series are lists of metals (sometimes with carbon or hydrogen thrown in).
But they're not just any old lists in any old order. As the name suggests, they tell you all about reactivities.

A **Reactivity Series** Shows How Well a Metal **Reacts**

1) A reactivity series is a table that lists metals in order of their reactivity.
2) As well as the metals, carbon is often included in reactivity series — a metal's position in the reactivity series compared to carbon determines how it's extracted from its metal oxide (see page 102).
3) Hydrogen can be included in reactivity series too — this shows the reactivity of metals with dilute acids (see next page).

If a metal is below hydrogen in the reactivity series, it's less reactive than hydrogen and won't react with dilute acids.

4) You need to know this reactivity series:

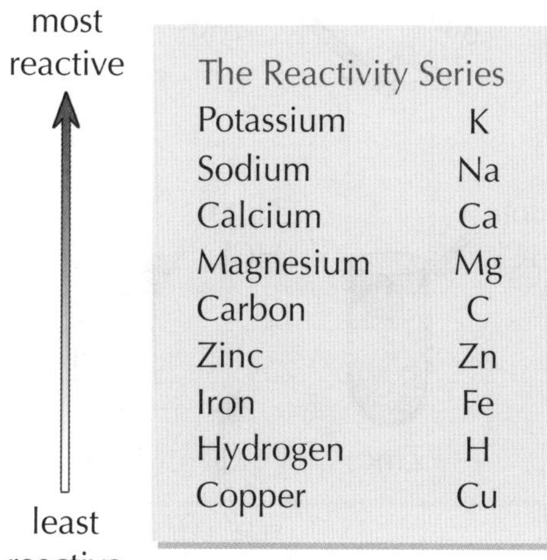
most reactive
least reactive

The Reactivity Series	
Potassium	K
Sodium	Na
Calcium	Ca
Magnesium	Mg
Carbon	C
Zinc	Zn
Iron	Fe
Hydrogen	H
Copper	Cu

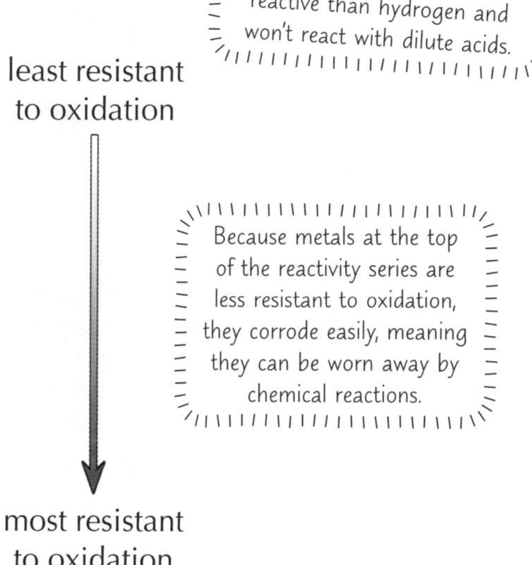
least resistant to oxidation
most resistant to oxidation
Because metals at the top of the reactivity series are less resistant to oxidation, they corrode easily, meaning they can be worn away by chemical reactions.

5) The metals at the top of the reactivity series are the most reactive. They're also oxidised easily (they gain oxygen to form oxides).
6) The metals at the bottom of the reactivity series are less reactive. They're more resistant to oxidation than the metals higher up the reactivity series.
7) You can determine a metal's position in the reactivity series by reacting it with water and dilute acids (see p.98-99).

Supplement

Aluminium Appears to be **Unreactive**

1) If aluminium was included in the reactivity series above, it would sit just below magnesium.
2) However, it is more resistant to corrosion (oxidation) than you would expect.
3) This is because the surface of aluminium reacts with oxygen in the air to form a layer of unreactive aluminium oxide (Al_2O_3) which acts as a barrier against further oxidation.
4) This can give the appearance that aluminium is less reactive than it actually is.

Metals at the top of a reactivity series are more reactive

Don't worry if you come across different reactivity series to the one shown above — they all work the same. The more reactive elements are at the top of the series and the less reactive ones are at the bottom.

Reactivity of Metals

You can determine a metal's position in the reactivity series by reacting it with dilute acids and water.

How **Metals** React With **Acids** Tells You About Their **Reactivity**

1) Reactive metals tend to fizz when you drop them into acid.
This is because the reaction releases hydrogen gas (see page 96).

2) Here's a classic experiment that you can do to show that some metals are more reactive than others.
All you do is place little pieces of various metals into dilute hydrochloric acid:

Sodium and potassium react explosively with dilute HCl — so it's best not to use them in this experiment.

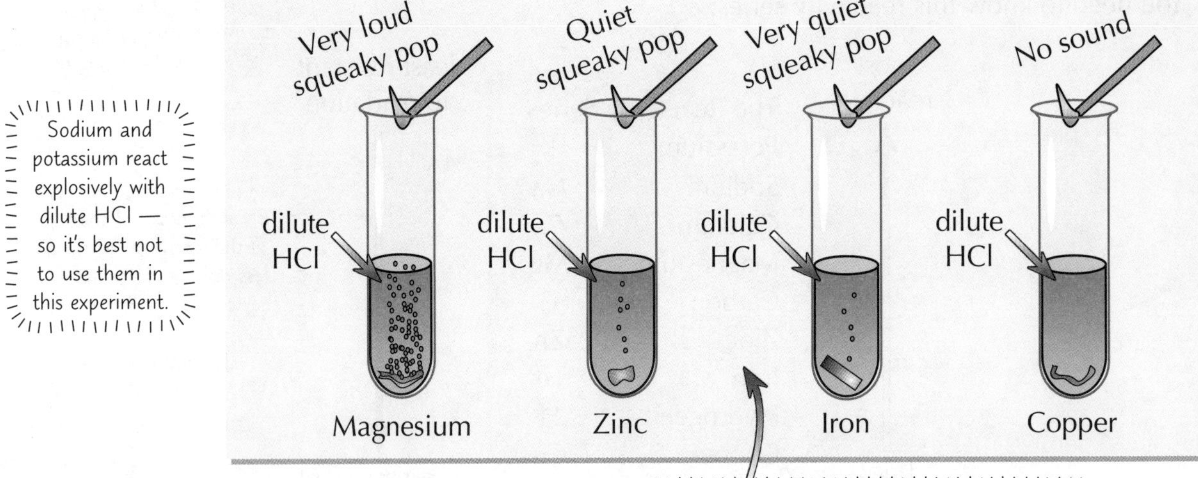

It's worth making sure the pieces of metal are a similar size and shape so as you can compare your results. Powdered metals will react much faster than lumps of metal as they've got a larger surface areas (see page 62).

3) The more reactive the metal is, the faster the reaction with the acid will go.

4) Very reactive metals (e.g. magnesium and calcium) will fizz vigorously, less reactive metals (e.g. zinc) will bubble a bit, and unreactive metals (e.g. copper) will not react with dilute acids at all.

5) You can show that hydrogen is forming using the lighted splint test (see page 87). The louder the squeaky pop, the more hydrogen has been made in the time period and the more reactive the metal is.

6) The speed of reaction is also indicated by the rate at which the bubbles of hydrogen are given off — the faster the bubbles form, the faster the reaction and the more reactive the metal.

You could also follow the rate of the reaction by using a gas syringe to measure the volume of gas given off at regular time intervals (see p.64) or using a thermometer to measure by how much the temperature changes (as the reaction of acids with metals is exothermic — see p.56).

Always take care when carrying out experiments

It's a good idea to think about how you could minimise the possible risks before doing any practical work. For example, when carrying out the reaction above, you should wear goggles to protect yourself from any acid that might spit out of the test tube when you add the metal.

Reactivity of Metals

Some Metals React With Water

1) In a similar way to their reactions with acids, the reactions of metals with water also show the reactivity of metals.

2) This is the general reaction:

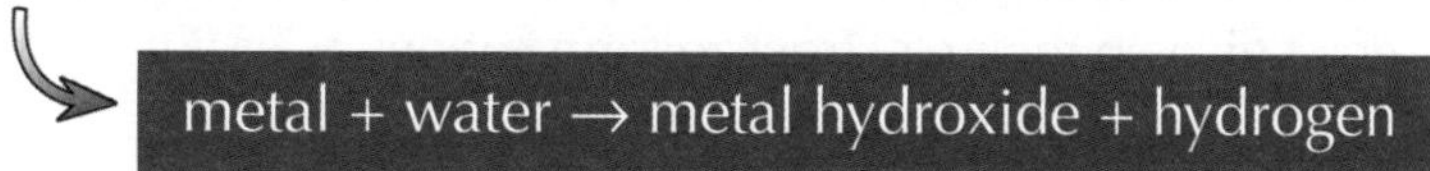

3) Very reactive metals like potassium, sodium and calcium will all react vigorously with water.

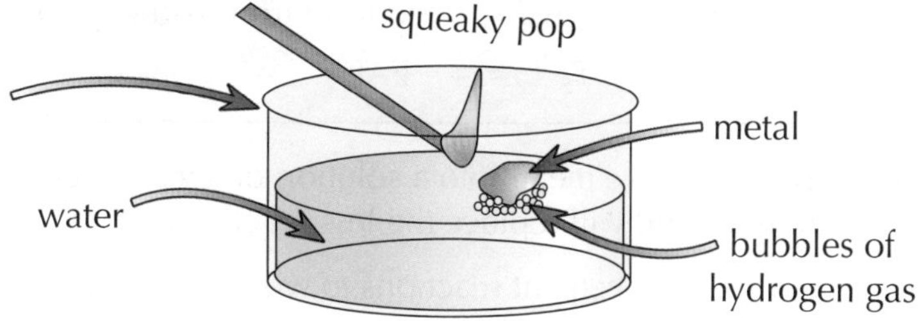

Less Reactive Metals Only React With Steam

1) Less reactive metals like magnesium, zinc and iron won't react much with cold water, but they will react with steam.

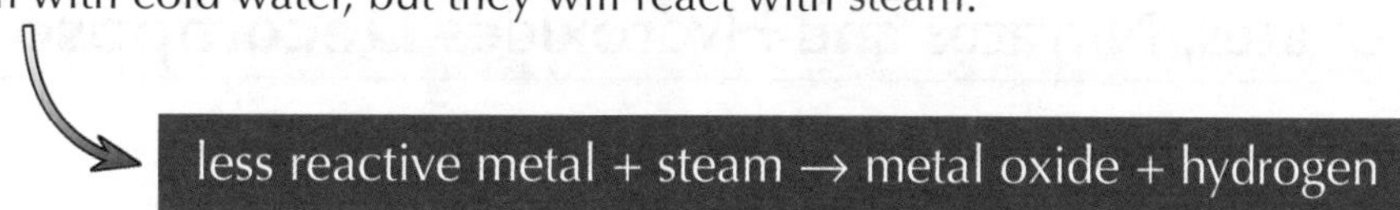

2) You could show this in the lab using this experiment:

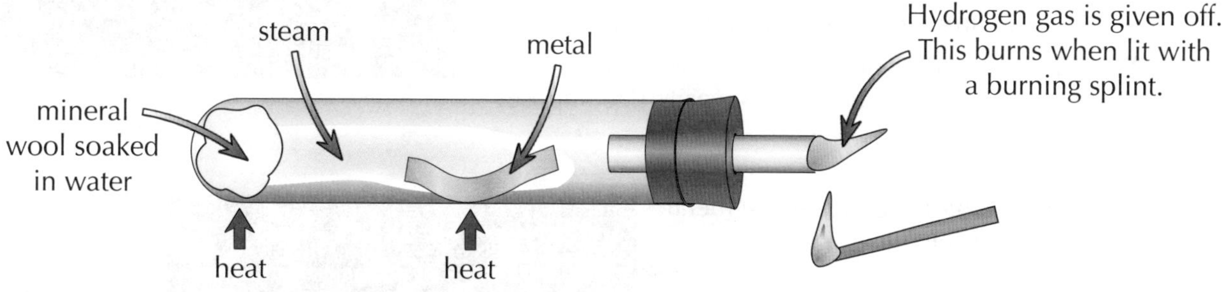

3) Copper is so unreactive that it won't react with either water or steam.

Less reactive metals need a bit of encouragement to react with H_2O

Some metals lower down the reactivity series aren't reactive enough to react with liquid water — they'll only react if you give the water a bit more energy by heating it to form steam. Splendid.

Reactivity of Metals

It is also possible to test the reactivity of metals by reacting them with other metals or by heating them.

A **More Reactive** Metal **Displaces** a **Less Reactive** Metal

1) More reactive metals react more strongly than less reactive metals. This is because they easily lose their electrons to form cations (positive ions). Less reactive metals don't give up their electrons to form cations as easily.
2) This means that a more reactive metal will displace a less reactive metal from its oxide because it will bond more strongly to the oxygen.

> Example: iron would be displaced from iron oxide by the more reactive aluminium.
>
> $$Fe_2O_3 + 2Al \rightarrow Al_2O_3 + 2Fe$$

Displacement reactions like this one are redox reactions (see p.72) — the metal is oxidised and the displaced metal ion is reduced.

3) If you put a reactive metal into a solution of a less reactive metal salt the reactive metal will replace the less reactive metal in the salt.
4) You can use displacement reactions to work out where in the reactivity series a metal is supposed to go.

> E.g. If you were given a lump of a mystery metal, you could try reacting it with different metal oxides and salts. If it reacted with copper oxide, you'd know it was higher in the series than copper. If it didn't react with magnesium sulfate, you'd know it was lower than magnesium in the reactivity series.

Supplement

Metal Carbonates, Nitrates and Hydroxides **Decompose** in **Heat**

Supplement

Thermal decomposition is the breakdown of a substance into simpler substances when heated. The thermal decomposition of metal carbonates, nitrates and hydroxides depends on the reactivity of the metal — the more reactive it is, the more strongly you have to heat the compound to get it to decompose.

1) When a metal carbonate thermally decomposes, it forms carbon dioxide and a metal oxide.
2) Metal carbonates of the most reactive metals (like potassium and sodium) do not easily decompose.

$$CuCO_{3(s)} \rightarrow CuO_{(s)} + CO_{2(g)}$$

copper(II) carbonate → copper oxide + carbon dioxide

3) Heating a nitrate of a reactive metal (like potassium or sodium) produces a metal nitrite and oxygen.

$$2KNO_{3(s)} \rightarrow 2KNO_{2(s)} + O_{2(g)}$$

potassium nitrate → potassium nitrite + oxygen

4) If you heat a nitrate of a less reactive metal, you produce a metal oxide, nitrogen dioxide and oxygen.

$$2Zn(NO_3)_{2(s)} \rightarrow 2ZnO_{(s)} + O_{2(g)} + 4NO_{2(g)}$$

zinc nitrate → zinc oxide + oxygen + nitrogen dioxide

You can tell when NO_2 is produced because you will see a red-brown gas.

5) When a metal hydroxide thermally decomposes, it produces a metal oxide and water.
6) As with metal carbonates, the hydroxides of the most reactive metals (like sodium and potassium) do not easily decompose.

$$Zn(OH)_{2(s)} \rightarrow ZnO_{(s)} + H_2O_{(g)}$$

zinc hydroxide → zinc oxide + water

Warm-Up & Exam Questions

Metals react in interesting ways, I'm sure you'll agree. See how much you remember with these questions.

Warm-Up Questions

1) Why are pure metals malleable?
2) What gas is released when a metal reacts with a dilute acid?
3) True or false? Zinc is less reactive than calcium.
4) Explain why a more reactive metal will displace a less reactive metal from its oxide.

Exam Questions

1 A student performed some experiments to investigate the reactivity of metals.

(a) The student placed pieces of four different metals, **A**, **B**, **C** and **D**, into dilute hydrochloric acid. The diagram below shows what the four experiments looked like after 1 minute.

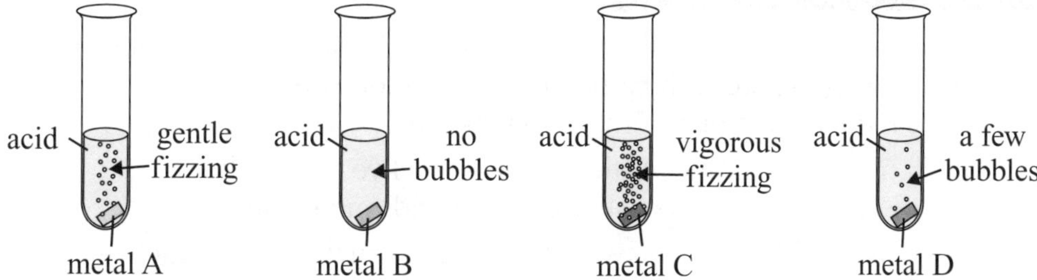

Use the information in the diagram to put these metals in order of decreasing reactivity.

[2]

(b) Next, the student performed experiments on three mystery metals, marked **X**, **Y** and **Z**. Her results are shown in the table below.

Metal	Any reaction with cold water?	Any reaction with steam?
X	Reacts vigorously. Hydrogen gas is produced.	
Y	no reaction	Reacts vigorously. Metal is coated with a white solid. Hydrogen gas is produced.
Z	no reaction	no reaction

(i) Metal **Y** was zinc. It reacted with the steam to produce hydrogen gas and a white solid. Name the white solid that was produced by this reaction.

[1]

(ii) One of the other metals the student was given was sodium. Suggest whether sodium was metal **X** or metal **Z**. Give a reason for your answer.

[1]

(c) A student heats samples of copper carbonate and sodium carbonate. State which of these compounds will react. Write a balanced symbol equation for the reaction that occurs.

[2]

[Total 6 marks]

Extraction of Metals

You've learnt about the reactivity series of metals over the last few pages. Now you need to apply it.

Most Metals are Found in **Ores** and have to be **Separated**

1) Metals that are unreactive don't tend to form compounds with other elements. Unreactive metals such as gold are found uncombined — so you just have to find them and dig them up.
2) However, most metals do react with other elements to form compounds, which can be found naturally in the Earth's crust. If a compound contains enough of the metal to make it worthwhile extracting, the compound is called a metal ore.
3) The more reactive a metal is, the harder it is to extract it from a compound.
4) Lots of common metals like iron and aluminium form metal oxide ores. The metal can be separated from its oxide by a reduction reaction (see p.72).

Methods of **Extraction** are Linked to the **Order of Reactivity**

Extraction by Reduction with Carbon

1) Some metals can be extracted from their ores using a reduction reaction with carbon. This is done by heating the ore with carbon or carbon monoxide. E.g. iron oxide is reduced in a blast furnace to make iron.
2) This method will only work for metals that are less reactive than carbon. This is because more reactive elements form compounds more readily.
3) So, carbon can only take the oxygen away from metals which are less reactive than itself.

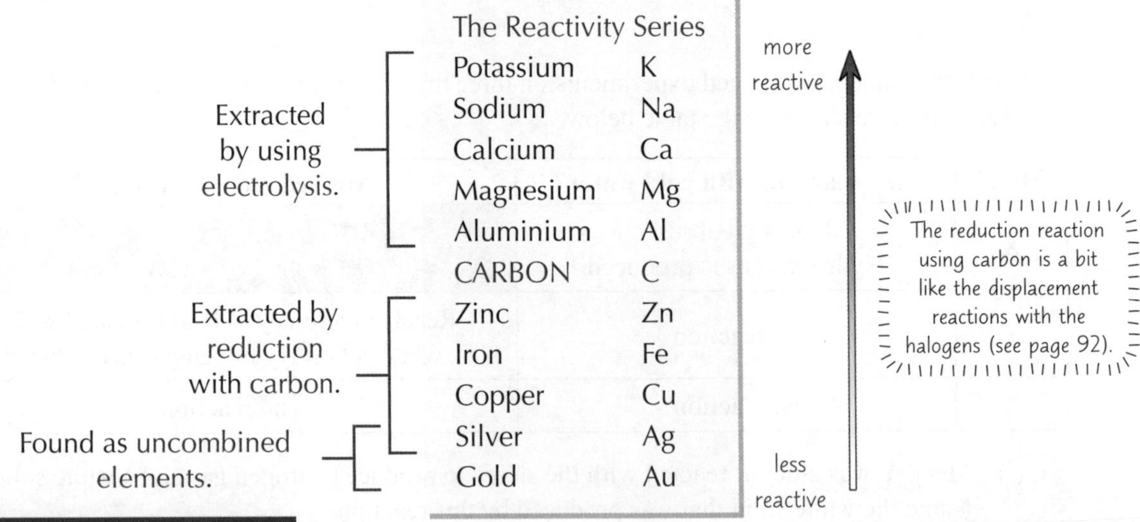

Extraction by Electrolysis

1) Very reactive metals form very stable ores — i.e. it's difficult to get the metal out of its compound.
2) So metals that are more reactive than carbon (they come higher in the reactivity series) have to be extracted using electrolysis.
3) Electrolysis uses electricity to separate the metal from the other elements in the compound (see p.47). For example, aluminium is extracted from bauxite ore using electrolysis.

Carbon can't reduce anything above it in the reactivity series

Knowing the reactivity series on page 97 will help you to remember which metals can be extracted from their ore by carbon. Write it out, cover it up and see if you can remember it.

Iron and Steel

Iron is mainly extracted from its ore in order to make steel. However, iron ore needs to undergo a series of chemical reactions under high temperatures before we can use the pure metal.

Iron is Extracted from Hematite

1) Iron is extracted from iron ore, which contains a form of iron oxide known as hematite (Fe_2O_3).
2) In order to produce iron, the hematite must be reacted with coke (a form of carbon) and limestone (calcium carbonate) in a blast furnace at very high temperatures.
3) The coke reacts with oxygen in the hot air to form carbon dioxide. This reaction is very exothermic and adds heat to the furnace. The carbon dioxide is then reduced to form carbon monoxide:

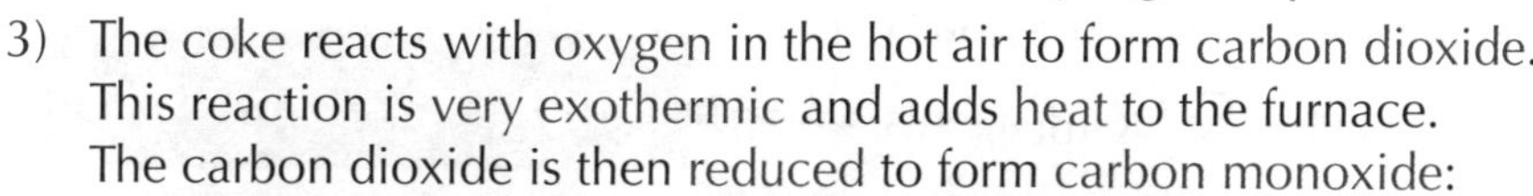

$$C + O_2 \rightarrow CO_2 \qquad C + CO_2 \rightarrow 2CO$$

4) Carbon monoxide then reduces the hematite, producing iron and carbon dioxide:

$$Fe_2O_3 + 3CO \rightarrow 2Fe + 3CO_2$$

5) At higher temperatures, the coke can also reduce the hematite:

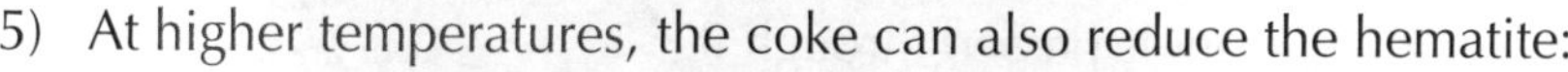

$$Fe_2O_3 + 3C \rightarrow 2Fe + 3CO$$

6) Molten iron settles at the bottom of the furnace and can be drawn off.

Mixture of hematite, coke and limestone
Waste gases
Lower temperatures
Waste gases
Higher temperatures
Hot air
Hot air
Molten slag
Molten iron

Limestone Neutralises Any Impurities

1) Iron ore is not just made up of hematite. It also contains impurities such as silicon dioxide (SiO_2).
2) Limestone ($CaCO_3$) is used in the blast furnace to neutralise silicon dioxide, producing calcium silicate ($CaSiO_3$). This is removed from the furnace as molten slag.

- Limestone breaks down at high temperatures, forming calcium oxide:
  $$CaCO_3 \rightarrow CaO + CO_2$$
- Calcium oxide can then act as a base to remove acidic silicon dioxide:
  $$CaO + SiO_2 \rightarrow CaSiO_3$$

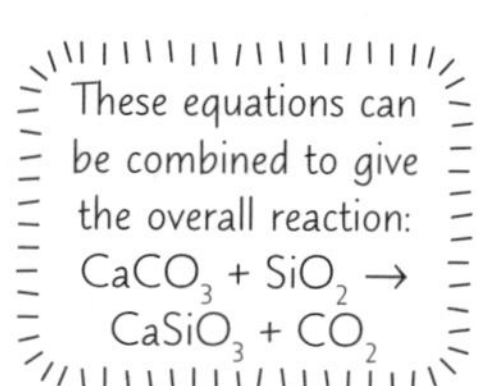

These equations can be combined to give the overall reaction: $CaCO_3 + SiO_2 \rightarrow CaSiO_3 + CO_2$

Oxygen Can Be Used to Remove Impurities from Iron

1) Steel is an alloy (p.96) of iron and carbon (and sometimes other metals).
2) The molten iron removed from the blast furnace is still not pure — any impurities must be removed from the molten iron before it can be used to make steel. This is done using oxygen and basic oxides, such as calcium oxide.
3) The main impurity is carbon, but other impurities can include phosphorus and silicon.
4) Oxygen is blown onto the impure iron mixture. Carbon impurities in the mixture will react with the oxygen to form carbon monoxide and carbon dioxide gas. However, not all of the carbon is removed — some needs to remain in order to make steel.
5) Other elements such as phosphorus and silicon react with the oxygen to form acidic oxides. These can be neutralised using calcium oxide, forming a waste layer of slag.

Zinc and Aluminium

Like iron, zinc can be extracted using carbon. However, aluminium is extracted from its ore using electricity.

Zinc is Extracted from **Zinc Blende**

1) Zinc blende is an ore of zinc, mostly made up of zinc sulfide (ZnS).
2) When the ore is heated in air, zinc sulfide reacts to produce zinc oxide: $2ZnS + 3O_2 \rightarrow 2ZnO + 2SO_2$
3) Zinc oxide can then be heated in a furnace with coke (C).
4) Like in the blast furnace, the coke reacts with oxygen in the air to form carbon dioxide, which is then reduced to carbon monoxide (see previous page).
5) Carbon and carbon monoxide both act as reducing agents when reacting with zinc oxide.

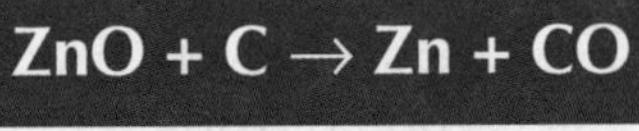

$ZnO + CO \rightarrow Zn + CO_2$

6) The zinc is removed from the top of the furnace as zinc vapour, then condensed.

Aluminium is **Extracted** by **Electrolysis**

1) Metals that are more reactive than carbon (see page 102) are extracted using electrolysis of molten compounds (see page 47 for more on this).
2) Once the metal ore is melted, an electric current is passed through it. The metal is discharged at the cathode and the non-metal at the anode.

The compounds have to be molten (i.e. liquid) so that the ions are free to move.

Aluminium is extracted from its ore, bauxite, using electrolysis with carbon electrodes. Aluminium oxide (Al_2O_3) has a high melting point, so the ore is first dissolved in molten cryolite (an aluminium compound with a lower melting point than Al_2O_3) to lower the melting point.

During electrolysis, aluminium is formed at the cathode: $Al^{3+} + 3e^- \rightarrow Al$

Aluminium metal sinks to the bottom of the cell and is siphoned off.

Oxygen forms at the anode: $2O^{2-} \rightarrow O_2 + 4e^-$

The overall equation is: $2Al_2O_{3(l)} \rightarrow 4Al_{(l)} + 3O_{2(g)}$

Electrolysis is a **More Expensive** Process than **Reduction** with Carbon

1) In order to run electrolysis to extract metals from their ores, you need large amounts of electricity. Electricity is expensive, making electrolysis a pretty pricey process. There are also costs associated with melting or dissolving the metal ore so it can conduct electricity.
2) In comparison, extracting metals using reduction with carbon is much cheaper. Carbon is cheap, and also acts as a fuel to provide the heat needed for the reduction reaction to happen.
3) This means that, in general, metals lower down the reactivity series (less reactive metals) are cheaper to extract than those higher up the reactivity series (more reactive metals).

Supplement

Supplement

Electrolysis is used to extract reactive metals from their ores

Extracting aluminium by electrolysis is handy, but it does have downsides. The large amounts of energy required often come from burning fossil fuels and this contributes to global warming (see p.116 for more).

Recycling Metals

We don't have an infinite amount of metals to keep making things from, so recycling is a really important way of making sure we don't run out of key natural resources such as aluminium or iron. What a good idea.

Recycling Metals Can Save **Energy** and **Money**

Important metals such as iron, steel and aluminium can be recycled. This has many benefits...

Recycling is the process of converting waste materials into new products.

Metals are usually recycled by melting them and then casting them into the shape of the new product.

1) Mining and extracting metals takes lots of energy, most of which comes from burning fossil fuels.

2) Recycling metals often uses much less energy than is needed to mine and extract new metal, conserves the finite amount of each metal in the earth and cuts down on the amount of waste getting sent to landfill.

3) Recycling also saves on the financial costs of mining and extracting iron from its ore. It also reduces the cost of sending waste from mining and extraction to landfill.

For example, for every 1 kg of aluminium cans you recycle, you save:

- 95% or so of the energy needed to mine and extract 'fresh' aluminium
- 4 kg of aluminium ore
- a lot of waste.

In fact, aluminium's about the most cost-effective metal to recycle.

4) Extracting metals also impacts on the environment. Mines are damaging to the environment and destroy habitats — not to mention the fact that they spoil the appearance of the landscape. Recycling more metals means that we don't need as many mines.

There are **Disadvantages** to **Metal Recycling**

1) Metals have be sorted and separated before they can be recycled, which takes time and money.

2) Energy is also required to collect, transport and recycle the metals. However, the energy cost is lower than the cost of extracting new metals from ores.

Recycling's great — it's useful in so many different ways...

The examiners might ask you to evaluate the benefits of metal recycling. Remember that recycling doesn't just reduce the use of raw materials, it reduces the amount of energy used, the amount of damage to the environment and the amount of waste produced. It also has economic benefits.

Uses of Metals

Metals have a variety of useful properties including conductivity and hardness. Combining metals with other metals or with entirely different elements can change their properties to produce a range of different alloys.

Metals Have Different Uses Depending on Their Properties

The uses of metals depend largely on their physical and chemical properties, including their reactivity, their density and their electrical and thermal conductivity.

Metal	Properties	Uses
Aluminium	Strong, low density	Aircraft manufacturing
	Resistant to corrosion	Food containers
Copper	Good electrical conductivity, malleable	Electrical wiring
	Low reactivity, good thermal conductivity	Cooking utensils
Mild steel	Durable, strong, malleable	Car bodies and machinery
Stainless steel	Resistant to corrosion, strong, hard	Cutlery, saucepans and industrial equipment in chemical plants
Zinc	Creates corrosion resistant, tough and conductive alloys	Galvanising (see p.112)
		Making brass (an alloy of copper and zinc)

Supplement

Using Additives can Change the Properties of Metals

1) Alloys are made by adding other elements to a metal (see page 96).
2) The properties of the alloy depend on the added elements and the metal you start with — they're different to the properties of the original pure metal.

For example, adding different chemical additives to iron can create steels with different properties:

- Adding small amounts of carbon to iron can create mild steel, which is more malleable.
- Adding more carbon makes the steel harder.
- Stainless steel, which is more resistant to rusting, contains chromium and sometimes nickel.

Supplement

Supplement

How a metal is used will depend on its properties

A property that is good for one application may be a disadvantage in another, e.g. some metals are used for pans as they conduct heat well, but they're rarely used for mugs — hot drinks would cool too quickly.

Warm-Up & Exam Questions

If you were hoping to test your knowledge of metals with some questions, then it's your lucky day...

Warm-Up Questions

1) True or false? Magnesium can be extracted from its ore using carbon.
2) What are the three reactants added to the blast furnace in the production of iron?
3) What is the name of the main ore of zinc? [S]
4) Give a disadvantage of recycling metals.
5) What properties of copper make it a good material for cooking utensils?

Exam Questions

1 Not all metals can be extracted using carbon. Some need to be extracted using a different method.

(a) Give the name of the process used to extract these metals.

[1]

(b) Predict whether sodium could be extracted from its ore using carbon. Explain your answer.

[1]

[Total 2 marks]

2 Iron can be extracted by the reduction of hematite (Fe_2O_3) with carbon monoxide (CO) in a blast furnace to produce iron and carbon dioxide.

(a) Write a balanced symbol equation for this reaction.

[2]

(b) Explain why the hematite is described as being reduced during this reaction.

[1]

In the blast furnace, calcium oxide (CaO) neutralises silicon dioxide (SiO_2), producing calcium silicate ($CaSiO_3$).

(c) Write a balanced symbol equation for this reaction.

[1]

(d) What happens to the calcium silicate produced by this reaction?

[1]

[Total 5 marks]

Supplement

3 Aluminium is extracted from aluminium oxide (Al_2O_3) by electrolysis.

(a) The aluminium oxide is dissolved in molten cryolite. State why.

[1]

(b) Name the two products of the electrolysis of aluminium oxide.

[1]

(c) State a common use of aluminium.

[1]

[Total 3 marks]

Supplement

Revision Summary for Sections 9 & 10

That's all for Sections 9 and 10 — have a go at these questions before moving on to Section 11.

- Try these questions and tick off each one when you get it right.
- When you've done all the questions for a topic and are completely happy with it, tick off the topic.

The Periodic Table (p.90)

1) What feature of atoms determines the order of the modern periodic table?
2) Are the elements in Group II metals or non-metals?
3) How many electrons are in the outer shell of an atom of a Group VII element?

Groups of the Periodic Table (p.91-94)

4) Give two properties of the Group I metals.
5) Write a balanced symbol equation for the reaction between potassium (K) and water.
6) Put these Group I metals in order of reactivity with water, starting with the least reactive: potassium, caesium, lithium, sodium.
7) What would you observe when reacting lithium with water?
8) How many atoms are in each molecule of a halogen?
9) Describe the difference between the appearances and physical states of bromine and iodine at room temperature and pressure.
10) If chlorine water is added to potassium bromide solution, what colour will the solution turn?
11) At room temperature, what colour are the Group VIII gases?
12) Why is argon used in filament lamps?
13) Where are transition elements on the periodic table?
14) True or false? Transition metals can form more than one type of ion.

Metals and their Reactivities (p.96-100)

15) Give three physical properties of metals.
16) What is an alloy?
17) What is produced by the reaction between a metal and oxygen?
18) Put these metals in order from most to least reactive: copper, zinc, sodium, iron.
19) Why is aluminium less reactive than predicted from a reactivity series?
20) If a metal easily loses electrons, is it reactive or unreactive?
21) What is produced during the thermal decomposition of a metal hydroxide?
22) What is produced during the thermal decomposition of potassium nitrate?

Extraction of Metals and their Uses (p.102-106)

23) Give an example of a metal extracted using electrolysis.
24) What two substances can reduce hematite in the blast furnace?
25) Describe how impurities are removed from iron to produce steel.
26) Describe how zinc is extracted from zinc oxide.
27) Give two uses of stainless steel.
28) Name an alloy of zinc.
29) How can the chemical properties of iron be changed?

Water

Water is pretty important for life, and also for your exams...

There are **Chemical Tests** for **Water**

The reaction between copper(II) sulfate and water (page 70) can be used as a test for water.

1) Anhydrous copper(II) sulfate is a white powder which contains no water.
2) If you add a couple of drops of water to the white powder, blue hydrated copper(II) sulfate is produced.

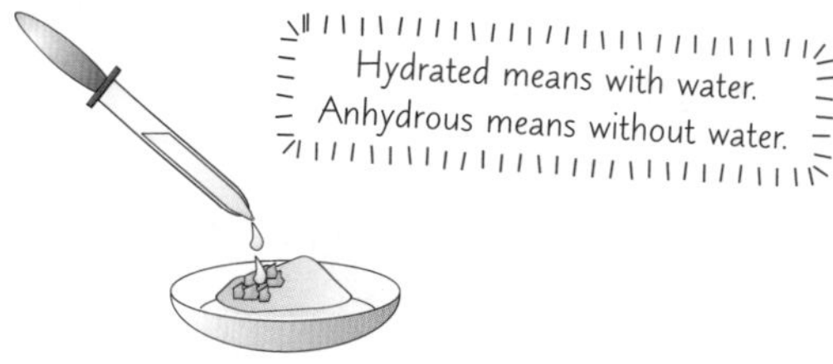
Hydrated means with water.
Anhydrous means without water.

So, to test for water, all you need to do is add a few drops of your test solution to anhydrous copper(II) sulfate and see if the white powder turns blue. This test will tell you if water is present in the solution but it won't tell you if the water is pure.

You can carry out a similar test for water using blue anhydrous cobalt(II) chloride. When water is added to the anhydrous cobalt(II) chloride powder, it turns pink and becomes hot. Blue cobalt(II) chloride paper is often used for this test — adding water turns the paper pink.

A **Clean** Water Supply is Essential for **Homes** and **Industry**

Water has many important uses in the home and in industry, for example:

At home
- Drinking water
- For cooking and cleaning
- Heating
- Watering plants

In Industry
- As a coolant
- As a solvent
- Raw material for industrial processes
- Irrigation (watering crops)

Supplement

The water we use for drinking and irrigating crops needs to be clean and safe.
An inadequate supply of clean water can lead to many problems, e.g:
- Some diseases can be spread by drinking water contaminated with bacteria.
- Fewer crops will be able to grow, leading to food shortages.

Water is **Purified** in **Water Treatment Plants**

We get the water that we use from sources such as surface water (e.g. lakes and rivers) or ground water (water that's underground). But the water that comes out of your taps doesn't just come straight from the source. Before we can drink it, it has to be treated to make it safe:

1) Filtration — a wire mesh screens out large debris such as leaves etc. Then gravel and sand beds filter out any other solid bits.
2) Chlorination — chlorine gas is bubbled through to kill harmful bacteria and other microbes.

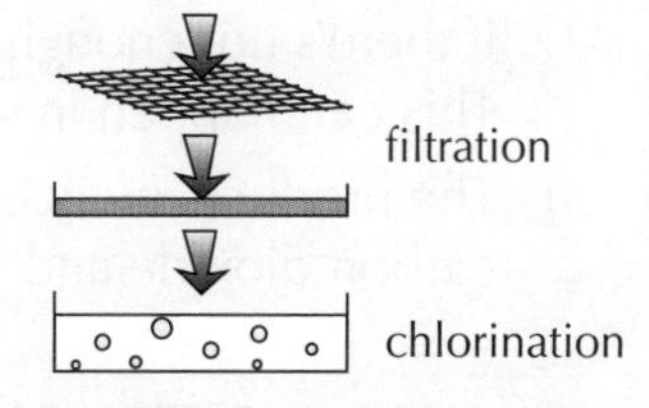
filtration
chlorination

The water that comes out of our taps has been treated

The big stuff (e.g. leaves and stones) is removed first, before smaller things such as microbes are dealt with.

Air

Air doesn't consist of pure oxygen — it's a mixture of different gases. Human activity has changed the composition of the air through pollution — we have increased the amount of pollutants in the air.

Air is Mostly Made Up of Nitrogen and Oxygen

Air is a mixture of different gases. The composition of clean, dry air is approximately:

- 78% nitrogen,
- 21% oxygen,
- and the remaining 1% is a mixture of carbon dioxide and noble gases.

The air we breathe isn't dry — it contains varying amounts of water vapour.

Supplement

Liquid Air can be Separated Using Fractional Distillation

1) The air is cooled slowly down to –200 °C. As part of the cooling process, water vapour, carbon dioxide and noble gases can be removed, leaving a liquid mixture of nitrogen and oxygen.

Water vapour and CO_2 are filtered out as solids. The noble gases are still gaseous at –200 °C so are easily separated from the liquid mixture.

2) This liquid mixture is passed into the bottom of a fractionating column.

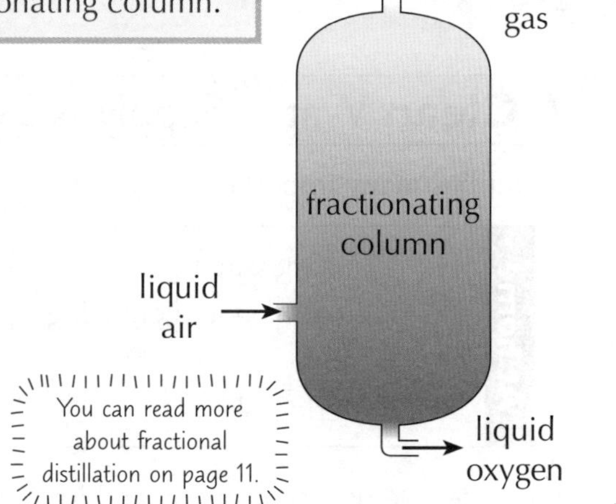

3) The temperature of the column is increased to around –196 °C so that the liquid nitrogen in the mixture begins to boil. The nitrogen gas rises to the top of the column and is collected and removed.

4) Oxygen has a higher boiling point than nitrogen (about –183 °C) so it does not vaporise at this temperature. Instead it is removed as a liquid from the bottom of the column.

You can read more about fractional distillation on page 11.

Air can Contain Pollutants

Pollutants such as sulfur dioxide and nitrogen dioxide can be found in the air due to human activities. They can have negative impact on our health, and can also damage the environment and buildings.

Incomplete Combustion Produces Carbon Monoxide

1) Complete combustion reactions of hydrocarbons (compounds that contain just carbon and hydrogen atoms) produce only carbon dioxide and water (see page 58).
2) If there's not enough oxygen around for complete combustion, you get incomplete combustion. This can happen in some appliances, e.g. boilers, that use carbon compounds as fuels.
3) The products of incomplete combustion contain less oxygen than carbon dioxide. As well as carbon dioxide and water, incomplete combustion produces carbon monoxide (CO).

Carbon monoxide is toxic. It can combine with red blood cells and stop your blood from doing its proper job of carrying oxygen around the body.
A lack of oxygen in the blood supply to the brain can lead to fainting, a coma or even death.

Air

Sulfur Dioxide Causes **Acid Rain**

1) Fossil fuels are non-renewable fuels created by the break down of plant and animal remains over millions of years.
2) When fossil fuels are burned, they release mostly CO_2.
3) But they also release other harmful gases such as sulfur dioxide.
4) The sulfur dioxide (SO_2) comes from sulfur compounds in the fossil fuels.
5) When sulfur dioxide mixes with clouds, it forms dilute sulfuric acid. This then falls as acid rain.

Coal and oil are fossil fuels.

Acid rain causes lakes to become acidic and many plants and animals die as a result. Acid rain also kills trees, damages limestone buildings and stone statues, and can also make metal corrode.

Oxides of Nitrogen Are Also **Pollutants**

1) Nitrogen oxides can be formed by reactions in the internal combustion engines of cars.
2) The large amount of energy released by the combustion of the fuel causes nitrogen and oxygen in the air to react together.

Supplement

3) Cars contain catalytic converters which reduce oxides of nitrogen present in the engine, forming nitrogen gas and oxygen gas:

$$2NO \rightarrow N_2 + O_2$$
$$2NO_2 \rightarrow N_2 + 2O_2$$

4) These gases are relatively harmless compared to oxides of nitrogen.

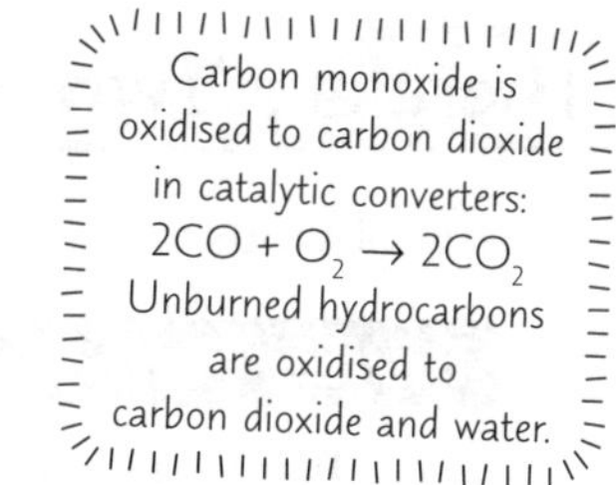

Carbon monoxide is
oxidised to carbon dioxide
in catalytic converters:
$2CO + O_2 \rightarrow 2CO_2$
Unburned hydrocarbons
are oxidised to
carbon dioxide and water.

Supplement

Nitrogen oxides are harmful pollutants — they can contribute to acid rain and, at ground level, can cause photochemical smog. Photochemical smog is a type of air pollution that can cause breathing difficulties, headaches and tiredness.

Lead Compounds are **Toxic**

Lead compounds used to be present in almost all petrol that was produced, and are still present in some today. The burning of leaded petrol releases lead compounds into the atmosphere.

Lead is toxic and affects almost all organs in the body. This can cause major health issues, particularly involving the central nervous system.

Each pollutant comes with its own set of problems

To help you to remember the effects caused by different pollutants, write out the pollutants and their effects on individual pieces of paper, then try to match the correct pairs together.

Rusting

Iron's strength has made it a very important metal that's used throughout the world for building construction, car manufacture and wrought iron garden furniture. But the problem is — it rusts...

Iron **Corrodes** to Make **Rust**

1) Iron corrodes easily. In other words, it rusts.
2) Rusting only happens when the iron's in contact with both oxygen (from the air) and water.
3) The chemical reaction that takes place when iron corrodes is an oxidation reaction (see page 72). The iron gains oxygen to form iron(III) oxide.
4) Water then becomes loosely bonded to the iron(III) oxide and the result is hydrated iron(III) oxide — which we call rust.

The word "rust" is only used for the corrosion of iron, not other metals.

iron + oxygen + water → hydrated iron(III) oxide (rust)

5) Unfortunately, rust is a soft crumbly solid that soon flakes off to leave more iron available to rust again.

There are **Two** Main Ways to **Prevent Rusting**

1) The obvious way to prevent rusting is to coat the iron with a barrier to keep out the water and oxygen.

Barrier Methods

- Painting/Coating with plastic — ideal for big and small structures alike. It can be decorative too.
- Oiling/Greasing — this has to be used when moving parts are involved, like on bike chains.

Supplement

2) The other way is sacrificial protection. This involves placing a more reactive metal with the iron. The water and oxygen then react with this sacrificial metal instead of with the iron.

Sacrificial Protection

- Zinc is often used as a sacrificial metal.
- The zinc is more reactive than iron — it's further up the reactivity series (see p.97).
- So, the zinc will be oxidised instead of the iron.
- A coating of zinc can be sprayed onto the object — this is known as galvanising.
- Or big blocks of zinc can be bolted to the iron. This is used on ships' hulls, or on underground iron pipes.

Galvanising initially acts as a barrier, but then sacrificially protects the iron underneath if the coating gets scratched.

Supplement

Rust is hydrated iron(III) oxide...

Remember that rust is the product of iron coming into contact with both oxygen and water. Paint, oil and grease have to be regularly re-applied to iron to stop it from rusting, which can get expensive.

Warm-Up & Exam Questions

Now that you've read the previous chunk of pages, you can check how well you've understood them.

Warm-Up Questions

1) Describe a test for water using cobalt(II) chloride.
2) What two things are needed for iron to rust?

Exam Questions

1 Which of the following statements about lead compounds is correct?

- ☐ **A** Lead compounds are produced by car batteries.
- ☐ **B** Lead compounds cause photochemical smog.
- ☐ **C** Lead compounds can be found in petrol.
- ☐ **D** Lead compounds react with carbon dioxide in the air to produce acid rain.

[Total 1 mark]

2 The diagram below shows how water can be treated.

Water from a suitable source — **Z** — Chlorination

(a) Give **two** uses of water in the home.

[2]

(b) Describe what happens during stage **Z** in the diagram.

[2]

[Total 4 marks]

3 Burning fossil fuels can produce pollutants like sulfur dioxide. Sulfur dioxide can cause acid rain.

(a) Explain why sulfur dioxide is produced when some fossil fuels are burned.

[1]

(b) Give **one** environmental problem caused by acid rain.

[1]

[Total 2 marks]

Supplement

4 There are several methods that can be used to prevent the corrosion of iron and its alloys (such as steel).

(a) A ship manufacturer wants to prevent the corrosion of a steel ship using sacrificial protection. Describe what is meant by sacrificial protection and explain how it protects the ship.

[3]

(b) A roofing company coats an iron roof with a layer of zinc to protect it from rusting. After a while, the zinc layer becomes scratched. Would you expect the iron roofing to begin to rust? Explain your answer.

[2]

[Total 5 marks]

Fertilisers and the Haber Process

There's more to using fertilisers than making your garden look nice and pretty...

Fertilisers Help Plants **Grow**

Fertilisers containing nitrogen, phosphorus and potassium are often called NPK fertilisers.

1) The three main essential elements in fertilisers are nitrogen, phosphorus and potassium. Plants absorb these nutrients from the soil.
2) If plants don't get enough of these elements, their growth and life processes are affected.
3) Fertilisers supply these elements if they're missing from the soil, or provide more of them. This helps to increase the crop yield, as the crops can grow faster and bigger.
4) Ammonia fertilisers have some important advantages compared to traditional fertilisers, like manure. You can control the compositions of chemicals in them, as well as how much is made. Ammonia fertilisers are also soluble, so all the chemicals can dissolve down into the soil to reach the plants.

Ammonia can be **Displaced** from its **Salts**

1) Basic substances are often added to acidic soil to help neutralise the excess acidity.
2) However, if the base is in excess, it can displace ammonia from ammonium compounds that have been added to fertilise the soil.
3) This displacement reaction produces ammonia gas, a salt and water (see p.76). For example:

This reaction is problematic for farmers because it results in the loss of nitrogen from the fertiliser.

ammonium chloride + sodium hydroxide → ammonia + sodium chloride + water

$$NH_4Cl + NaOH \rightarrow NH_3 + NaCl + H_2O$$

Supplement

Nitrogen and **Hydrogen** are Needed to Make **Ammonia**

The Haber process is used to make ammonia from hydrogen and nitrogen using the following reaction:

nitrogen + hydrogen ⇌ ammonia (+ heat)

$$N_{2(g)} + 3H_{2(g)} \rightleftharpoons 2NH_{3(g)}$$

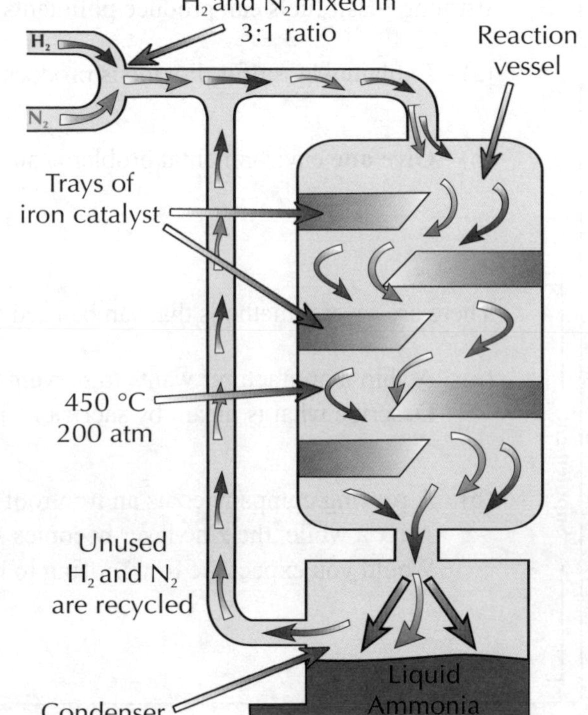

1) The reactant gases are passed over an iron catalyst. A high temperature (450 °C) and a high pressure (200 atmospheres) are used.
2) Because the reaction is reversible (it occurs in both directions), some of the ammonia produced converts back into hydrogen and nitrogen again. It eventually reaches equilibrium (see p.70).
3) The ammonia is formed as a gas, but as it cools in the condenser it liquefies and is removed. The unused hydrogen (H_2) and nitrogen (N_2) are recycled, so nothing is wasted.
4) The ammonia produced can then be used to make ammonium nitrate — a very nitrogen-rich fertiliser.

Supplement

Fertilisers and the Haber Process

Supplement

The Reactants are **Easily Sourced**

The Haber process reaction is well suited for an industrial scale as the reactants aren't too difficult or expensive to obtain.

- The nitrogen is obtained easily from the air, which is 78% nitrogen.
- The hydrogen can be produced by reacting hydrocarbons with steam.

The Conditions Used are a **Compromise**

1) Energy costs (costs associated with reaching and maintaining the conditions required for the reaction, e.g. temperature and pressure) affect whether a reaction is profitable.
2) Generally, high temperatures and pressures cost more to maintain, so lower temperatures and pressures are used wherever possible.
3) The conditions of the Haber process are chosen to maximise the rate and yield of the reaction, while making sure the reaction is still profitable.

Pressure of Reaction

Higher pressures favour the forward reaction, since there are fewer moles of gas on the right hand side. So the pressure is set as high as economically possible to give the best yield, while still remaining safe.

Temperature of Reaction

The forward reaction is exothermic, which means the yield of ammonia would be greater at lower temperatures. The trouble is, lower temperatures mean a lower rate of reaction. So in industry, the temperature is increased anyway to get a much faster rate of reaction.

Catalysts Affect How **Quickly** Equilibrium is Reached

1) The temperature, pressure and concentration of reactants also affect how quickly equilibrium is reached. If you increase the rate of reaction (see p.61), you also increase the rate at which you reach equilibrium.
2) So equilibrium is always reached faster using high temperatures, high pressures and high concentrations (but remember, high temperatures decrease the yield of ammonia).
3) Catalysts are also useful in speeding up how quickly equilibrium is reached.

In the Haber process, the iron catalyst makes the reaction go faster, so it reaches equilibrium faster too. But the catalyst doesn't affect the position of equilibrium, or the percentage yield.

Without the catalyst, the Haber process would have to be carried out at an even higher temperature in order to get a quick enough reaction — and that would reduce the % yield of ammonia even further. So the catalyst is very important.

The Haber process is a really important reaction

The Haber process is a little complicated and can take a while to get your head around. Have a good read over the previous couple of pages to make sure you're happy with why the conditions are chosen before moving on. After all, it could end up being worth precious marks in the exam.

The Greenhouse Effect

You've probably heard of carbon dioxide — it's always in the news. This page will tell you why.

Carbon Dioxide and Methane are Greenhouse Gases

1) The temperature of the Earth is a balance between the heat it gets from the Sun and the heat it radiates back out into space.

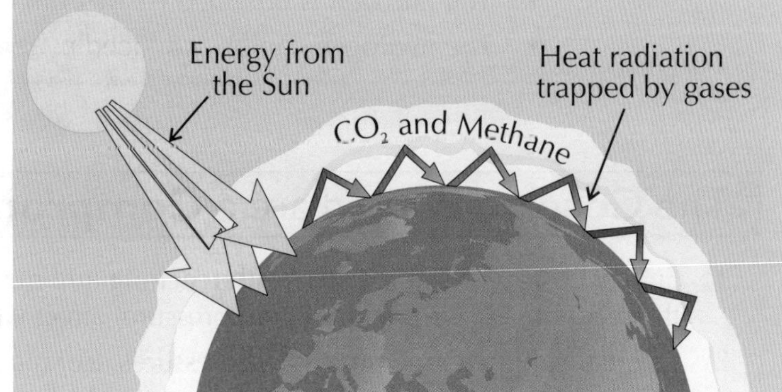

2) Gases in the atmosphere like carbon dioxide, methane and water vapour naturally act like an insulating layer. They are often called 'greenhouse gases'. They absorb most of the heat that would normally be radiated out into space, and re-radiate it in all directions — including back towards the Earth.

3) Human activity affects the amount of carbon dioxide and methane in the atmosphere — examples include:

Deforestation: fewer trees means less CO_2 is removed from the atmosphere via photosynthesis.
Burning fossil fuels: carbon that was 'locked up' in these fuels is being released as CO_2.
Agriculture: farm animals produce methane through their digestive processes. Increased agricultural waste means more methane is released by decomposing vegetation.

4) It is because of this human activity that over the last 200 years or so, the concentration of greenhouse gases in the atmosphere has been increasing. For this to have happened, they must be being released into the air faster than they're being removed — this is linked to climate change (see below).

Increasing Greenhouse Gases are Linked to Climate Change

1) There's a correlation between increasing levels of greenhouse gases and the gradual heating up of the Earth's atmosphere (global warming). Although the Earth's temperature varies naturally, there's a scientific consensus that the extra greenhouse gases have caused the average temperature of the Earth to increase.

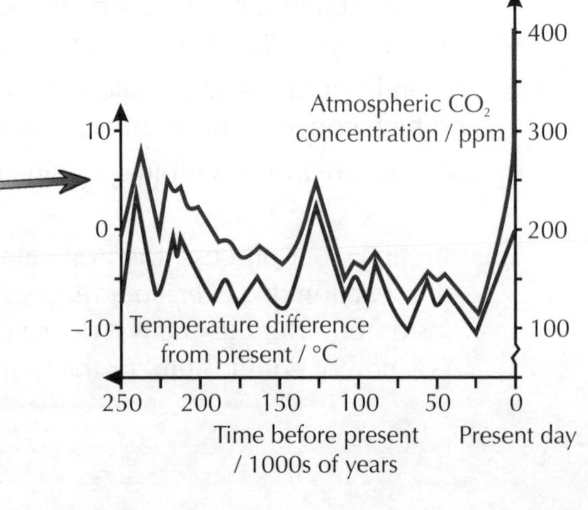

2) Global warming is a type of climate change and causes other types of climate change, e.g. changing rainfall patterns. It could also cause severe flooding due to the polar ice caps melting and sea level rise.

Human activity has increased the concentration of CO_2

There's a strong correlation between rising carbon dioxide levels and global temperature, and so many scientists believe that global warming is caused by increasing CO_2 emissions or human activity. However, some scientists don't believe that we have enough data to prove this link.

The Carbon Cycle

Carbon is constantly being recycled — there's a nice balance between what goes in and what goes out.

Carbon Dioxide is Released into the Atmosphere

1) When plants, algae and animals respire (to produce energy), carbon is released into the atmosphere as CO_2.

glucose + oxygen → carbon dioxide + water

$$C_6H_{12}O_6 + 6O_2 \rightarrow 6CO_2 + 6H_2O$$

2) The complete combustion (burning with oxygen) of carbon-containing substances (such as wood and fossil fuels) also releases CO_2 back into the air. For example:

methane + oxygen → carbon dioxide + water

$$CH_4 + 2O_2 \rightarrow CO_2 + 2H_2O$$

3) Carbon dioxide is also produced when carbonates react with acids (see p.76) or thermally decompose (see p.100).

Supplement

Plants can Remove Carbon Dioxide from the Atmosphere

1) CO_2 is removed from the atmosphere by green plants and algae during photosynthesis.

carbon dioxide + water → glucose + oxygen

$$6CO_2 + 6H_2O \rightarrow C_6H_{12}O_6 + 6O_2$$

2) The carbon is used to make glucose, which can be turned into important biological molecules.
3) This glucose is also used to fuel respiration, releasing CO_2 back into the atmosphere.

The Constant Cycling of Carbon is called the Carbon Cycle

Carbon is constantly being cycled — from the air, through organisms and eventually back out into the air again.

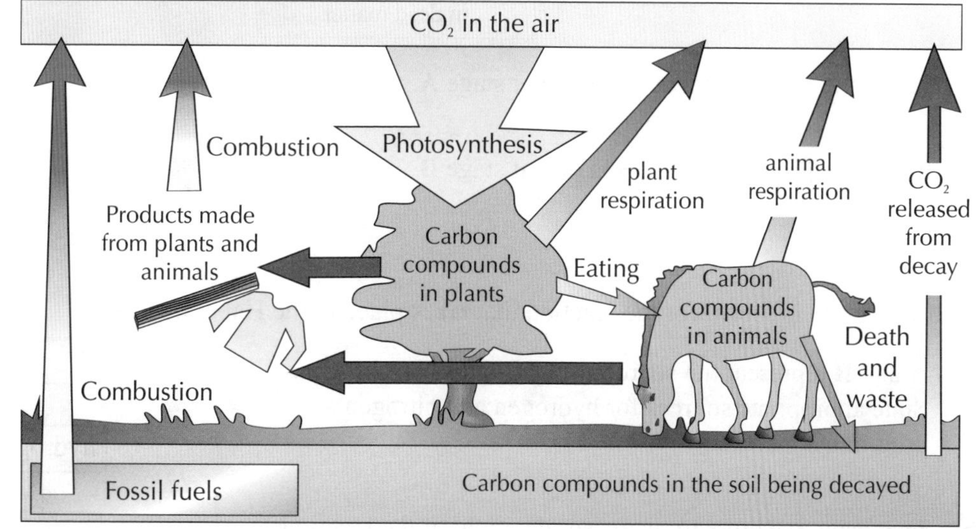

Fossil fuels are gradually made from decayed plant and animal matter.

Supplement

Respiration and combustion release carbon dioxide into the air...

... plants take it up again. The carbon cycle is a continuous process where carbon moves between organisms and the environment. If you are taking the Extended course, make sure you know the whole cycle.

Warm-Up & Exam Questions

It's time to see how much you remember from the previous few pages by having a go at these questions.

Warm-Up Questions

1) What is produced when ammonia is displaced from ammonium compounds?
2) Name the catalyst used in the Haber process.
3) Name two greenhouse gases.
4) True or false? Carbon dioxide can be formed through combustion reactions.

Exam Questions

1 Farmers often use fertilisers.

(a) Fertilisers usually contain nitrogen. Name the **two** other elements they usually contain.

[2]

(b) Explain why farmers apply fertilisers to their crops.

[2]

[Total 4 marks]

Supplement

2 The diagram shows a simplified version of the carbon cycle.

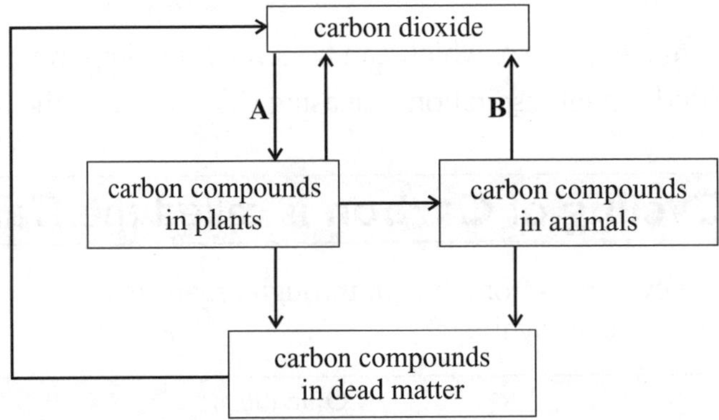

(a) Name the process that is occurring at stage **A**.

[1]

(b) Name the process that is occurring at stage **B**.

[1]

[Total 2 marks]

3 A flow diagram is shown for the reaction that takes place in the Haber process.

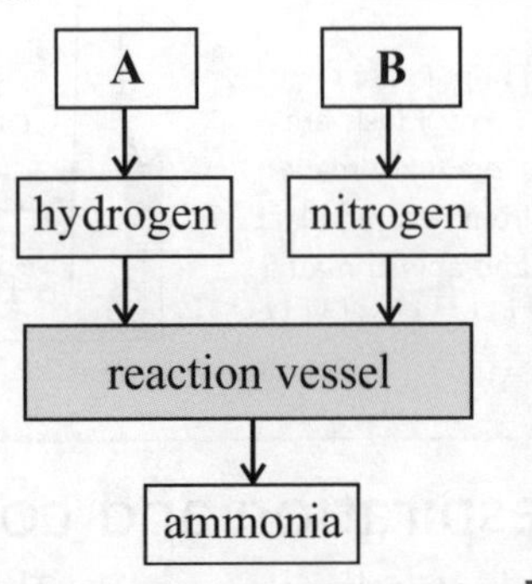

(a) **A** and **B** represent the sources of hydrogen and nitrogen. State appropriate sources for hydrogen and nitrogen used in the reaction.

[2]

(b) Increasing the pressure increases the yield of the reaction. Suggest why a pressure greater than 200 atm isn't used.

[1]

[Total 3 marks]

Sulfur

You've seen air, you've seen water, you've seen nitrogen — now here's a page on the chemistry of sulfur.

Sulfur is Used to Produce **Sulfuric Acid** and **Sulfur Dioxide**

1) Elemental sulfur is found near volcanoes and hot springs, and can be mined from deposits in the ground. It can also be removed from fuels such petrol before they're sold for use.
2) Sulfur is mainly used to produce sulfuric acid (H_2SO_4) in the Contact process.
3) It can also be burnt to produce sulfur dioxide (SO_2). Sulfur dioxide can be used as bleach in the manufacture of wood pulp. This lightens the pulp so that it can be used to make paper. Sulfur dioxide can also be used as a food preservative where it prevents rotting by killing bacteria.

Supplement

The **Contact Process** is Used to Make **Sulfuric Acid**

1) The first stage is to make sulfur dioxide (SO_2) — usually by burning sulfur in air.

sulfur + oxygen → sulfur dioxide

$$S_{(s)} + O_{2(g)} \rightarrow SO_{2(g)}$$

2) The sulfur dioxide is then oxidised (with the help of a catalyst) to make sulfur trioxide (SO_3).

sulfur dioxide + oxygen ⇌ sulfur trioxide

$$2SO_{2(g)} + O_{2(g)} \rightleftharpoons 2SO_{3(g)}$$

3) Next, the sulfur trioxide is used to make sulfuric acid.

sulfur trioxide + water → sulfuric acid

$$SO_{3(g)} + H_2O_{(l)} \rightarrow H_2SO_{4(aq)}$$

In reality, it's a bit more complicated than this — SO_3 is dissolved in sulfuric acid first to make oleum ($H_2S_2O_7$). The oleum is then converted to sulfuric acid by adding water.

The **Conditions** Used to Make SO_3 are **Carefully Chosen**

The reaction in step 2 above is reversible. So, the reaction conditions can be controlled to change the equilibrium position. The conditions used in industry for the Contact process are a compromise between the rate of reaction, the yield and cost.

1) Temperature of reaction: The forward reaction is exothermic, so increasing the temperature increases the rate of reaction, but also reduces the yield. 450 °C is a compromise between maximum yield and speed of reaction.
2) Pressure of reaction: Higher pressures favour the forward reaction (as it makes fewer moles of gas) but are expensive, so the reaction is usually carried out at 2 atmospheres.
3) Catalyst: To increase the rate of reaction a vanadium(V) oxide catalyst (V_2O_5) is used. It doesn't change the position of the equilibrium.

Sulfuric Acid has Many **Uses**

1) Sulfuric acid is a strong, corrosive acid which has oxidising and dehydrating properties.
2) Concentrated sulfuric acid is used in car batteries and in the manufacture of detergents. It can also be used in fertiliser production, as well as for making paints and dyes.
3) Dilute sulfuric acid is often used to catalyse organic reactions. It can also be used to clean metals.

Supplement

Sulfuric acid has many useful applications

Sulfuric acid isn't just something you use in experiments at school, it is used a lot in manufacturing too.

Carbonates

This page is all about lime, limestone and slaked lime — none of which involve citrus fruit...

Lime is Produced by Thermal Decomposition

1) Limestone is a type of rock mostly made of calcium carbonate.
2) Heating calcium carbonate causes it to decompose into lime (calcium oxide) and carbon dioxide:

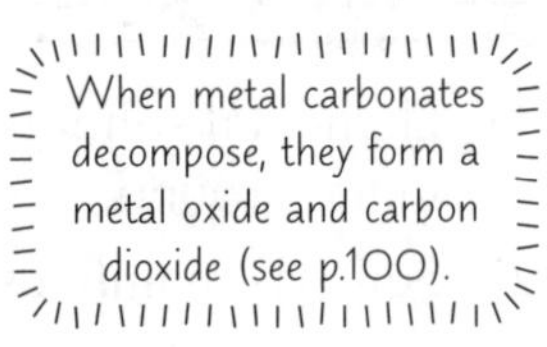
When metal carbonates decompose, they form a metal oxide and carbon dioxide (see p.100).

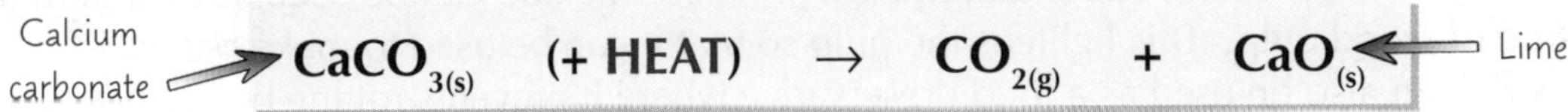
Calcium carbonate
Lime

$$CaCO_{3(s)} \quad (+ \text{HEAT}) \rightarrow CO_{2(g)} + CaO_{(s)}$$

Lime and Slaked Lime Are Basic Compounds

1) When lime is added to water, it reacts to give slaked lime (calcium hydroxide).
2) Lime and slaked lime are bases that can be used to neutralise acidic substances.
3) For example, they can be used to treat acidic soils. Neutralising the soil allows plants that don't thrive in acidic conditions to grow.
4) They can also be used to neutralise acidic industrial waste products. For example:

> Flue gas is the mixture of gases (including sulfur dioxide) produced by factories and power stations that is released into the atmosphere. Flue gas desulfurisation involves spraying slaked lime at the flue gas to neutralise the sulfur dioxide before it moves out of the chimneys. This reduces atmospheric pollution.

Sulfur dioxide is an acidic oxide.

Calcium Carbonate is Used in Manufacture

Calcium carbonate isn't just used to make lime — it also has roles in the manufacture of iron and cement.

Iron

1) Iron needs to be extracted from its ore in a blast furnace (see p.103).
2) Calcium carbonate is added to the blast furnace where it thermally decomposes to form calcium oxide and carbon dioxide (see above).
3) The calcium oxide then reacts with silicate impurities present in the ore (e.g. silicon dioxide, SiO_2). This produces molten calcium silicate (slag) which is then removed.

$$CaO + SiO_2 \rightarrow CaSiO_3$$

Cement

1) Powdered calcium carbonate can be heated with clay in a rotary kiln.
2) This mixture is then ground to a fine powder and mixed with calcium sulfate and water to form cement.

Slaked lime neutralises acidic substances

The use of slaked lime to neutralise industrial waste products, such as flue gas, is really important for reducing sulfur dioxide emissions. This helps to combat environmental issues such as acid rain (see p.111).

Warm-Up & Exam Questions

Here is a page of questions to help make sure you've got to grips with what you've learnt about sulfur and carbonates. If you have any problems, have a look back at the relevant page until you understand it.

Warm-Up Questions

1) What application does sulfur dioxide have in the food industry?
2) Give a use of concentrated sulfuric acid.
3) Name the compound otherwise known as limestone.
4) State one use of slaked lime.

Exam Questions

1 Which type of reaction produces calcium oxide from calcium carbonate?

- **A** oxidation
- **B** displacement
- **C** thermal decomposition
- **D** neutralisation

[Total 1 mark]

Supplement

2 The Contact process is a multi-stage industrial process used to manufacture sulfuric acid. The flow chart below shows the overall reactions that take place during the process.

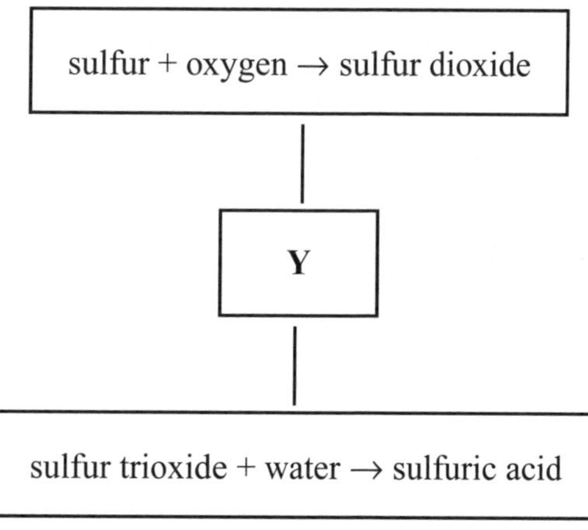

(a) Give the word equation for the reaction that happens during stage **Y** of the flow chart.

[2]

(b) Give the temperature, pressure and catalyst used for stage **Y** of the Contact process.

[3]

[Total 5 marks]

Revision Summary for Section 11

That's all for Section 11 — but before you move onto Section 12, let's find out how much you really know.

- Try these questions and tick off each one when you get it right.
- When you've done all the questions for a topic and are completely happy with it, tick off the topic.

Water, Air and Rusting (p.109-112)

1) Give two uses of water in industry.
2) Give one problem associated with an inadequate supply of safe drinking water.
3) Name the process used in water treatment where harmful microbes are killed.
4) What percentage of the air is made up of nitrogen?
5) Name the process used to separate oxygen and nitrogen in liquid air.
6) Describe the effect that carbon monoxide has on health.
7) What is the purpose of a catalytic converter?
8) Give one effect that nitrogen oxides have on health.
9) True or false? Iron rusts if it is in contact with carbon dioxide and water.
10) Describe one way of preventing iron from rusting.

Fertilisers and the Haber Process (p.114-115)

11) What causes the displacement of ammonia from its salts in fertilisers?
12) What temperature is used in the Haber process?
13) True or false? Increasing the temperature of the Haber process increases the rate and decreases the yield of the reaction.

The Greenhouse Effect and the Carbon Cycle (p.116-117)

14) What are greenhouse gases?
15) Give two sources of methane.
16) Describe the link between carbon dioxide and global warming.
17) Give two types of reaction that produce carbon dioxide.
18) True or false? Carbon dioxide is taken out of the atmosphere by photosynthesis.

Sulfur and Carbonates (p.119-120)

19) True or false? Sulfur is mainly used as a fuel.
20) Which gas is used as a bleach in the manufacture of wood pulp?
21) Why are the conditions for the Contact Process a compromise?
22) True or false? Lime also known as calcium oxide.
23) Name two things that are made using calcium carbonate.

Fuels and Fractional Distillation

Fossil fuels like coal, petroleum and gas are non-renewable fuels — they take so long to form that they're being used up much faster than they're being formed. They're finite resources — one day they'll run out.

There are **Three Key Fuels** You Need to Know About

1) Coal — a solid fuel made from carbon.
2) Natural gas — a mixture of gases which forms underground. It is mostly made up of methane.
3) Petroleum — a complex mixture of lots of different hydrocarbons (compounds which contain just carbon and hydrogen). The hydrocarbons found in petroleum are mostly alkanes (see page 128).

Petroleum is **Separated** into Different Hydrocarbon **Fractions**

1) Petroleum can be separated out into fractions — simpler, more useful mixtures containing groups of hydrocarbons of similar lengths (i.e. they have similar numbers of carbon atoms).
2) The different fractions in petroleum are separated by fractional distillation (see page 11). The petroleum is heated until most of it has turned into gas. The gases enter a fractionating column (and the liquid bit, bitumen, is drained off at the bottom).
3) In the column there's a temperature gradient (i.e. it's hot at the bottom and gets cooler as you go up).
4) Longer hydrocarbons have higher boiling points. They turn back into liquids and drain out of the column early on, when they're near the bottom. The shorter hydrocarbons have lower boiling points. They turn to liquid and drain out much later on, near to the top of the column where it's cooler.
5) You end up with the petroleum mixture separated out into different fractions. Each fraction contains a mixture of hydrocarbons with similar boiling points and relative molecular masses.

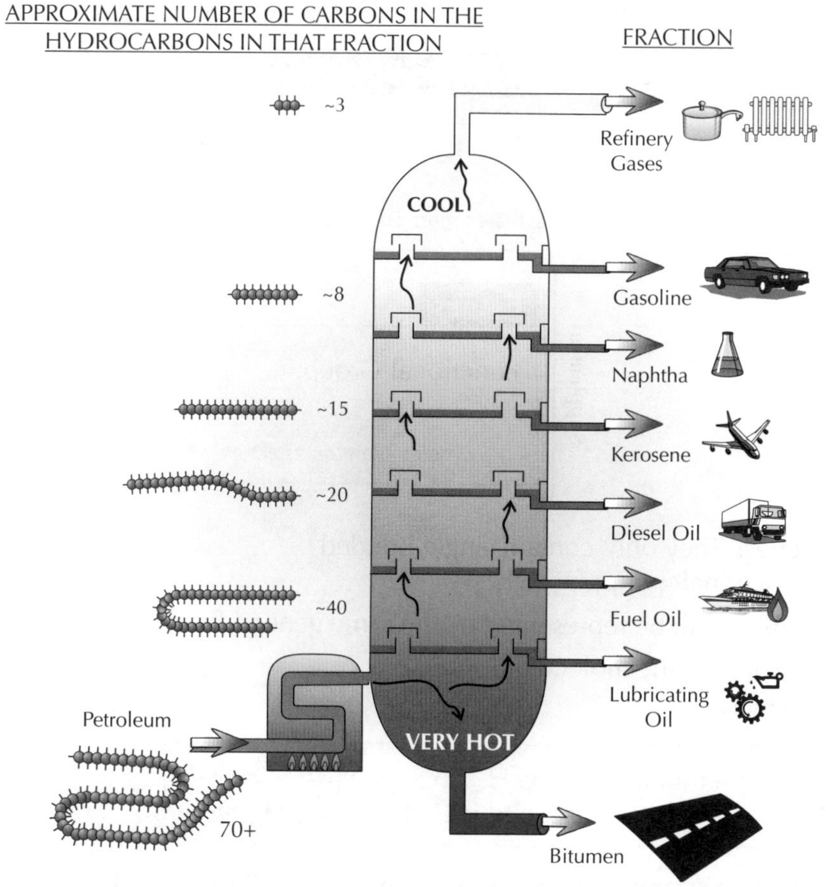

Refinery gas can be used for heating and cooking.

Gasoline is used as fuel (petrol) in cars.

Naphtha is used in the chemical industry.

Kerosene (paraffin) is used as jet fuel.

Diesel oil (gas oil) is used as a fuel in diesel engines.

Fuel oil is used to fuel large ships and to heat homes.

Lubricating oil is used to make lubricants, waxes and polishes.

Bitumen is used to make roads.

Each fraction has molecules of similar lengths and similar boiling points

Each fraction is used in a slightly different way — make sure you remember the different uses for each one.

Organic Compounds

This section's all about organic chemistry — in other words, molecules that contain carbon.

There are **Several Ways** of Representing **Organic Compounds**

Type of formula	What it shows you	Formula for Ethene
Molecular formula	The actual number of atoms of each element in a molecule.	C_2H_4
Displayed formula	Shows how all the atoms are arranged, and all the bonds between them.	$H_2C{=}CH_2$ (displayed: H, H on each C, C=C)
Structural formula	Shows the arrangement of atoms carbon by carbon, with the attached hydrogens and functional groups (see below).	CH_2CH_2
General formula	An algebraic formula that can describe any member of a family of compounds.	C_nH_{2n} (for all alkenes)

S

Organic Compounds can Belong to a Certain **Homologous Series**

1) A homologous series is a family of similar compounds with similar chemical properties due to the presence of the same functional group.
2) A functional group is a group of atoms that determine how a compound typically reacts, so compounds in a homologous series often react in similar ways.
3) Make sure you learn these homologous series and their functional groups:

Alkenes

Functional Group: $>C{=}C<$

There's more on alkenes on p.131-132.

Alcohols

Functional Group: $-O-H$

There's more on alcohols on p.134-135.

Carboxylic Acids

Functional Group: $-\overset{O}{\overset{\|}{C}}-OH$

There's more on carboxylic acids on p.136-137.

Supplement

Esters

Functional Group: $-\overset{O}{\overset{\|}{C}}-O-$

There's more on esters on p.137.

4) Alkanes are also a homologous series. They only contain single-bonded carbon and hydrogen atoms (no functional group).

Supplement

5) Compounds in a homologous series can all be represented by the same general formula.
6) You can use a general formula to work out the molecular formula of any member of a homologous series.

E.g. The general formula for alkanes is C_nH_{2n+2}. So the first alkane in the series is $C_1H_{(2\times1)+2} = CH_4$, the second is $C_2H_{(2\times2)+2} = C_2H_6$, etc.

7) The molecular formulae of neighbouring compounds in a homologous series differ by a CH_2 unit.
8) The physical properties of molecules in a homologous series show trends down the series. For example, the bigger a molecule is, the higher its boiling point will be.

Supplement

Naming Organic Compounds

Organic compounds used to be given whatever names people liked, but these names led to confusion between different countries. Luckily, chemists got together and came up with a system...

There's a **Method** for **Naming Organic Compounds**

The IUPAC system for naming organic compounds was invented as an international language for chemistry. It can be used to give any organic compound a name using these rules...

1) Count the carbon atoms in the carbon chain — this gives you the stem.

No. of Carbons	Stem
1	meth-
2	eth-
3	prop-
4	but-

2) The main functional group of the molecule usually tells you what homologous series the molecule is in (see previous page), and so gives you the suffix — see the table below.

Homologous Series	Suffix	Example
alkanes	–ane	ethane — CH_3CH_3
alkenes	–ene	ethene — CH_2CH_2
alcohols	–ol	ethanol — CH_3CH_2OH
carboxylic acids	–oic acid	ethanoic acid — CH_3COOH
esters	Prefix: alkyl– (–yl) Suffix: –anoate	ethyl ethanoate — $CH_3COOCH_2CH_3$

How to name esters is covered in more detail on page 137.

3) Number the carbon chain so that the functional group has the lowest possible number.

4) If there's more than one identical functional group, use di- (2), tri- (3) or tetra- (4) before the suffix.

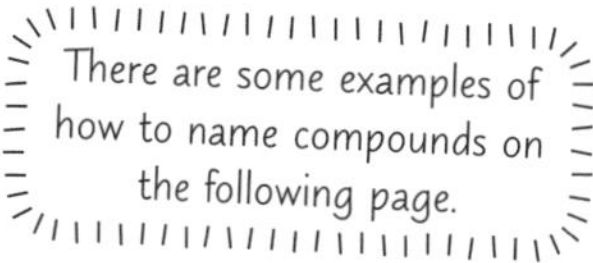

There are some examples of how to name compounds on the following page.

Use these rules to help you name compounds correctly

It's not the most exciting task, but learning the stems and suffixes will really help you out in the rest of this section. You can work out a lot about organic molecules just from knowing what their names are telling you. Go back and re-read this page until you've understood it all.

Naming Organic Compounds

Here are a couple of examples of how to name organic compounds.

You Can Work Out the **Name** of CH_3COOH Like This...

CH_3COOH

1) The carbon chain is 2 carbons long. So the stem is 'eth–'.
2) The main functional group is –COOH, so it is a carboxylic acid and the suffix is '–oic acid'.
3) This means that the systematic name for the molecule is: ethanoic acid.

In carboxylic acids, the functional group is always on carbon 1, so it doesn't need a number.

S

Supplement

...And an **Alkene** Like This...

Here's how you'd go about naming the alkene $CH_2CHCH_2CH_3$:

$CH_2CHCH_2CH_3$

1) The carbon chain is 4 carbons long. So the stem is 'but–'.
2) The main functional group is a carbon-carbon double bond. So it is an alkene and the name will end in '–ene'.
3) Numbering the carbon chain so that one of the carbons in the C=C group has the lowest possible number puts the C=C group on carbon 1.
4) This means that the systematic name for the molecule is: but-1-ene.

...And an **Alcohol** Like This...

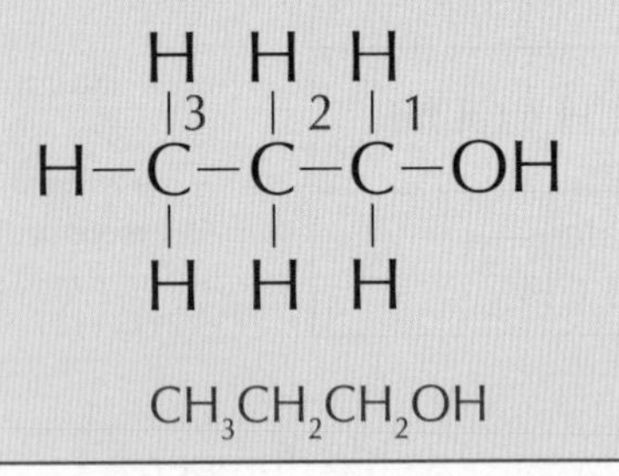

$CH_3CH_2CH_2OH$

1) The carbon chain is 3 carbons long. So the stem is 'prop-'.
2) The main functional group is -OH, so it is an alcohol and the suffix is -ol.
3) Numbering the carbon chain puts the OH on carbon 1.
4) This means that the systematic name for the molecule is: propan-1-ol.

This molecule is sometimes just called propanol.

If this molecule had 2 -OH groups it would be called propanediol — see page 140.

Supplement

Start by counting the carbon atoms

In an exam, you might be given the name of a compound and asked to draw its displayed formula. But don't panic — it's not actually too tricky. The stem tells you how many carbon atoms to draw and if there's a number, that tells you which carbon to attach the functional group to. Then just look at the suffix to check which group you're drawing.

Isomers

The molecular formula alone can't tell you the structure of a molecule, thanks to the existence of isomers.

Isomers Have the Same **Molecular Formula**

1) Two molecules are isomers of one another if they have the same molecular formula but the atoms are arranged differently.
2) This means their structural formulae are different.
3) Structural isomers can be hard to spot — here are some things you need to look out for:

Differently Shaped Carbon **Chains**

1) The carbons could be arranged differently — for example, as a straight chain, or branched (one of the carbons being bonded to more than two other carbons) in different ways.
2) These isomers have similar chemical properties (they will react in similar ways) — but their physical properties, like boiling point, will be different because of the change in shape of the molecule.

E.g. both of these molecules have the formula C_4H_{10}:

```
                            H
                            |
   H  H  H  H             H-C-H
   |  |  |  |           H   |   H
 H-C--C--C--C-H         |   |   |
   |  |  |  |         H-C---C---C-H
   H  H  H  H           |   |   |
                        H   H   H
```

Butane

Methylpropane

Functional Groups in **Different Places**

1) The arrangement of carbon atoms could be the same, and the isomers could have the same functional group, but the functional group could be attached to a different carbon atom.
2) These isomers also have different physical properties.

E.g. both of these molecules have the formula C_4H_8:

```
   H  H  H  H             H  H  H  H
   |  |  |  |             |  |  |  |
 H-C==C--C--C-H         H-C--C==C--C-H
         |  |             |        |
         H  H             H        H
```

But-1-ene

But-2-ene

Supplement

Supplement

Structural isomers can be difficult to spot

You need more than just molecular formulae to distinguish structural isomers — look for differences in their displayed formulae, such as which carbon the functional group is attached to, or any branching present.

Alkanes

Time to take a look at the different types of hydrocarbons you can get. First up is alkanes...

Alkanes are **Saturated Hydrocarbons**

1) Alkanes are hydrocarbons — they're chains of carbon atoms surrounded by hydrogen atoms.

2) Different alkanes have chains of different lengths.

3) Here are the names and the structures of the first four alkanes.

1) Methane

Molecular formula: CH_4
Structural formula: CH_4

```
  H
  |
H-C-H
  |
  H
```

Each line represents a covalent bond.

2) Ethane

Molecular formula: C_2H_6
Structural formula: CH_3CH_3

```
  H H
  | |
H-C-C-H
  | |
  H H
```

Supplement

3) Propane

```
  H H H
  | | |
H-C-C-C-H
  | | |
  H H H
```

Molecular formula: C_3H_8
Structural formula: $CH_3CH_2CH_3$

4) Butane

```
  H H H H
  | | | |
H-C-C-C-C-H
  | | | |
  H H H H
```

Molecular formula: C_4H_{10}
Structural formula: $CH_3CH_2CH_2CH_3$

The general formula for alkanes is C_nH_{2n+2}.

Supplement

To help remember the names of the first four alkanes just remember: Mice Eat Peanut Butter.

4) The diagrams above show that all the atoms have formed bonds with as many other atoms as they can. There are only single covalent bonds between the carbon atoms — this means the molecules are saturated.

Hydrocarbons only contain hydrogen and carbon

Alkanes are the most basic homologous series, but that doesn't make them unimportant.
Learning their names and structures is a great starting point for understanding other organic compounds.

Alkanes

You saw on page 124 that compounds in a homologous series react in similar ways. Alkanes are no exception — here are two reactions of alkanes that you need to know about.

Alkanes Burn in **Combustion Reactions**

1) Alkanes, such as methane, are generally unreactive.
2) However, they readily undergo combustion reactions (burning).
3) Alkanes make up the majority of hydrocarbons in petroleum and tend to combust completely in a good supply of oxygen.
4) The complete combustion of alkanes produces carbon dioxide and water. For example:

methane + oxygen → carbon dioxide + water

$$CH_4 + 2O_2 \rightarrow CO_2 + 2H_2O$$

Supplement

Alkanes also React with **Chlorine** to make **Chloroalkanes**

1) Chlorine reacts with alkanes in the presence of ultraviolet light.

Ultraviolet light can also be called ultraviolet radiation.

2) In these reactions, a hydrogen atom from the alkane is substituted with (replaced by) chlorine. So this is called a substitution reaction.

3) This is how chlorine and methane react together to form chloromethane.

methane + chlorine → chloromethane + hydrogen chloride

$$\mathrm{CH_4} + Cl_2 \xrightarrow{UV} \mathrm{CH_3Cl} + HCl$$

(H–C–H with H above and below, + Cl_2 → H–C–H with Cl above and H below, + HCl)

The UV here shows that the reaction needs ultraviolet light.

Supplement

Alkanes are useful fuels as they release energy when burnt

The best way to learn key reactions and equations is to practise writing them out. That way, you'll learn all the little details that will end up getting you marks in your final exams.

Warm-Up & Exam Questions

That's your first chunk of organic chemistry finished. Now test your new-found knowledge with these questions before moving on to the next section.

Warm-Up Questions

1) True or false? In fractional distillation, naphtha condenses lower in the column than fuel oil.
2) Which two elements are present in alkanes?
3) Name the carboxylic acid with three carbons in its carbon chain.
4) What are structural isomers?

S

Exam Questions

1 Which of the following is a displayed formula?

☐ **A** $H_2C{=}CH_2$ (displayed: H, H on each C, C=C) ☐ **B** $CH_3CH_2CH_3$ ☐ **C** C_2H_4 ☐ **D** CH_2O_2

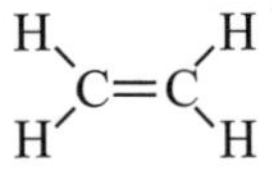

[Total 1 mark]

2 Fractional distillation is a method of separating petroleum into fractions containing hydrocarbon chains of similar lengths.

(a) What are the following hydrocarbons fractions primarily used for?

(i) Kerosene

(ii) Naphtha

(iii) Bitumen

[3]

(b) Why do shorter hydrocarbons condense higher in the column than longer hydrocarbons?

[1]

[Total 4 marks]

3 Alkanes are typically unreactive, but can react under certain conditions.

(a) Complete the symbol equation for the combustion of methane:

CH_4 + __O_2 → CO_2 + 2_____

[2]

S (b) Propane reacts with chlorine in a substitution reaction.
Write the symbol equation for this reaction, and state any necessary conditions.

[2]

[Total 4 marks]

Supplement

4 An organic molecule is shown below.

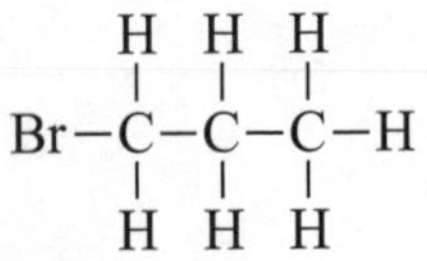

```
    H  H  H
    |  |  |
Br—C—C—C—H
    |  |  |
    H  H  H
```

(a) Draw the displayed formula of a structural isomer of this molecule.

[1]

(b) The molecular formula of a straight chain organic molecule is C_4H_9Cl.
Draw the displayed formula of **both** straight-chain isomers of this molecule.

[2]

[Total 3 marks]

Supplement

Alkenes and Cracking

You've read how fractional distillation can split up petroleum into hydrocarbon fractions. Well, now read about how cracking can make those fractions even more useful.

Cracking — Splitting Up Long-Chain Hydrocarbons

1) Long hydrocarbons have high boiling points and are viscous (thick and sticky), whereas shorter hydrocarbons have lower boiling points and are much thinner and paler in colour.
2) Demand for short-chain hydrocarbons like octane, which is used in petrol (gasoline), is much higher than for longer-chain hydrocarbons.
3) So, to meet this demand, long-chain hydrocarbons are split into more useful short-chain molecules using cracking:

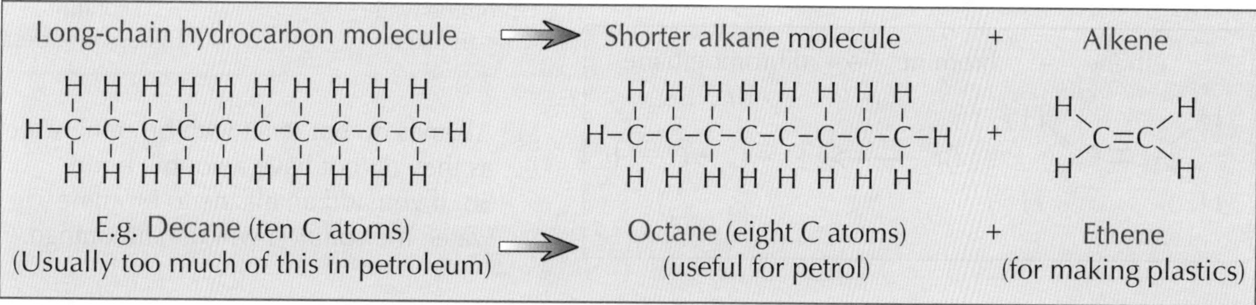

4) Cracking is a form of thermal decomposition, which just means breaking molecules down into simpler molecules by heating them.
5) Cracking is an important method for producing alkenes. It can also be used to produce hydrogen, H_2.

Conditions for Cracking — Heat, Plus a Catalyst

1) In industry, vaporised hydrocarbons are passed over a powdered catalyst at high temperature (about 500 °C). Silica (SiO_2) and/or alumina (Al_2O_3) are used as catalysts.
2) The vaporised hydrocarbons break down when they come into contact with the catalyst, producing a mixture of short-chain alkanes and alkenes (and sometimes hydrogen).

Cracking using a catalyst is called catalytic cracking.

Alkenes Have a C=C Double Bond

1) Alkenes are hydrocarbons which have a double bond between two of the carbon atoms in their chain.
2) The double bond means that alkenes are unsaturated molecules — they can make more bonds. The double bond can open up, allowing the carbon atoms to bond with other atoms (see next page).
3) The first member of the alkene homologous series is ethene, C_2H_4.

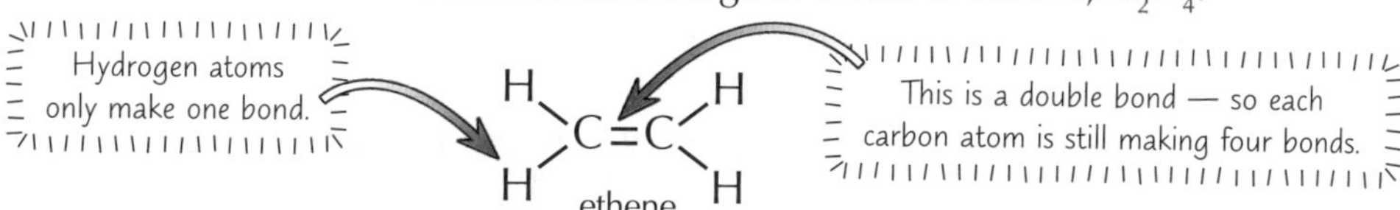

4) The next two are propene, C_3H_6, and butene, C_4H_8.
5) All alkenes have the general formula: C_nH_{2n} — they have twice as many hydrogens as carbons.

S

Alkanes and alkenes are both types of hydrocarbon

Watch out — it's easy to get confused between alkanes and alkenes. They may look (and sound) similar, but that double bond makes a lot of difference, especially to their reactivities (see next page for more).

Reactions of Alkenes

The double bond means that alkenes can react with lots of different compounds.

Bromine Reacts with **Alkenes** to Form **Bromoalkanes**

1) The reaction between aqueous bromine and alkenes is often used as a test for carbon-carbon double bonds.
2) When you shake an alkene with orange bromine water, the solution becomes colourless — this is because the bromine molecules, which are orange, are reacting with the alkene to make a dibromoalkane, which is colourless.

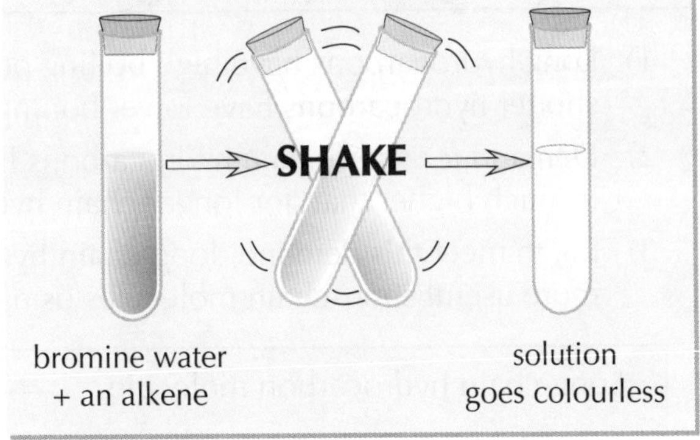

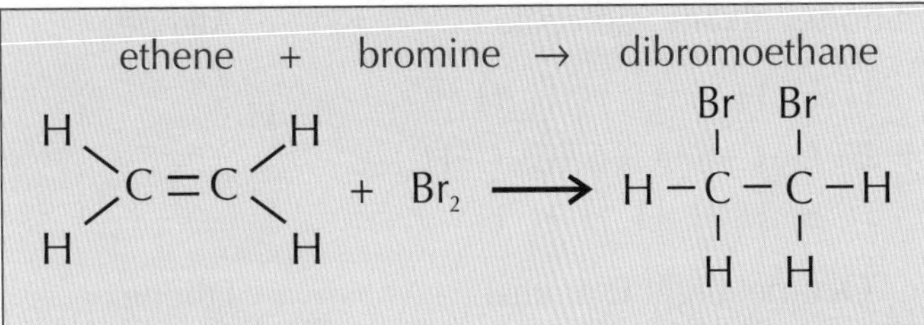

3) Alkanes do not react with bromine water, as they do not have a double bond. So, if you add an alkane to bromine water, the solution will remain orange.

Supplement

4) The reaction of bromine with an alkene is called an addition reaction because the C=C double bond is split and a bromine atom is added to each of the carbons.

Addition of **Hydrogen** is Known as **Hydrogenation**

Hydrogen can react with the double-bonded carbons to open up the double bond and form the equivalent saturated alkane. The alkene is reacted with hydrogen in the presence of a nickel catalyst:

$$H_2C{=}CH_2 + H_2 \xrightarrow{\text{nickel catalyst}} H{-}CH_2{-}CH_2{-}H$$

Steam can React with **Alkenes** to Form **Alcohols**

1) When alkenes react with steam, water is added across the double bond and an alcohol is formed.
2) For example, ethanol can be made by mixing ethene with steam and then passing it over a catalyst:

$$H_2C{=}CH_2 + H_2O \xrightarrow{\text{phosphoric acid catalyst}} H{-}CH_2{-}CH_2{-}O{-}H$$

ethene + water → ethanol

Have a look at p.134-135 for more on alcohols and the production of ethanol.

Supplement

A few more reactions to learn here...

Using bromine water is a really good test to see if you've got an alkane or an alkene. With the alkane, the bromine water will stay orange, whereas an alkene will turn the solution colourless.

Addition Polymers

Alkenes can do even more than that. They can be used to form long chains of molecules called polymers.

Addition Polymers are Made From Unsaturated Monomers

1) Polymers are large molecules made by joining up lots of small repeating units called monomers.
2) Alkene monomers can open up their carbon-carbon double bonds and join together to form polymer chains. This is called addition polymerisation.

The brackets and the n show that the repeat unit is repeated many times.

E.g. ethene (C_2H_4) becoming poly(ethene) $(C_2H_4)_n$:

many single ethenes

poly(ethene)

The 'n' represents 'any number' — it just means you start with lots of ethene molecules.

This is a shorthand way of showing the polymer chain. The bit inside the brackets is called the repeat unit.

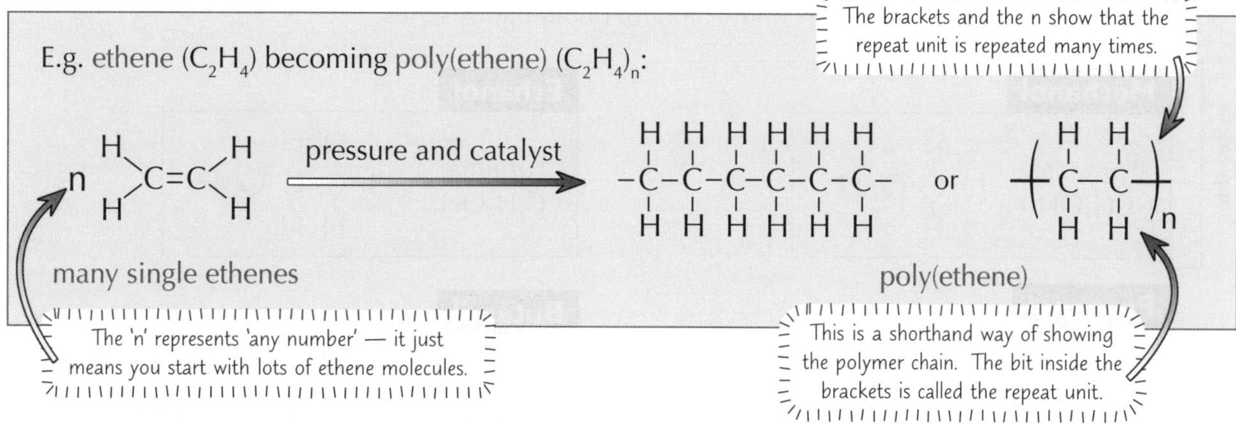

3) The name of the polymer comes from the type of monomer it's made from — you just put brackets around it and stick the word "poly" in front of it. So ethene becomes poly(ethene), etc.
4) To get the formula of the polymer, you just put the formula of the monomer in brackets and put a little 'n' after it. So C_2H_4 becomes $(C_2H_4)_n$. Simple.

Supplement

You May Need to Draw the Structure of a Polymer

1) Drawing the structure of an addition polymer from the structure of its monomer is easy.

   1) Join the carbons together in a row with no double bonds between them.
   2) Stick a pair of brackets around the repeat unit, and put an 'n' after it.
   3) You should also draw a bond from each of the two carbons in the chain that pass through the brackets — this shows that the chain continues.

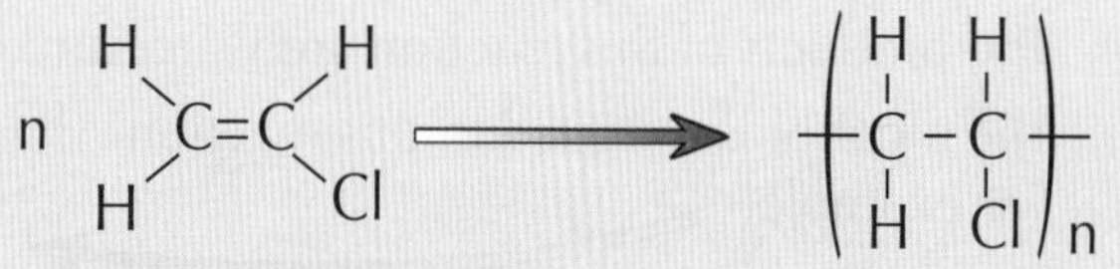

Chloroethene — Poly(chloroethene)

2) To get from the structure of the polymer to the structure of the monomer, just do the reverse.

Draw out the repeating bit of the polymer, get rid of the two bonds going out through the brackets and put a double bond between the carbons.

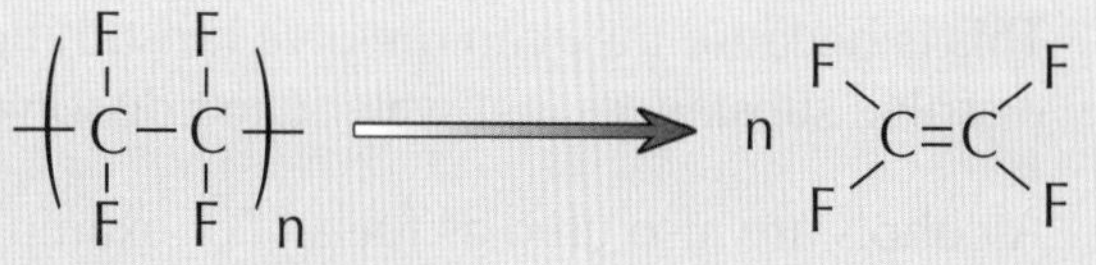

Poly(tetrafluoroethene) — Tetrafluoroethene

Polymer chemistry is really important to modern life

Polymers can be used for lots of different things, which you'll find out about on page 141. But for now, just make sure that you understand that they're long chains built up from lots of smaller units.

Alcohols

Alcohols look a bit like alkanes, but with an -OH functional group attached.

Alcohols Have an '-OH' Functional Group

1) All alcohols have names ending -ol and contain an -OH functional group.
2) When writing the formulae for alcohols, make sure you show the -OH functional group. E.g. ethanol is written as C_2H_5OH not C_2H_6O.
3) Here are the first four members of the alcohol homologous series:

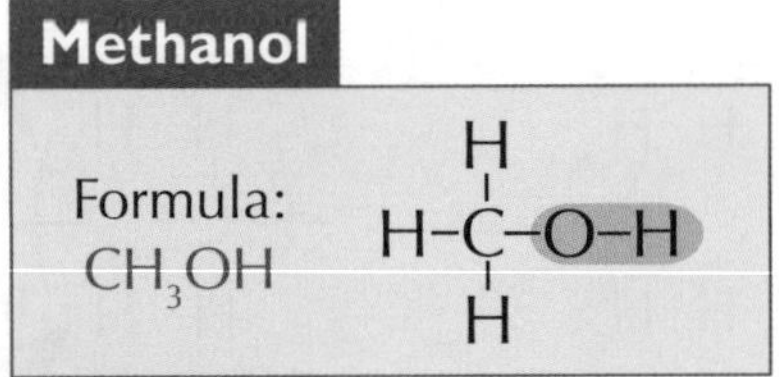

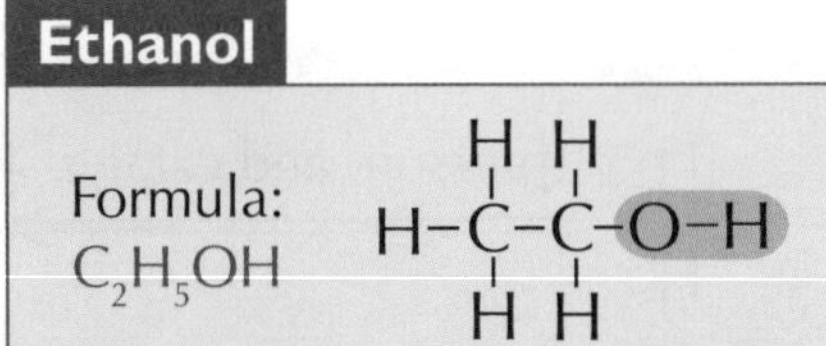

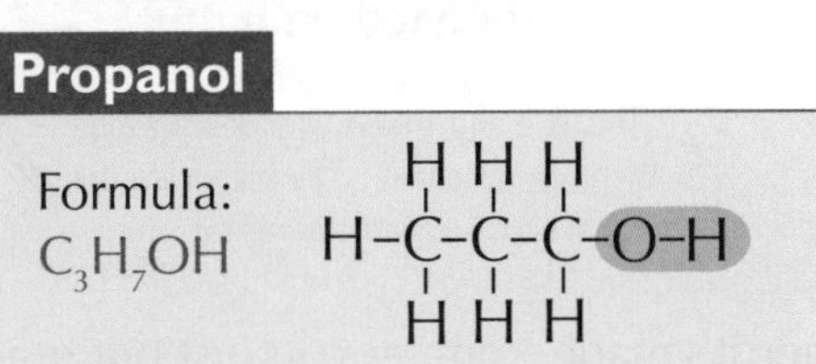

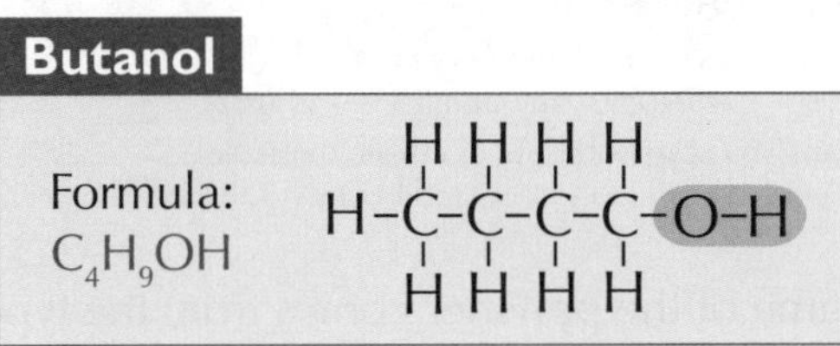

Supplement

4) The general formula of an alcohol is $C_nH_{2n+1}OH$.
5) It is possible to get alcohols where the -OH group is attached to different carbon atoms in the carbon chain, or alcohols with more than one -OH group (like the ones that form condensation polymers on page 140).

Supplement

Alcohols are Oxidised when they are Burnt

1) When alcohols are burnt in enough oxygen (or air), they undergo complete combustion (see page 58).
2) The products of this reaction are water and carbon dioxide.
3) The alcohol is oxidised in this reaction. For example:

ethanol + oxygen → carbon dioxide + water

$C_2H_5OH + 3O_2 \rightarrow 2CO_2 + 3H_2O$

Alcohols are Used as Solvents and Fuels

1) Alcohols such as ethanol are used as solvents in industry. This is because they can dissolve most things water can dissolve, but they can also dissolve substances that water can't dissolve — e.g. hydrocarbons, oils and fats.
2) Alcohols are also used as fuels. For example, ethanol is used as a fuel in spirit burners — it burns fairly cleanly and it's non-smelly.

All alcohols have names ending in -ol

For the exam, make sure you learn the structure of ethanol, as well as its combustion reaction. When balancing the equation, remember — there will be as many CO_2 molecules as there are carbons in ethanol (two) and half as many H_2O molecules as there are hydrogen atoms.

Production of Ethanol

The best way to make ethanol often depends on which resource is most easily available — oil or sugar.

Ethanol Can Be Produced from Ethene and Steam

1) Ethene (C_2H_4) is produced from petroleum (by cracking — see page 131).
2) Ethene will react with steam (H_2O) to make ethanol.
3) This is an addition reaction because water is added to the molecule.
4) The reaction needs a high temperature (300 °C) and a high pressure (60-70 atmospheres).
5) Phosphoric acid is used as a catalyst.

You've met addition reactions of alkenes already on page 132.

S

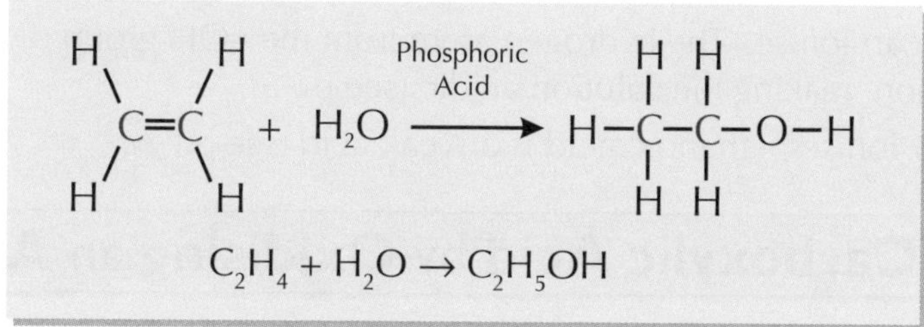

Supplement

6) At the moment this is a cheap process, because ethene's fairly cheap and not much of it is wasted.
7) The trouble is that petroleum is a non-renewable resource, which will start running out at some point. This means that using ethene to make ethanol will become very expensive.
8) The process also requires a lot of energy to maintain the high temperature and pressure.

Ethanol Can Also Be Produced by Fermentation

The alcohol in beer and wine, etc. isn't made from ethene — it's made by fermentation.

1) The raw material for fermentation is simple sugars, e.g. glucose. The sugars are converted into ethanol using yeast.

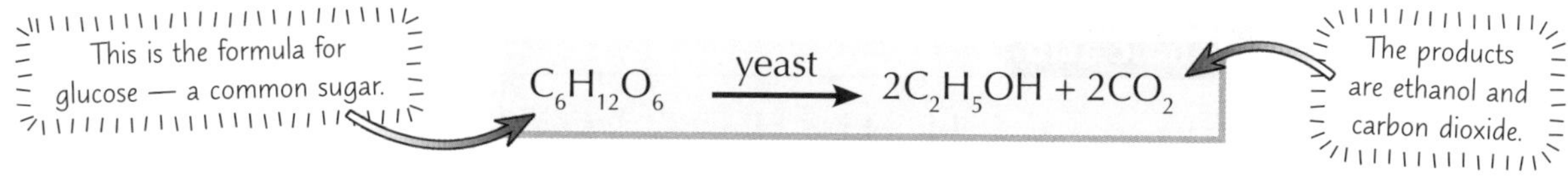

2) Yeast cells contain enzymes. Enzymes are natural catalysts (see p.63) — they speed up reactions.
3) The fermentation mixture needs to be about 30 °C — fermentation happens fastest at this temperature. At lower temperatures, the reaction slows down. If it's too hot, the enzymes in the yeast denature (are destroyed) and the reaction will stop.
4) It's important to keep the mixture in anaerobic conditions (no oxygen). Oxygen converts the ethanol to ethanoic acid (which is what you get in vinegar).
5) After fermentation, the ethanol is distilled to increase its concentration.

Supplement

6) An advantage of this process compared to the reaction of ethene with steam is that the raw materials are all renewable resources. Sugar (sugar cane) is grown as a major crop in several parts of the world, including many poorer countries. Yeast is also easy to grow.
7) There are some disadvantages to fermentation though. The ethanol you get from this process isn't very concentrated, so it needs to be distilled to increase its strength (as in whisky distilleries). The ethanol also needs to be purified to remove any contaminants such as leftover yeast.
8) Fermentation is also slower than the addition of steam to ethene, as it is a batch process (it has to be stopped and started). In contrast, the addition of steam to ethene is a continuous process.

Supplement

Yeast enzymes work best at a specific temperature

Remember — it's very important to keep the temperature as close as possible to 30 °C during fermentation.

Carboxylic Acids

Carboxylic acids are another homologous series you need to know about. Here's a bit about them.

Aqueous Ethanoic Acid Shares Properties with **Other Acids**

1) Carboxylic acids have a -COOH functional group and their names end in '-oic acid'.
2) Ethanoic acid (CH_3COOH) is the carboxylic acid with two carbon atoms.
3) Ethanoic acid reacts like other acids (see p.76). E.g. it reacts with carbonates to produce carbon dioxide, a salt and water.
4) When in solution, it can ionise. The hydrogen atom from the –OH group is released as an H^+ ion, making the solution acidic (see p.75).
5) Since it only partially ionises, ethanoic acid is a weak acid (see p.77).

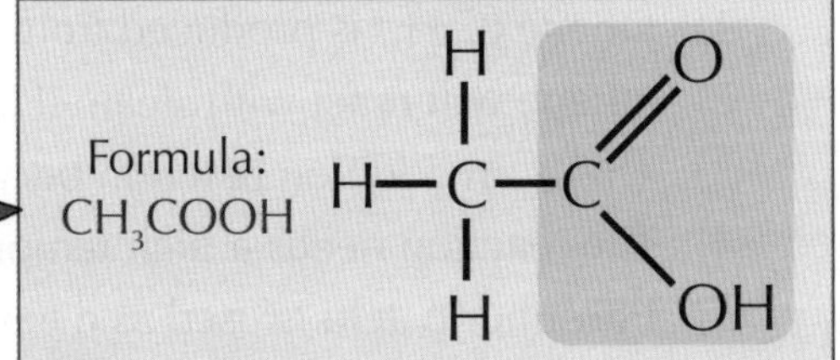

You Can Make a **Carboxylic Acid** by **Oxidising** an **Alcohol**

1) Carboxylic acids have the general formula $C_{n-1}H_{2n-1}COOH$.
2) As well as ethanoic acid, you need to know the three carboxylic acids shown below.

n is the total number of C atoms in the molecule, including the one in the COOH group.

Methanoic acid

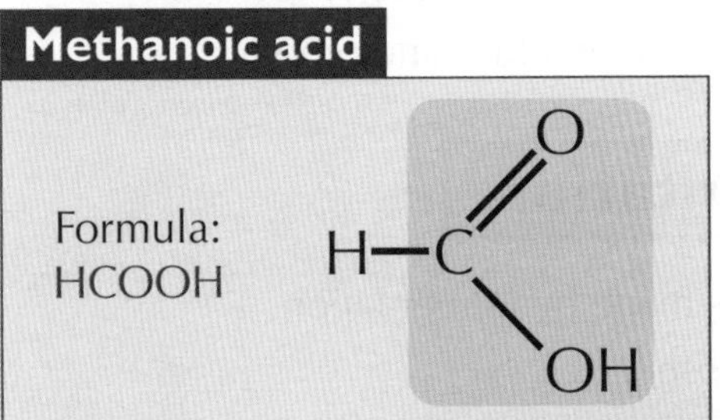

Propanoic acid

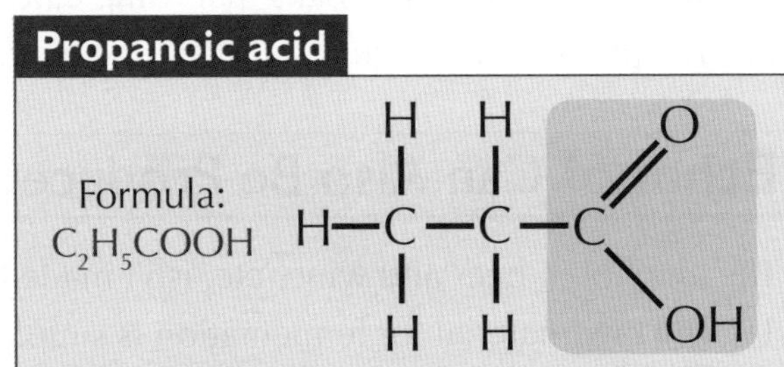

Butanoic acid

Formula: C_3H_7COOH

3) They can each be formed by oxidising the alcohol which contains the same total number of carbons (i.e. methanol is oxidised to methanoic acid, ethanol is oxidised to ethanoic acid, and so on). You need an oxidising agent for this, such as acidified potassium manganate(VII).

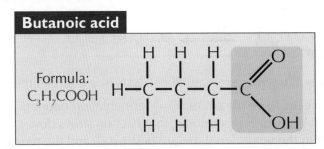

Remember — when something's oxidised, it gains oxygen (or loses electrons). See p. 72.

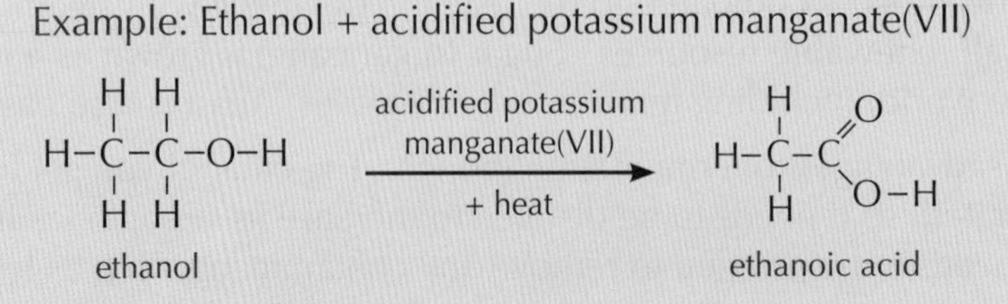

Alcohols can only form carboxylic acids in this way if the -OH group is attached to a carbon that's only attached to one carbon itself.

Supplement

Ethanoic acid is made by oxidising ethanol

Remember — members of a homologous series have similar reactions because they contain the same functional group. So if you know how a certain molecule in a homologous series reacts (e.g. ethanol forming ethanoic acid), you can predict how other molecules in that series react.

Carboxylic Acids

You have already learned about the fermentation of glucose to form ethanol on page 135. Here is what happens if that reaction is allowed to carry on a step further.

Supplement

Carboxylic Acids can also be Made by Fermenting Alcohols

1) Ethanol can be oxidised by fermentation into a carboxylic acid.
2) In this process, ethanol reacts with oxygen in the air to produce ethanoic acid (and water). The reaction is carried out by bacteria in the solution.
3) This process occurs quite slowly, and is the reason why beer and wine can taste sour if they are left exposed to the air for a couple of days (as ethanoic acid tastes sour).

C_2H_5OH	+	O_2	$\longrightarrow$	CH_3COOH	+	H_2O
ethanol		oxygen		ethanoic acid		water

Esters can be Made from Carboxylic Acids and Alcohols

1) Esters have the functional group '-COO-'.
2) Esters are formed from an alcohol and a carboxylic acid.
3) An acid catalyst is usually used (e.g. concentrated sulfuric acid).

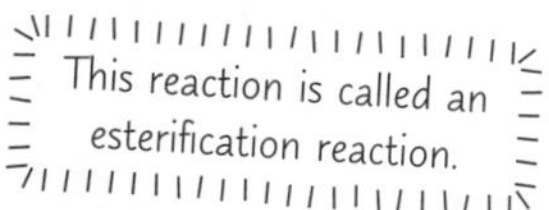

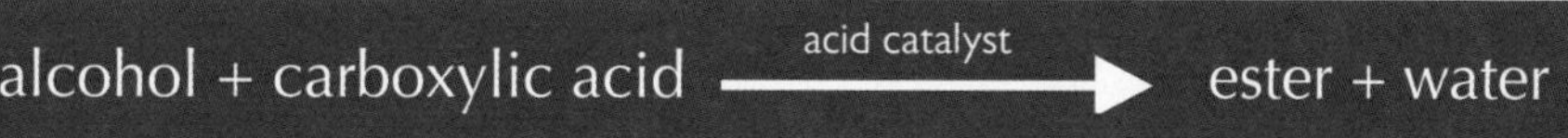

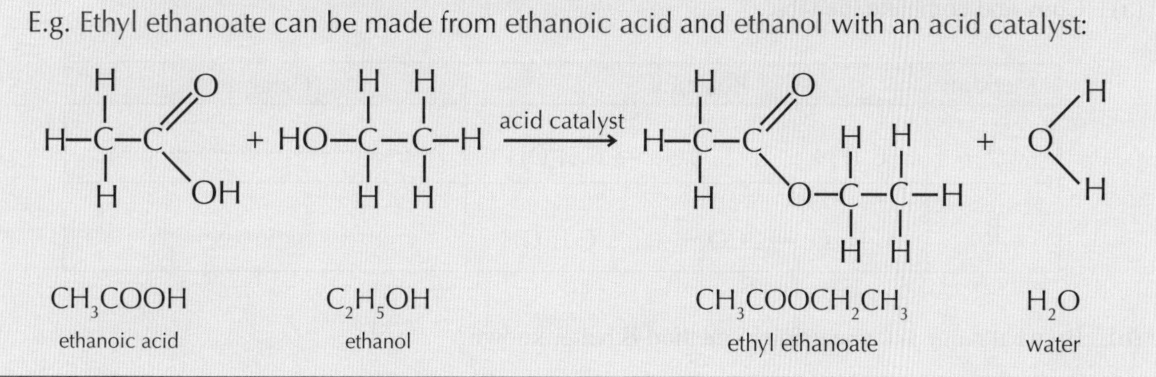

4) Their names end in '-oate'. The alcohol forms the first part of the ester's name, and the acid forms the second part.

ethanol + ethanoic acid → ethyl ethanoate + water
methanol + propanoic acid → methyl propanoate + water

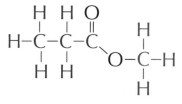

You can use an ester's molecular formula to work out the acid and alcohol used to make it. The carbon chain before the ester link (-COO-) comes from the acid and the chain after the ester link comes from the alcohol.

methyl propanoate

Carboxylic acids react with alcohols to form esters

EXAM TIP

There's a lot going on in those esterification reactions but, if you break it down, they're not too tricky to understand. If you're asked to draw the structure of an ester, just take the -OH from the acid and the -H from the alcohol to make water and combine the rest.

Warm-Up & Exam Questions

Time to test how much you know about those key organic compounds...

Warm-Up Questions

1) Why are alkenes described as unsaturated?
2) What type of reaction does ethene undergo to produce poly(ethene)?
3) State two conditions that are required when producing ethanol by fermenting glucose.
4) Name the ester which has the structural formula $CH_3COOCH_2CH_3$.

Exam Questions

1 Cracking is a process used in the petroleum industry.

(a) Briefly describe what is meant by cracking.

[2]

(b) Give an example of a compound that may be used as a catalyst in cracking.

[1]

(c) Cracking can sometimes be used to produce a gas that doesn't contain any carbon atoms. Name this gas.

[1]

[Total 4 marks]

2 The incomplete table below shows some information about two methods of manufacturing ethanol.

(a) Copy and complete the table.

Method	Reaction	Catalyst
A	C_2H_4 + ... → C_2H_5OH	....
B	$C_6H_{12}O_6 \rightarrow 2CO_2$ + ...C_2H_5OH	....

[4]

(b) By what name is the reaction in method **B** better known?

[1]

(c) Draw the displayed formulae for both organic molecules in method **A** and circle their functional groups.

[2]

[Total 7 marks]

3 Alkenes are unsaturated hydrocarbons.

(a) Describe how bromine water is used to determine if a sample of hydrocarbons contains alkenes.

[2]

(b) Write the equation for the reaction of bromine water with propene.

[1]

[Total 3 marks]

Exam Questions

4 A student has a small sample of a carboxylic acid, **A**.
The structural formula of carboxylic acid **A** is CH_3COOH.

(a) Name carboxylic acid **A**.

[1]

(b) Draw the displayed formula of carboxylic acid **A**.

[1]

(c) What would happen to the pH of a solution if carboxylic acid **A** was added to it?

[1]

[Total 3 marks]

5 Alcohols are a series of organic compounds with a wide range of industrial applications.

(a) An alcohol containing 3 carbons is commonly used as a solvent.
What is the name given to this alcohol?

[1]

(b) Butanol is also commonly used as a solvent. Give the structural formula for butanol.

[1]

(c) Methanol can be used as an additive to fuels to improve combustion.
Draw the displayed formula for methanol.

[1]

[Total 3 marks]

Supplement

6 Ethanoic acid is an example of a carboxylic acid.

(a) (i) Name the alcohol that can be oxidised to produce ethanoic acid.

[1]

(ii) Give an example of an oxidising agent that can be used to convert the alcohol from part (i) to ethanoic acid.

[1]

(b) Ethanoic acid is reacted with butanol.
Name the **two** products of this reaction.

[2]

[Total 4 marks]

7 Draw the displayed formulae of the carboxylic acid and the alcohol that can be reacted together to produce propyl methanoate.

[Total 2 marks]

Supplement

Polymers

You might remember addition polymerisation from page 133, but there's more to polymers than just that.

There are **Different Types** of **Polymer**

1) Different polymers are made up of different monomers.
2) The way the monomers are linked together can vary as well, depending on the type of polymer. E.g. in addition polymers, the monomers are joined together by C-C single bonds.

Polymers can be Made by **Condensation Polymerisation**

1) Condensation polymerisation involves monomers which contain different functional groups.
2) The monomers react together and bonds form between them, making polymer chains.
3) For each new bond that forms, a small molecule (for example, water) is lost. This is why it's called condensation polymerisation.
4) Many common condensation polymers are made from two different monomers, with each one having two of the same functional groups.
5) For example, polyesters form when dicarboxylic acid monomers and diol monomers react together.

Within the repeating unit of a polyester you'll always have the ester link and the carbon chain of both monomers.

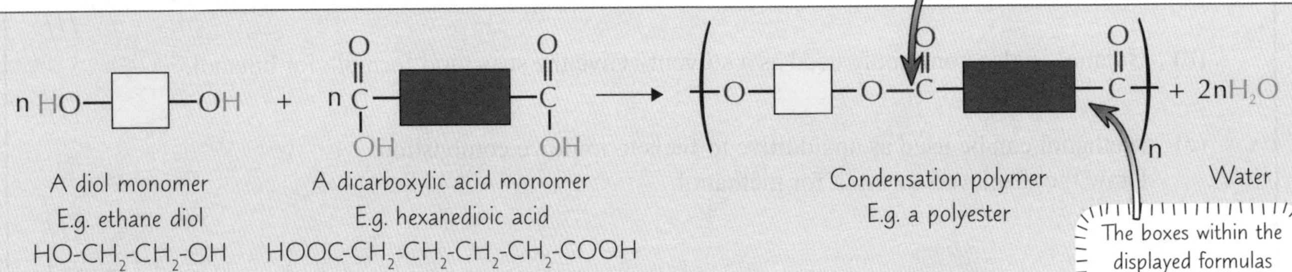

The boxes within the displayed formulas represent the carbon chains.

6) Polyamides are another example of a condensation polymer. They form from the reaction of dicarboxylic acid monomers with diamine monomers (see next page for an example).

H_2N—■—NH_2

A diamine monomer

Addition and **Condensation Polymerisation** are Different

	Addition Polymerisation	Condensation Polymerisation
Number of products	Only one product formed.	Two types of product — the polymer and a small molecule (e.g. water).
Number of types of monomers	Only one monomer type, containing a C=C bond.	Two monomer types each containing two of the same functional groups. or One monomer type with two different functional groups (see page 142).
Functional groups involved in polymerisation	Carbon-carbon double bond in monomer.	Two reactive groups on each monomer.

Condensation polymerisation involves losing a small molecule

It is important that you learn the differences between addition and condensation polymerisation. Study this table — particularly the difference in number of products — until you've got it.

Synthetic Polymers

In the last 100 years, synthetic polymers and plastics have become vital to our lives. However, there are now serious problems surrounding the disposal of these polymers.

Synthetic Polymers Have Many Uses

1) Plastics are a group of synthetic (man-made) polymers, traditionally produced from petroleum.
2) Plastics are used in a wide range of applications such as packaging, fabrics, gadgets and vehicles.
3) Useful synthetic polymers also include nylon (a polyamide) and *Terylene* (a polyester). These fibres are commonly used in the making of clothing and other fabrics.

Supplement

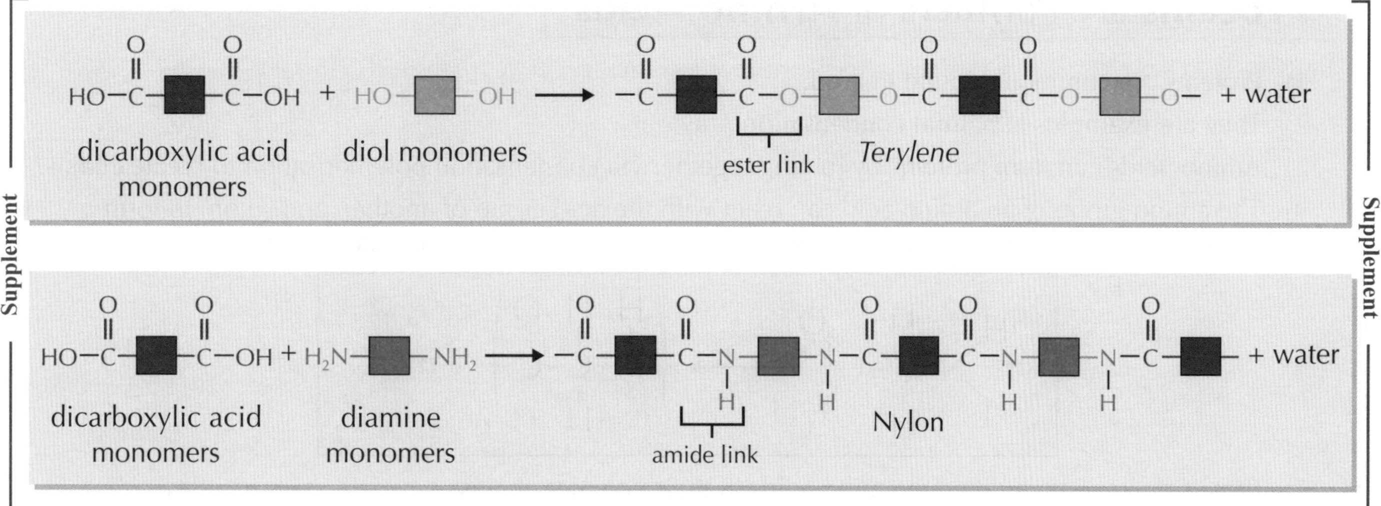

The Disposal of Plastics Comes with Pollution Problems

1) It takes a long time for some plastics to biodegrade (be broken down by bacteria or other organisms) — if you bury them in a landfill site, they'll still be there centuries later.

Substances that aren't easily broken down by microorganisms are called 'non-biodegradable'.

2) Most addition polymers are difficult to biodegrade because they are inert — they don't react easily. This is because the carbon-carbon bonds in the polymer chain are very strong and aren't easily broken.

3) Plastics sometimes get dumped in landfill sites when the different polymers are too difficult or expensive to separate and recycle.

4) Burning plastics produces a lot of energy and can be used to generate electricity.

5) However, burning plastics also releases toxic gases, such as HCl, or carbon dioxide (CO_2) which contributes to global warming. So that isn't an ideal solution either.

Disposing of synthetic polymers and plastics is a serious problem

As you can see, it's difficult to dispose of polymers in a way that doesn't harm the environment in some way. The best thing we can do is to reuse polymers as many times as possible and then recycle them.

Proteins

Proteins are a key part of our diet, but they also perform many important functions in the body.

Amino Acids have an Amino Group and a Carboxyl Group

Supplement

1) An amino acid contains two different functional groups — a basic amino group ($-NH_2$) and an acidic carboxyl group ($-COOH$).
2) An example of an amino acid is glycine — the smallest and simplest amino acid possible.

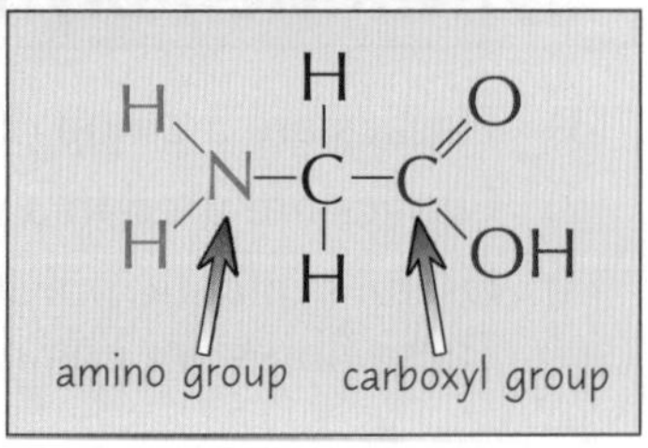

amino group carboxyl group

Proteins are Polymers of Amino Acids

1) Proteins are commonly found in food.
2) They are examples of natural condensation polymers.
3) Amino acids can form proteins by joining together via condensation polymerisation to create chains.
4) The amino group of an amino acid can react with the acid group of another, and so on, to form a polyamide chain. For every new bond that is formed, a molecule of water is lost.

E.g.

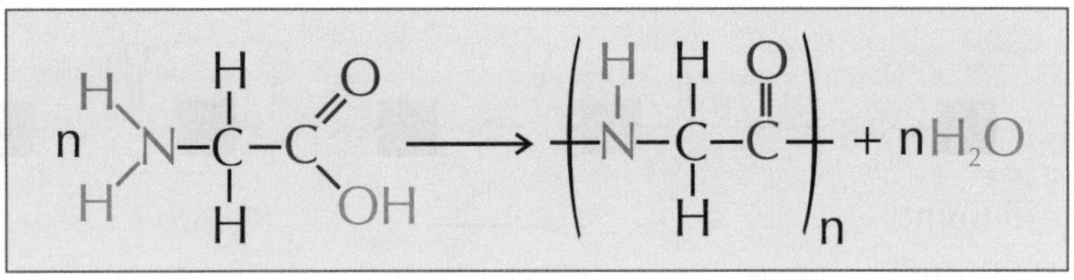

$$n\,H_2N{-}CH_2{-}COOH \longrightarrow {-}\!\left(NH{-}CH_2{-}CO\right)\!_n{-} + nH_2O$$

5) Proteins can contain different amino acids in their polymer chains. The order of the amino acids is what gives proteins their different properties and structures. The structure of a protein can be represented like this:

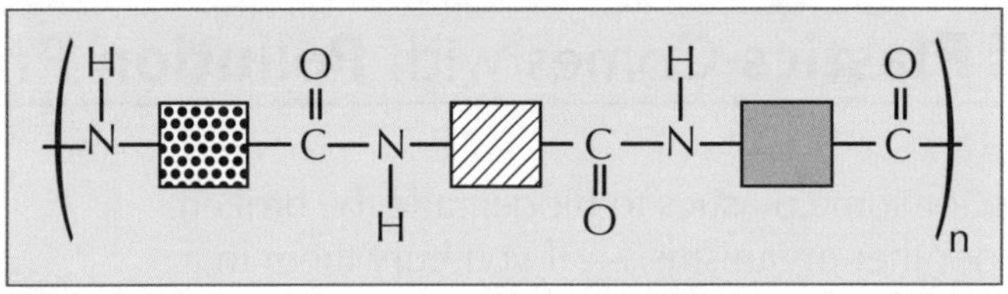

$$-\!\left(NH{-}\blacksquare{-}CO{-}NH{-}\blacksquare{-}CO{-}NH{-}\blacksquare{-}CO\right)\!_n-$$

6) The amide links found in protein chains are the same as the ones formed when producing nylon. However, the monomer units in these polymers are different.

Supplement

Proteins Can be Broken Down by Hydrolysis

1) Proteins can be broken back into their amino acids through hydrolysis.
2) Hydrolysis is when a molecule is split apart by water.
3) A water molecule is added into each amide bond, breaking them apart and re-forming the carboxylic acid functional group and the amino functional groups.
4) In the lab, this reaction is typically carried out with an acid catalyst such as hydrochloric acid (HCl).

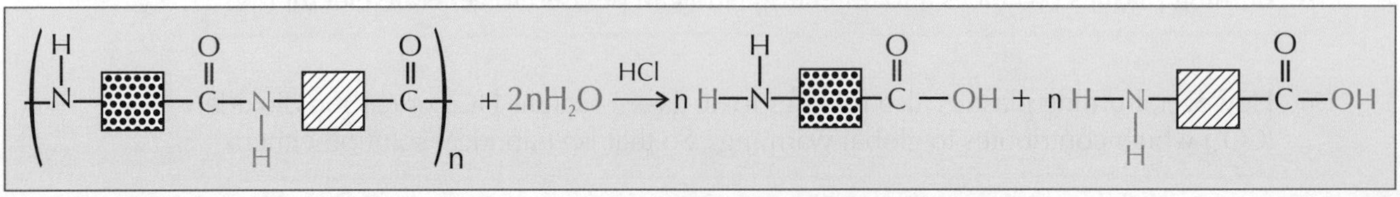

$$-\!\left(NH{-}\blacksquare{-}CO{-}NH{-}\blacksquare{-}CO\right)\!_n- + 2nH_2O \xrightarrow{HCl} n\,H{-}NH{-}\blacksquare{-}C{-}OH + n\,H{-}NH{-}\blacksquare{-}C{-}OH$$

Proteins are made up of long chains of amino acids.

You saw earlier how condensation polymers can be formed from different types of monomer. Amino acids are a great example of single unit monomers with two different functional groups.

Complex Carbohydrates

Like proteins, complex carbohydrates are another component of our food which is a natural polymer. But instead of using amino acids as monomers, carbohydrates are made up of simple sugar molecules.

Complex Carbohydrates are **Polymers** Made Up of **Sugars**

1) Complex carbohydrates, such as starch, are common constituents in many foods, including bread, rice and pasta.

Supplement

2) Complex carbohydrates are polymers made up of a large number of sugar monomers.

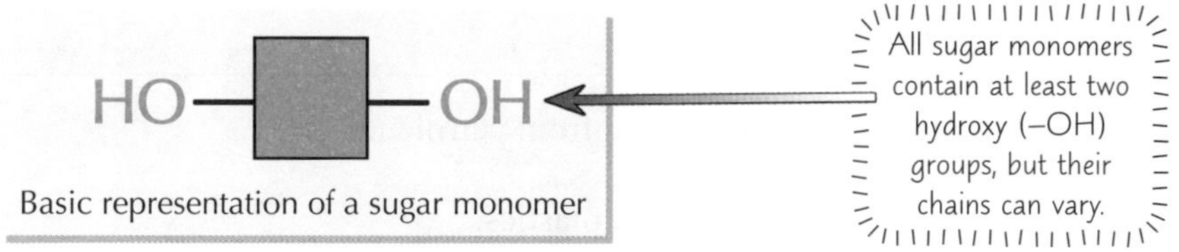

HO — ■ — OH
All sugar monomers contain at least two hydroxy (–OH) groups, but their chains can vary.

Basic representation of a sugar monomer

3) As with proteins, the monomers are joined together by condensation polymerisation.

n HO—■—OH ⟶ (—O—■—O—■—O—■—O—)$_n$ + nH_2O

sugar monomers — complex carbohydrate — water

4) Complex carbohydrates can be broken up into simple sugars by hydrolysis. Water is added to the polymer link and the simple sugar monomers are re-formed.

5) This reaction can be catalysed by either enzymes or by heating the solution with an acid.

Chromatography Can **Separate** the Products of **Hydrolysis**

1) Hydrolysing carbohydrates or proteins can produce a mixture of products.

2) Paper chromatography (see page 9) is a useful method for separating and identifying the simple sugars or amino acids produced from the hydrolysis of carbohydrates and proteins.

3) A locating agent is used to make the colourless compounds visible once they have separated.

4) You can then identify the products of the hydrolysis reaction from their R_f values.

5) However, sometimes the amino acids or proteins in the mixture have very similar R_f values. This means they can't be distinguished by a single paper chromatography experiment.

6) In this case, the chromatogram can be rotated by 90° and a second chromatography experiment, using a different solvent, can be carried out to further separate the products. This is called two-dimensional chromatography.

Supplement

Carbohydrate polymers are made up of simple sugars

Carbohydrates and proteins have quite similar chemistry. They're both polymers that can undergo acid hydrolysis. Just make sure you remember the differences between their monomers and their bonding.

Warm-Up & Exam Questions

That's the end of the organic chemistry section. Now it's time to have a go at some exam-style questions.

Warm-Up Questions

S

1) How many different products are formed in a condensation polymerisation reaction?
2) True or false? Nylon is a polyamide.
3) What is meant by "non-biodegradable"?

Exam Questions

1 Plastics are polymers produced from petroleum.

(a) Give three typical uses of plastics.

[3]

(b) Describe one pollution problem caused by non-biodegradable plastics.

[1]

[Total 4 marks]

Supplement

2 Proteins are polymers which are key constituents of food.

(a) What type of links are found between the monomers in a protein chain?

[1]

(b) Name the type of reaction which can be used to break proteins into amino acids.

[1]

[Total 2 marks]

3 Synthetic polymers can be produced by either addition polymerisation or condensation polymerisation.
State whether each of these monomers would take part in addition or condensation polymerisation.

(a) H—N(—H)—■—C(=O)—OH *[1]*

(b) H₂C=CH₂ (H, H on each C) *[1]*

(c) HO—C(=O)—▨—C(=O)—OH *[1]*

[Total 3 marks]

4 A scientist is researching the composition of a complex carbohydrate.
They carry out the hydrolysis of the carbohydrate and obtain a chromatogram of the resulting solution.

(a) Suggest why the scientist carried out a chromatography experiment on the product solution.

[2]

(b) The spots on the chromatogram are colourless.
What should the scientist do to make them visible?

[1]

(c) Name the type of molecule produced by hydrolysing complex carbohydrates.

[1]

[Total 4 marks]

Revision Summary for Section 12

Now that you're all done with the organic chemistry section, have a go at these revision questions to check your knowledge before moving on.

- Try these questions and tick off each one when you get it right.
- When you've done all the questions for a topic and are completely happy with it, tick off the topic.

Fuels and Fractional Distillation (p.123)

1) Name three types of non-renewable fuel.
2) True or false? Hydrocarbons with low boiling points are collected at the bottom of the fractionating column.
3) Which petroleum fraction is used for heating homes?

Naming Organic Compounds (p.124-127)

4) What is the molecular formula for ethanol?
5) What is the IUPAC name for the compound with the structural formula $CH_3CH_2CH_2CH_2OH$?
6) True or false? Structural isomers have identical physical and chemical properties.

Alkanes (p.128-129)

7) True or false? Alkanes are saturated molecules.
8) Alkanes will react with chlorine in the presence of what?

Alkenes (p.131-133)

9) True or false? Catalytic cracking is carried out at a low temperature.
10) What is the name of the alkene with two carbon atoms?
11) Name the type of reaction that is used to convert alkenes into polymers.
12) Give the name and formula of the polymer that is formed from C_2H_4.

Alcohols (p.134-135)

13) State one use of ethanol in industry.
14) Give a disadvantage of producing ethanol by fermentation.
15) Why might it become more expensive to produce ethanol from ethene in the future?

Carboxylic Acids (p.136-137)

16) What is the functional group of carboxylic acids?
17) What are the products when a carboxylic acid reacts with an alcohol?
18) Is ethanoic acid a strong or weak acid?

Polymers (p.140-143)

19) What monomers are needed to make a polyester?
20) What is *Terylene* used for?
21) How can burning plastics contribute to global warming?
22) What type of molecules are used as monomers when forming proteins?
23) What sort of catalyst is required to perform protein hydrolysis?

Planning Experiments

Dig out your lab coat and dust off your badly-scratched safety goggles... it's investigation time.

Evidence Can **Support** or **Disprove** a **Hypothesis**

1) Scientists observe things and come up with hypotheses to test them. A hypothesis is just a possible explanation for what they've observed. For example:

> Observation: People with big feet have spots. Hypothesis: Having big feet causes spots.

2) To determine whether or not a hypothesis is right, you need to do an investigation to gather evidence. To do this, you need to use your hypothesis to make a prediction — something you think will happen that you can test. E.g. people who have bigger feet will have more spots.

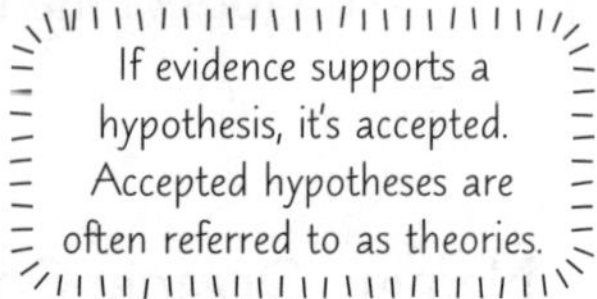

If evidence supports a hypothesis, it's accepted. Accepted hypotheses are often referred to as theories.

3) Investigations are used to see if there are patterns or relationships between two variables, e.g. to see if there's a pattern or relationship between the variables 'number of spots' and 'size of feet'.

Results Need to be **Reliable** and **Valid**

1) RELIABLE results come from experiments that give the same data each time the experiment is repeated (by you) and each time the experiment is reproduced (copied) by other scientists.
2) VALID results are both reliable and come from experiments that were designed to be a fair test.

Make an Investigation a **Fair Test** By **Controlling the Variables**

1) In a lab experiment you usually change one variable and measure how it affects another variable.
2) To make it a fair test, everything else that could affect the results should stay the same — otherwise you can't tell if the thing you're changing is causing the results or not.
3) The variable you CHANGE is called the INDEPENDENT variable.
4) The variable you MEASURE when you change the independent variable is the DEPENDENT variable.
5) The variables that you KEEP THE SAME are called CONTROL variables.

> You could find how temperature affects reaction rate by measuring the volume of gas formed over time. The independent variable is the temperature.
> The dependent variable is the volume of gas produced. Control variables include the concentration and amounts of reactants, the time period you measure, etc.

6) Because you can't always control all the variables, you often need to use a control experiment. This is an experiment that's kept under the same conditions as the rest of the investigation, but doesn't have anything done to it. This is so that you can see what happens when you don't change anything at all.

Results Also Need to be **Accurate**

1) Accurate results are those that are close to the true answer.
2) The accuracy of your results usually depends on your method — you need to make sure you're measuring the right thing and that you don't miss anything that should be included in the measurements.

> E.g. estimating the amount of gas released from a reaction by counting the bubbles isn't very accurate because you might miss some of the bubbles and they might have different volumes. It's more accurate to measure the volume of gas released using a gas syringe (see p.64).

Planning Experiments

In the exam, you could be asked to plan or describe how you'd carry out an experiment. The experiment might be one you've already come across or you might be asked to come up with an experiment of your own.

You Need to Be Able to Plan a **Good Experiment**

Even if you can't remember all the details of an experimental method you've learned about, you could still get marks for describing things like the independent and dependent variables.

Here are some general tips on what to include when planning an experiment:

1) Say what you're measuring (i.e. what the dependent variable is going to be).
2) Say what you're changing (i.e. what the independent variable is going to be) and describe how you're going to change it.
3) Describe the method and the apparatus you'd use.
4) Describe what variables you're keeping constant — and how you're going to do it.
5) Say that you need to repeat the experiment at least three times, to make the results more reliable.
6) Say whether you're using a control or not.

Here's an idea of the type of question you might be asked in the exam and what your answer might be...

Exam-style Question

Describe an experiment to investigate the effect of concentration on the reaction of dilute hydrochloric acid and magnesium metal. [6 marks]

Example Answer

Set up a flask containing a measured mass of magnesium metal. Place the flask on a mass balance.

Pour a measured volume of dilute hydrochloric acid into the flask and start the timer. Take readings of the mass at regular time intervals until the mass doesn't change anymore. The mass of gas lost from the reaction mixture can be calculated using this data.

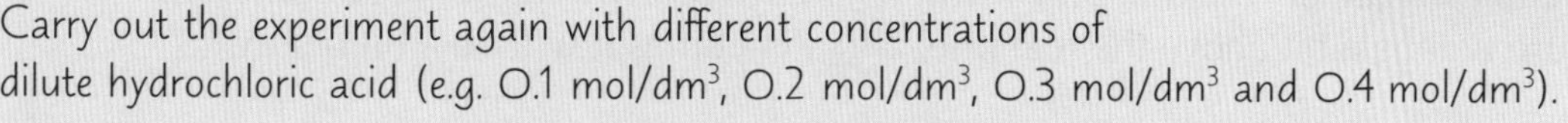

Carry out the experiment again with different concentrations of dilute hydrochloric acid (e.g. 0.1 mol/dm^3, 0.2 mol/dm^3, 0.3 mol/dm^3 and 0.4 mol/dm^3).

The mass should be measured at the same time intervals for each acid concentration. The volume of acid should always be the same and the same mass of magnesium metal should be used each time. The temperature must also remain constant.

Repeat the experiment three times at each acid concentration and use the results to find the average mass of gas lost at each time interval for each concentration.

You could also collect the hydrogen in a gas syringe and measure its volume.

You Can Make **Reasoned Predictions** Based on Your **Knowledge**

1) You can use your hypothesis (p.146) and the stuff you know to make sensible predictions about what the results of an experiment might be.
2) For example, you could use your knowledge of how concentration affects the rate of reaction to predict the results of the experiment above. You might predict that as the concentration of the acid increases, the rate of reaction increases.
3) The results of your experiment would then tell you if your prediction was correct. This will help you to determine if your hypothesis is likely to be correct, or whether it needs to change.

Planning Experiments

Your **Equipment** has to be **Right for the Job**

1) The measuring equipment you use has to be sensitive enough to measure the changes you're looking for. For example, if you need to measure changes of 1 cm^3 you need to use a measuring cylinder that can measure in 1 cm^3 steps — it'd be no good trying with one that only measures 10 cm^3 steps.

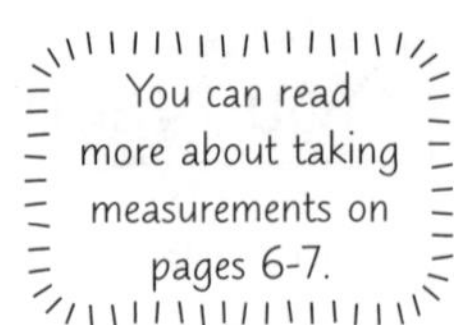

You can read more about taking measurements on pages 6-7.

2) The smallest change a measuring instrument can detect is called its resolution. E.g. some mass balances have a resolution of 1 g, some have a resolution of 0.1 g, and some are even more sensitive.

3) The more sensitive your equipment is, the more precise your measurements will be. E.g. a measurement of 10.1 g is more precise than a measurement of 10 g. You should make sure you record your measurements with the same precision (number of digits) as your measuring instrument.

4) Unfortunately, your readings may not always perfectly match the scale on the instrument. When this happens, you need to interpolate (estimate) where your reading lies between two marks on the scale.

5) Also, equipment needs to be calibrated by measuring a known value. If there's a difference between the measured and known value, you can use this to correct the inaccuracy of the equipment.

You Need to Look out for **Errors** in Your Results

1) The results of your experiment will always vary a bit because of random errors — unpredictable differences caused by things like human errors in measuring. E.g. the errors you make when you take a reading from a burette are random. You have to estimate or round the level when it's between two marks — so sometimes your figure will be a bit above the real one, and sometimes it will be a bit below.

2) You can reduce the effect of random errors by taking repeat readings and finding the mean (see p.151). This will make your results more reliable.

3) You can also reduce the effect of random errors by using more sensitive equipment.

4) If a measurement is wrong by the same amount every time, it's called a systematic error. For example, if you measured from the very end of your ruler instead of from the 0 cm mark every time, all your measurements would be a bit small. Repeating the experiment in the exact same way and calculating a mean won't correct a systematic error.

If there's no systematic error, then doing repeats and calculating a mean could make your results more accurate.

5) You can compensate for some systematic errors if you know about them, e.g. if a mass balance always reads 1 gram before you put anything on it, you can subtract 1 gram from all your results.

All investigations need to be planned before you begin

The number of marks available for a question like the one on the previous page will vary, but it'll usually be between four and six. Think about what you're going to say in advance and in what order. That way you're less likely to forget something important (like what you're measuring).

Safety and Heating Substances

Safety is really important when carrying out experiments. This is because experiments in chemistry can often involve using hazardous chemicals or heating substances. Read on to find out how to be safe in the lab.

Be Careful When You **Handle** or **Mix** Substances

1) There are lots of hazards in chemistry experiments, so before you start any experiment, you should read any safety precautions to do with your method or the chemicals you're using.
2) The substances used in chemical reactions are often hazardous. For example, they might catch fire easily (they're flammable), or they might irritate or burn your skin if you come into contact with them.
3) Whenever you're doing an experiment, you should wear a lab coat, safety goggles and gloves.
4) Always be careful that the chemicals you're using aren't flammable before you go lighting any Bunsen burners, and make sure you're working in an area that's well ventilated.
5) If you're doing an experiment that might produce nasty gases (such as chlorine), you should carry out the experiment in a fume hood so that the gas can't escape out into the room you're working in.
6) Never directly touch any chemicals (even if you're wearing gloves). Use a spatula to transfer solids between containers. Carefully pour liquids between different containers, using a funnel to avoid spills.
7) Be careful when you're mixing chemicals, as a reaction might occur. If you're diluting a liquid, add the concentrated substance to the water (not the other way around) or the mixture could get very hot.

Water Baths Can Be Used To Heat **Flammable Substances**

1) A water bath is a container filled with water that can be heated to a specific temperature.

- Set the temperature on the water bath, and allow the water to heat up.
- Place the vessel containing your substance in the water bath using a pair of tongs.
- The level of the water outside the vessel should be just above the level of the substance inside the vessel.
- The substance will then be warmed to the same temperature as the water.
- As the substance in the vessel is surrounded by water, the heating is very even. Water boils at 100 °C though, so you can't use a water bath to heat something to a higher temperature than this — the water won't get hot enough.

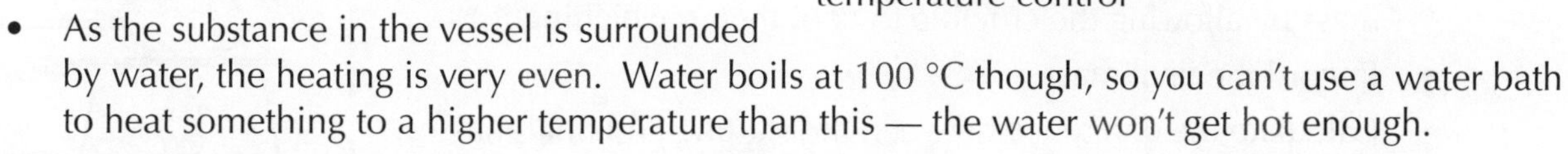

reaction vessel

temperature control

Handle any glassware you've heated with tongs until you're sure it's cooled down.

2) Electric heaters are often made up of a metal plate that can be heated to a certain temperature. The vessel containing the substance you want to heat is placed on top of the hot plate. You can heat substances to higher temperatures than you can in a water bath but, as the vessel is only heated from below, you'll usually have to stir the substance inside to make sure it's heated evenly.
3) Water baths and electric heaters can be used to safely heat flammable substances because there is no naked flame.

Heating Substances

Bunsen Burners Have a Naked **Flame**

1) Bunsen burners are good for heating things quickly. You can easily adjust how strongly they're heating.
2) Here's how to use a Bunsen burner:

- Connect the Bunsen burner to a gas tap, and check that the hole is closed. Place it on a heat-proof mat.
- Light a splint and hold it over the Bunsen burner. Now, turn on the gas. The Bunsen burner should light with a yellow flame.
- The more open the hole is, the more strongly the Bunsen burner will heat your substance. Open the hole to the amount you want. As you open the hole more, the flame should turn more blue.

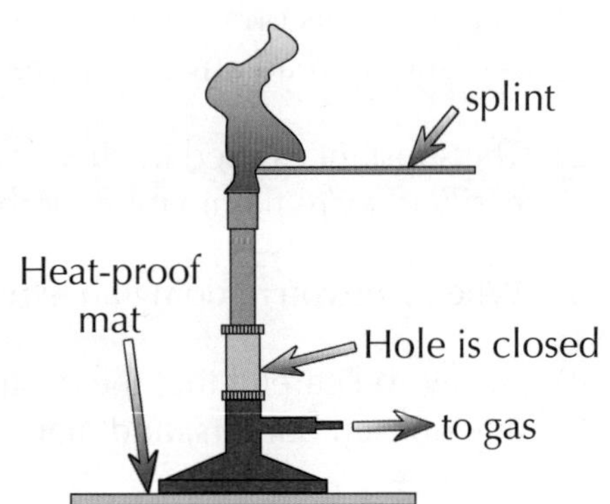

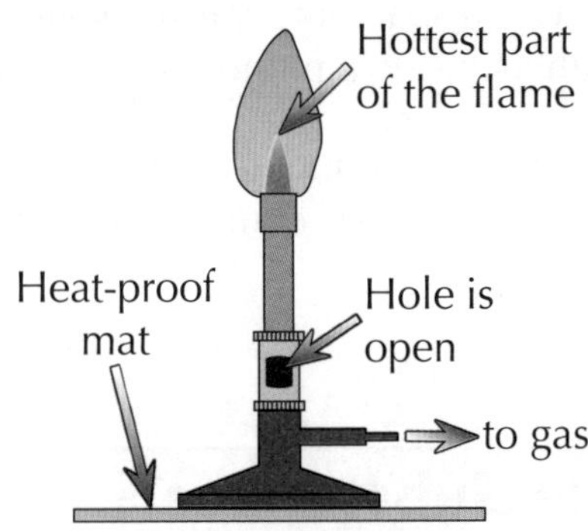

- The hottest part of the flame is just above the blue cone, so you should heat things here.
- If your Bunsen burner is alight but not heating anything, make sure you close the hole so that the flame becomes yellow and clearly visible.
- If you're heating something so that the container (e.g. a test tube) is in the flame, you should hold the vessel at the top, furthest away from the substance (and so the flame) using a pair of tongs.
- If you're heating something over the flame (e.g. an evaporating dish), you should put a tripod and gauze over the Bunsen burner before you light it, and place the vessel on this.

3) You'd use a Bunsen burner with a blue flame to carry out flame tests to identify metal ions in a compound — see page 83.

4) You'd also use a Bunsen burner with a blue flame to work out how much water is in a mass of hydrated crystals, e.g. hydrated copper(II) sulfate (p.70):

The water lost by heating the hydrated crystals is called the water of crystallisation.

- Weigh the mass of hydrated crystals in a crucible.
- Heat the crystals in the crucible to remove the water.
- Stop heating when the mass is constant. (You can check the mass by allowing the crucible to cool then reweighing it.)
- Record the final mass.
- Calculate the difference between the starting and final masses.

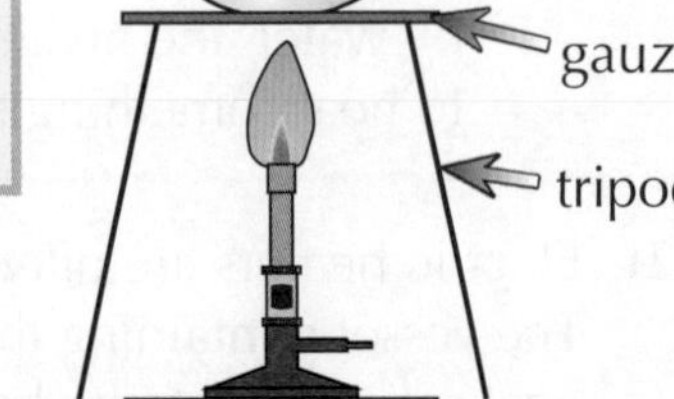

You can work out the number of moles of water that are lost by dividing the difference in mass by the M_r of water.

You might not expect the blue flame to be hotter, but it is

Bunsen burners are a crucial piece of equipment in a chemistry lab, but you need to be aware of how to use them safely. Make sure the flame is only blue when you need it to heat something.

Processing Data

Processing your data means doing some calculations with it to make it more useful.

You Should Be Able to Identify **Anomalous Results**

1) Most results vary a bit, but any that are totally different are called anomalous results.
2) These are caused by errors — see page 148.
3) You could be asked to identify an anomalous result in the exam and suggest what caused it. To do this, just look for a result that doesn't fit in with the rest (e.g. it's too high or too low) then try to figure out what could have gone wrong with the experiment to have caused it.
4) If you're calculating an average, you can ignore any anomalous results.

You Might Have to **Process Your Data**

1) When you've done repeats of an experiment you should always calculate the mean (average). To do this, add together all the data values and divide by the total number of values in the sample.
2) You might also need to calculate the range (how spread out the data is). To do this, find the largest number and subtract the smallest number from it.

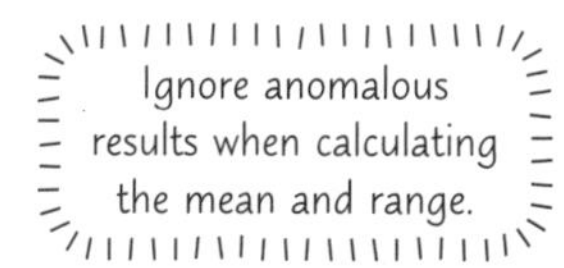

Ignore anomalous results when calculating the mean and range.

The results of an experiment to find the mass of gas lost from two reactions are shown below. Calculate the mean and the range for the mass of gas lost in each reaction.

Test tube	Repeat 1 / g	Repeat 2 / g	Repeat 3 / g	Mean / g	Range / g
A	28	37	32	(28 + 37 + 32) ÷ 3 = 32	37 − 28 = 9
B	47	51	60	(47 + 51 + 60) ÷ 3 = 53	60 − 47 = 13

Round to the **Lowest Number** of **Significant Figures**

The first significant figure of a number is the first digit that's not zero. The second and third significant figures come straight after (even if they're zeros). You should be aware of significant figures in calculations.

1) In any calculation where you need to round, you should round the answer to the lowest number of significant figures (s.f.) of the numbers used in the calculation.
2) Remember to write down how many significant figures you've rounded to after your answer.
3) If your calculation has multiple steps, only round the final answer, or it won't be as accurate.

Over the first 30 seconds of a reaction, 35.0 cm³ of gas was produced. Calculate the rate of reaction during the first 30 seconds of the reaction.

Rate of reaction = 35.0 cm³ ÷ 30 sec = 1.1666... = 1.2 cm³/s (2 s.f.)

3 s.f. (35.0) — 2 s.f. (30) — Final answer should be rounded to 2 s.f.

Don't forget your calculator...

EXAM TIP

In an exam you could be given some data and asked to process it in some way. Make sure you're comfortable with things like calculating a mean (using the right number of significant figures). Check you know what an anomalous result is and how to identify them, too.

Drawing Graphs

Once you've processed your data, you can present your results in a chart or graph.

Bar Charts can be Used to Show **Different** Types of **Data**

1) Bar charts can be used to display categoric data — data that comes in distinct categories, e.g. compound colour, metals, that is not numerical.
2) There are some golden rules you need to follow for drawing bar charts:

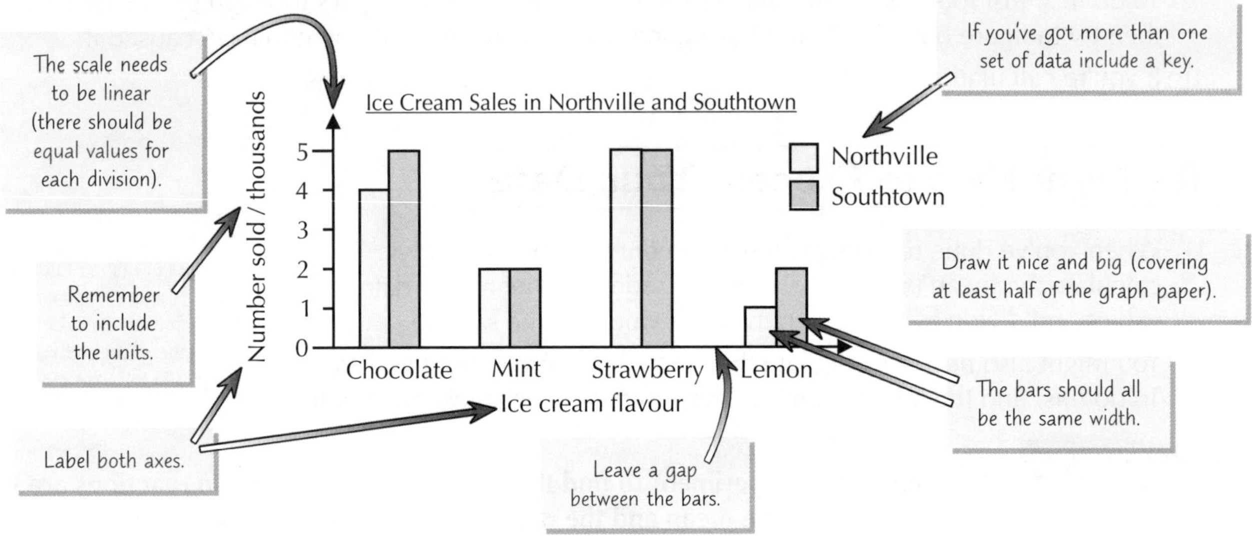

Graphs can be Used to Plot **Continuous Data**

1) If both variables are continuous you should use a graph to display the data. Continuous data is numerical data that can have any value in a range, e.g. length, volume, temperature.
2) Here are the rules for plotting points on a graph:

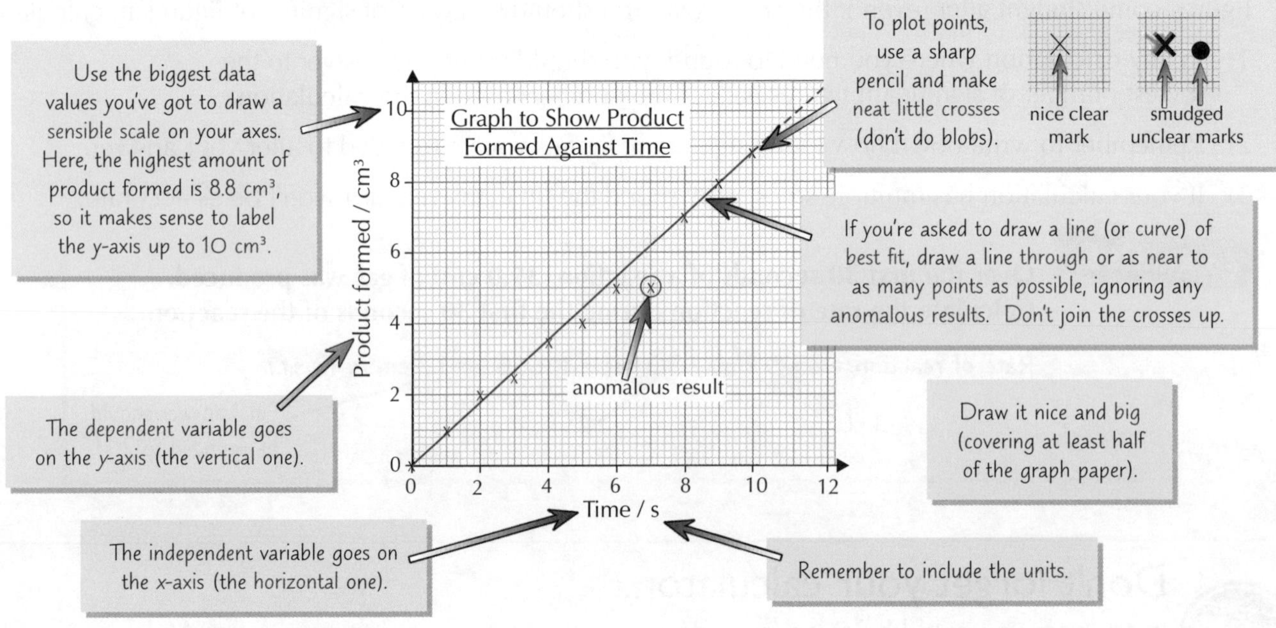

Interpreting Graphs

You Need to be Able to **Interpret** Graphs

1) A graph is used to show the relationship between two variables — you need to be able to look at a graph and describe this relationship.

> E.g. the graph on the previous page shows that as time goes on, more product is formed and that the amount of product formed is directly proportional to time.

A relationship is directly proportional if one variable increases at the same rate as the other variable (so if one variable doubles, the other also doubles, etc.). A graph shows direct proportion when the line is straight and goes through the origin (0,0).

2) You also need to be able to read information off a graph.

> In the example on the previous page, if you wanted to know how much product had been formed by 11 s, you'd draw a vertical line up to the graph line from the *x*-axis at 11 s and a horizontal line across to the *y*-axis. This would tell you that the amount of product formed by 11 s was around 9.8 cm^3.

Graphs Show the **Correlation** Between Two Variables

1) You can get three types of correlation (relationship) between variables:

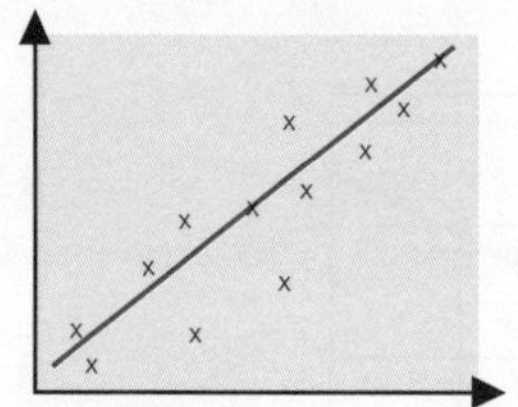

POSITIVE correlation: as one variable increases, the other increases.

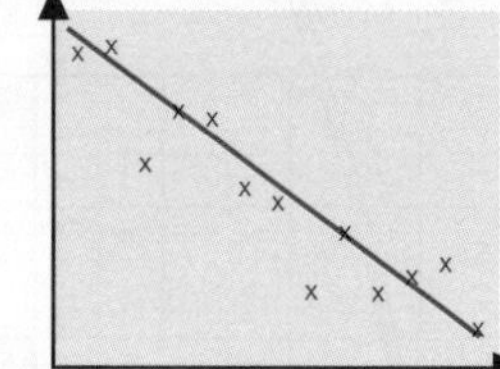

INVERSE (negative) correlation: as one variable increases the other decreases.

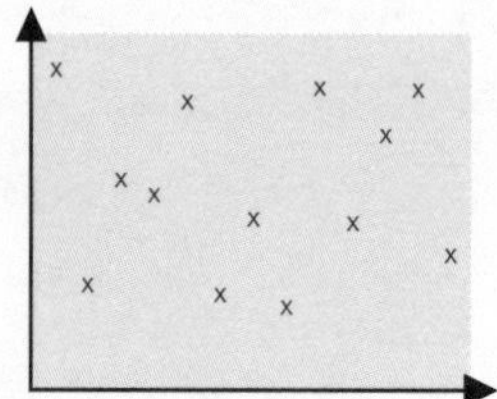

NO correlation: no relationship between the two variables.

2) Just because there's correlation, it doesn't mean the change in one variable is causing the change in the other — there might be other factors involved.
3) There are three possible reasons for a correlation:

> CHANCE: It might seem strange, but two things can show a correlation purely due to chance.

> LINKED BY A 3RD VARIABLE: A lot of the time it may look as if a change in one variable is causing a change in the other, but it isn't — a third variable links the two things.

> CAUSE: Sometimes a change in one variable does cause a change in the other. You can only conclude that a correlation is due to cause when you've controlled all the variables that could be affecting the result.

Correlation is just a relationship

It's important to remember that a correlation between two variables doesn't mean that a change in one is causing a change in the other — there could be another explanation for the results. However, if you've controlled all other variables properly, it's a sign there might be a pattern.

Calculating Rates from Graphs

You saw how to carry out some rate of reaction experiments back on pages 64-66. If you plot the results of experiments like those on a graph, you can calculate the rate of reaction. Here's how...

Faster Rates of Reaction are Shown by **Steeper Gradients**

1) If you have a graph of amount of product formed (or reactant used up) against time, then the gradient (slope) of the graph will be equal to the rate of the reaction — the steeper the slope, the faster the rate.

2) The gradient of a straight line is given by the equation:

gradient = change in y ÷ change in x

EXAMPLE:

Calculate the rate of the reaction shown on the graph below.

1) Find two points on the line that are easy to read the *x* and *y* values of (ones that pass through grid lines).

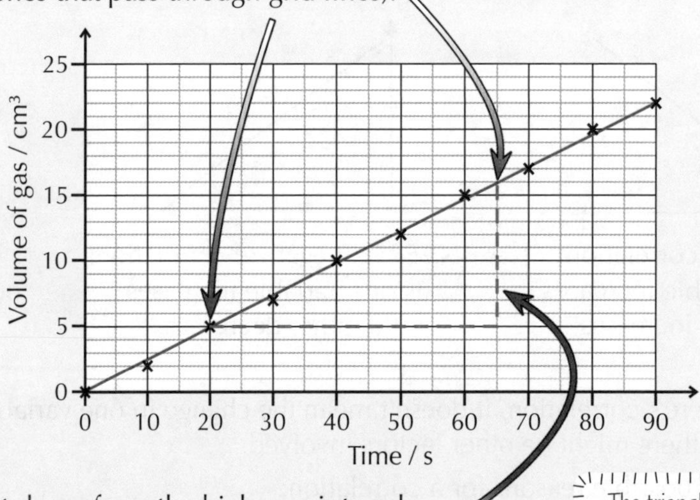

The triangle should be at least half the length of the graph line.

2) Draw a line straight down from the higher point and straight across from the lower one to make a triangle.

3) The height of your triangle = change in *y*

Change in y = 16 – 5 = 11

The base of your triangle = change in *x*

Change in x = 65 – 20 = 45

4) Use the formula to work out the gradient, and therefore the rate.

Gradient = change in y ÷ change in x = 11 ÷ 45 = 0.24 cm^3/s

The units of the rate are just "units of y-axis ÷ units of x-axis".

Use a gradient to work out reaction rate

When calculating rates, always be sure to give your answer to an appropriate number of significant figures. And don't forget to write the units, too. You can work out the correct units for the rate by taking the units on the *y*-axis and dividing them by the units on the *x*-axis. That's why the answer above is in cm^3/s.

Drawing Conclusions

Congratulations — you're nearly at the end of a gruelling investigation, time to draw some conclusions.

You Can **Only Conclude** What the Data Shows and **No More**

1) Drawing conclusions might seem pretty straightforward — you just look at your data and say what pattern or relationship you see between the dependent and independent variables.

The table below shows the rate of a reaction in the presence of two different catalysts.

Catalyst	Rate of reaction / cm^3/s
A	13.5
B	19.5
No catalyst	5.5

CONCLUSION:
Catalyst B makes this reaction go faster than catalyst A.

2) But you've got to be really careful that your conclusion matches the data you've got and doesn't go any further.

You can't conclude that catalyst B increases the rate of any other reaction more than catalyst A — the results might be completely different.

3) You also need to be able to use your results to justify your conclusion (i.e. back up your conclusion with some specific data).

The rate of this reaction was 6 cm^3/s faster using catalyst B compared with catalyst A.

4) When writing a conclusion you need to refer back to the original hypothesis and say whether the data supports it or not.

The hypothesis for this experiment might have been that adding a catalyst would increase the rate of reaction because it would decrease the activation energy.
The prediction may have been that catalyst B would decrease the activation energy by a greater amount so would increase the rate of reaction more than catalyst A.
If so, the data supports the hypothesis.

5) You could also make more predictions based on your conclusion, then further experiments could be carried out to test them.

Conclusions sum up what you've learnt from your data

There's no point doing an investigation unless you're going to draw some kind of conclusion from it — even if that conclusion is that you were completely wrong about your original hypothesis. Don't worry if you're wrong, there will still be something that you can learn from your data. That's how science works, after all.

Evaluations

So you've planned and carried out an investigation, processed and interpreted your data and drawn some conclusions. There's only one thing left to do — an evaluation.

Evaluations — Describe How it Could be Improved

An evaluation is a critical analysis of the whole investigation.

1) You should comment on the method — was it valid? Did you control all the other variables to make it a fair test?

2) Comment on the quality of the results — was there enough evidence to reach a valid conclusion? Were the results reliable, valid and accurate?

3) Were there any anomalous results? If there were none then say so. If there were any, try to explain them — were they caused by errors in measurement? Were there any other variables that could have affected the results?

4) All this analysis will allow you to say how confident you are that your conclusion is right.

5) Then you can suggest any changes to the method that would improve the quality of the results, so that you could have more confidence in your conclusion. For example, you might suggest changing the way you controlled a variable, or increasing the number of measurements you took. Taking more measurements at narrower intervals could give you a more accurate result.

For example, enzymes have an optimum temperature (a temperature at which they work best). Say you do an experiment to find an enzyme's optimum temperature and take measurements at 10 °C, 20 °C, 30 °C, 40 °C and 50 °C. The results of this experiment tell you the optimum is 40 °C. You could then repeat the experiment, taking more measurements around 40 °C to get a more accurate value for the optimum.

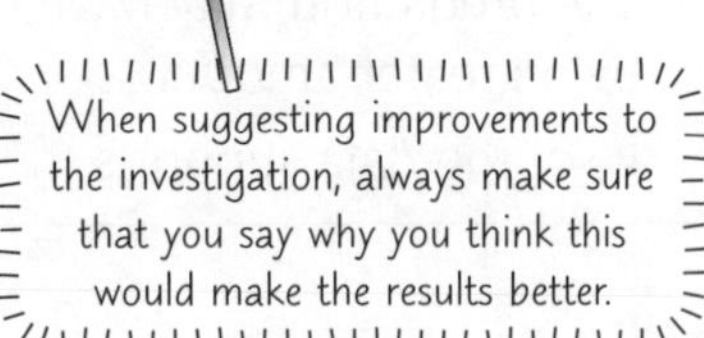

When suggesting improvements to the investigation, always make sure that you say why you think this would make the results better.

6) You could also make more predictions based on your conclusion, then further experiments could be carried out to test them.

Evaluations help us to improve scientific methods

That's it for this section. The practical paper is worth 20% of your total exam marks, so make sure that you're completely happy with everything in this section before you go into the exam. Best of luck.

Practice Papers

Once you've been through all the questions in this book, you should feel pretty confident about the exams.
As final preparation, here is a set of practice exam papers to really get you ready for the real thing.

Cambridge International GCSE Chemistry

Paper 1 Multiple Choice (Core)

In addition to this paper you should have:
- A soft pencil and eraser.
- A calculator.
- A Periodic Table

Centre name					
Centre number					
Candidate number					

Time allowed:
- 45 minutes

Candidate name
Candidate signature

Instructions to candidates
- Write your name and other details in the spaces provided above.
- Use pencil to record your answers.
- For each question, clearly shade the oval next to your chosen answer. For example: ⬬
  If you wish to change your answer, use an eraser to remove your original answer.
- Do all rough work on the paper.

Information for candidates
- There are 40 marks available for this paper.
- Each question is worth one mark.

1 Which change of state occurs when a substance changes from a liquid to a gas?

A condensation ○
B sublimation ○
C melting ○
D evaporation ○

2 The melting points of two compounds are shown in the table below.

Compound	Melting point (°C)
ammonium nitrate (NH_4NO_3)	170
citric acid ($C_6H_8O_7$)	156

An unidentified substance is found to have a melting point of around 163 °C.
Which of the following **best** describes what this tells you about the unidentified substance?

A The substance could be impure ammonium nitrate, but isn't impure citric acid. ○
B The substance could be impure citric acid, but isn't impure ammonium nitrate. ○
C The substance could be either impure ammonium nitrate or impure citric acid. ○
D The substance could be a mixture of equal parts ammonium nitrate powder and citric acid powder. ○

3 The diagrams below show the apparatus used in four different methods for separating mixtures.

Which of the separation methods would be most suitable for obtaining a pure, dry sample of sodium chloride from a solution of sodium chloride dissolved in water?

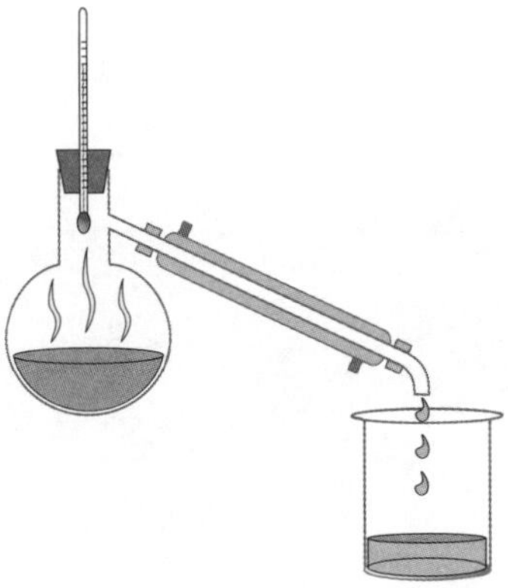

A 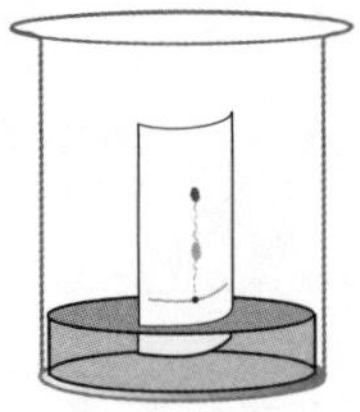 ○ **B**  ○ **C** 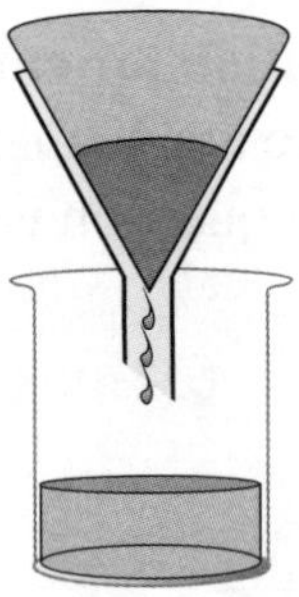 ○ **D** ○

4 The nucleon number of every atom of a certain element, X, is the same.
Which of the following statements must be **true** for element X?

A Atoms of element X contain no neutrons. ○
B Atoms of element X have an equal number of protons and neutrons. ○
C Atoms of element X have a full outer electron shell. ○
D Element X only has one isotope. ○

5 The atomic number of neon is 10.
Which diagram shows the correct electronic structure of neon?

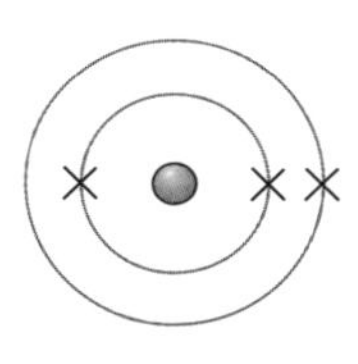

A

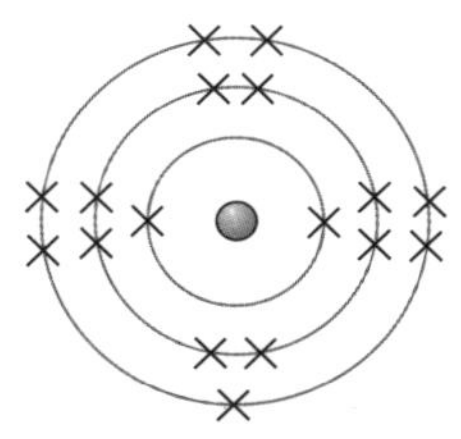

B

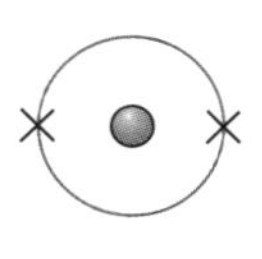

C

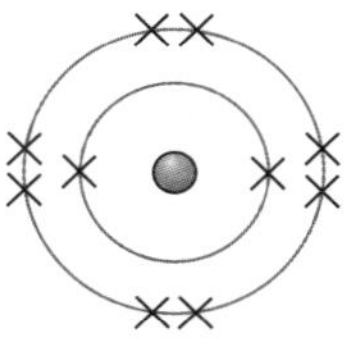

D

6 Eight elements have been labelled on the periodic table below.

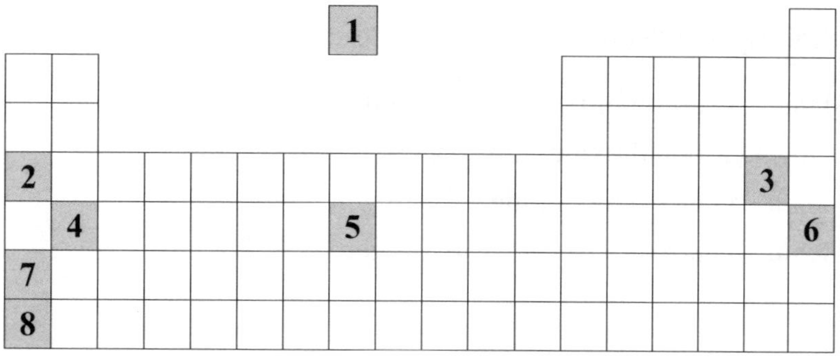

Which of the labelled elements have the same number of electrons in their outer shells?

A 2 and 3
B 2, 7 and 8
C 4, 5 and 6
D 1 and 6

7 Barium is in Group II of the periodic table.
When it reacts, it loses electrons to form an ion with a full outer shell.
What ion does barium form?

A Ba^{2+}
B Ba^{+}
C Ba^{2-}
D Ba^{-}

8 Group I metals can react with Group VII non-metals to form ionic compounds.
What are the charges on Group I and Group VII ions in an ionic compound?

	Group I Ion	Group VII Ion
A	+1	–2
B	–2	+2
C	+1	–1
D	0	+1

9 Which of the following substances is a macromolecule?

A graphite ○
B neon ○
C ammonia ○
D water ○

10 Hydrogen gas can be made at high temperatures using the following reaction:

$$CH_4 + H_2O \rightarrow CO + 3H_2$$

Which of the following word equations correctly describes this reaction?

A methane + steam → carbon dioxide + hydrogen ○
B ethane + steam → carbon dioxide + hydrogen ○
C methane + steam → carbon monoxide + hydrogen ○
D methane + steam → carbon + oxygen + hydrogen ○

11 The displayed formula of an organic compound is shown below.

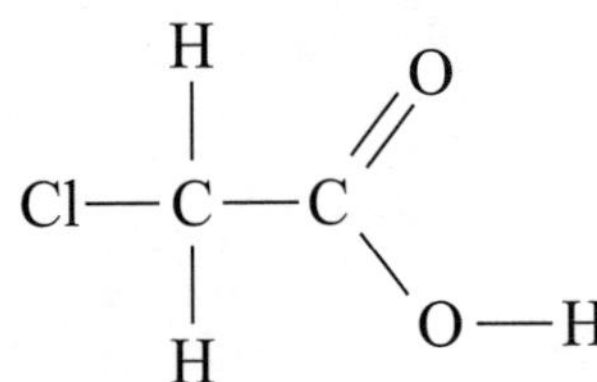

What is the molecular formula of this compound?

A $C_3H_3O_2$ ○
B C_3H_6O ○
C $Cl_2H_4O_2$ ○
D $C_2H_3ClO_2$ ○

12 Which of the following compounds has a relative formula mass of 62?

A sodium chloride, NaCl ○
B potassium bromide, KBr ○
C magnesium fluoride, MgF_2 ○
D sodium bromide, NaBr ○

13 The set-up of an electrolysis experiment is shown below.

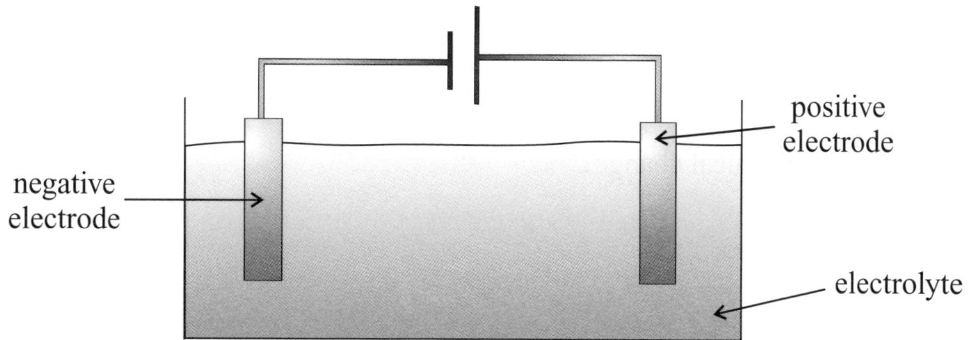

What names are given to the positive and negative electrodes?

	Positive electrode	Negative electrode
A ⬭	cation	anion
B ⬭	anode	cathode
C ⬭	anion	cation
D ⬭	cathode	anode

14 Which of the following shows the correct product at each electrode in the electrolysis of molten potassium chloride (KCl)?

	At the cathode	At the anode
A ⬭	chlorine gas	hydrogen gas
B ⬭	chlorine gas	molten potassium
C ⬭	molten potassium	water
D ⬭	molten potassium	chlorine gas

15 During an exothermic reaction, the energy of the products is ..... **1** ..... than the energy of the reactants, and the temperature of the surroundings ..... **2** ..... .

Which pair of words correctly completes the sentence above?

	1	**2**
A ⬭	higher	increases
B ⬭	lower	decreases
C ⬭	lower	increases
D ⬭	higher	decreases

16 Some examples of physical and chemical changes are listed below.

1. sugar dissolving in water
2. ethanol burning to form carbon dioxide
3. water vapour condensing

Which are examples of a chemical change?

A 1 and 2 ○
B 2 only ○
C 1 and 3 ○
D 3 only ○

17 A student reacts nitric acid (HNO_3) with calcium carbonate ($CaCO_3$) to form calcium nitrate, water and carbon dioxide gas.

The student carries out the reaction twice, using different quantities of reactants each time. Reaction **X** used 0.50 g of calcium carbonate and an excess of 0.10 g/dm³ nitric acid. Which of the sets of conditions below could have resulted in reaction **Y**?

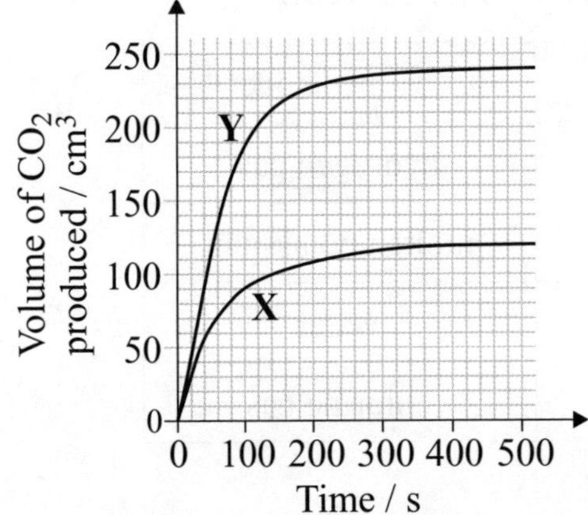

	Mass of $CaCO_3$ / g	Concentration of HNO_3 / g/dm³
A ○	0.25	0.01
B ○	1.00	0.10
C ○	0.25	0.20
D ○	1.00	0.01

18 A student investigated the rate of a reaction between marble chips and hydrochloric acid (HCl). The graph below shows the mass of the reaction mixture lost over time for two different reactions, between which only the concentration of hydrochloric acid was varied.

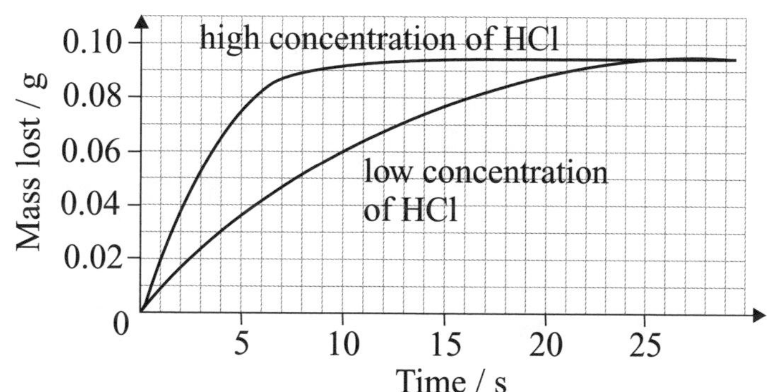

Which of the following options represents a valid conclusion that can be drawn from the graph about the reaction between hydrochloric acid and marble chips?

A The reaction rate depends on the temperature of the reactants.

B Increasing the concentration of the acid has no effect on the rate of reaction.

C The reaction rate depends on the acid concentration.

D The reaction rate depends on the mass of the marble chips used.

19 Which of the following equations shows a neutralisation reaction?

A $HNO_3 + LiOH \rightarrow LiNO_3 + H_2O$

B $Mg + H_2O \rightarrow MgO + H_2$

C $Na_2O + H_2O \rightarrow 2NaOH$

D $C_4H_{10} + 6\frac{1}{2}O_2 \rightarrow 4CO_2 + 5H_2O$

20 A student allows a metal carbonate and an acid to react together in a flask. The experiment is shown in the diagram below.

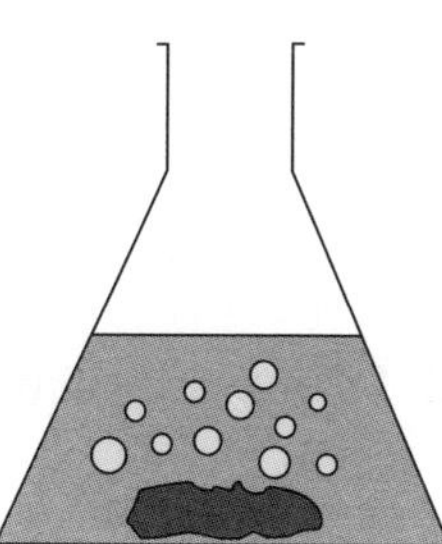

Which of the following chemicals is **not** produced?

A carbon dioxide

B a salt

C water

D hydrogen

21 A student was analysing a solution containing a mystery metal ion.
The student added a few drops of sodium hydroxide and a green precipitate formed.
The precipitate redissolved in excess sodium hydroxide to form a green solution.

What metal ion would you expect to be in the solution?

A zinc(II) ○
B chromium(III) ○
C copper(II) ○
D iron(II) ○

22 The table below shows some of the physical properties of the first metals in Group I.

Metal	Atomic number	Melting Point / °C	Boiling Point / °C
Lithium	3	181	1342
Sodium	11		883
Potassium	19	63	759
Rubidium	37	39	688

Which of the following options is most likely to be the melting point of sodium?

A 272 °C ○
B 20 °C ○
C 98 °C ○
D 61 °C ○

23 Which of these properties is associated with Group VII elements?

A solid at room temperature ○
B diatomic ○
C high melting point ○
D unreactive ○

24 The table below shows the colour changes associated with several halogen displacement reactions.

Start with:	Potassium chloride solution (KCl)	Potassium bromide solution (KBr)	Potassium iodide solution (KI)
Add chlorine water (Cl_2)	**A**	**B**	brown solution (I_2) formed
Add bromine water (Br_2)	no reaction	no reaction	**C**
Add iodine water (I_2)	**D**	no reaction	no reaction

Which reaction would result in an orange solution being formed?

A ⬭
B ⬭
C ⬭
D ⬭

25 Which of these statements is **true** for the noble gases?

A They can be used as fuels. ⬭
B They have only 1 electron in their outer shells. ⬭
C They are monatomic. ⬭
D They react with alkali metals to form salts. ⬭

26 The structure of bronze can be represented by the diagram below.

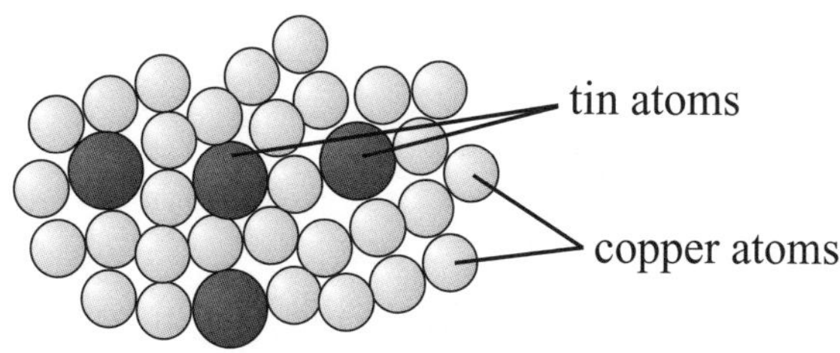

Which of the following statements could be made about bronze?

1. Bronze is more malleable than copper.
2. Bronze can conduct electricity.
3. Bronze is stronger than both tin and copper.

A 2 and 3 ⬭
B 1 and 2 ⬭
C 1, 2 and 3 ⬭
D 1 and 3 ⬭

27 Iron is extracted from its ore, hematite, in a blast furnace.
Which of these shows the correct balanced equation for the extraction of iron from hematite?

A $Fe_2O_3 + 4C \rightarrow 3Fe + 3CO_2$ ○
B $2FeCO_3 + C \rightarrow 2Fe + 3CO_2$ ○
C $FeO_3 + CO_2 \rightarrow 2Fe + CO_2$ ○
D $Fe_2O_3 + 3C \rightarrow 2Fe + 3CO$ ○

28 The table below shows some properties of four different metals.
Which row contains two properties of copper?

	Property 1	Property 2
A ○	Good thermal conductivity	Highly reactive
B ○	Resistant to corrosion	Low electrical conductivity
C ○	Low density	Hard
D ○	Good electrical conductivity	Malleable

29 Fresh water can come from a variety of different sources and is used for drinking, domestic use and industrial processes. Which of the following statements is **incorrect**?

A Water can be used as a cheap raw material in industry. ○
B Rivers are a source of fresh water. ○
C Filtration of water removes bacteria. ○
D Water can be used as a coolant for industrial processes. ○

30 Carbon monoxide is a gas that is toxic to humans.
How is carbon monoxide produced?

A By incomplete combustion in car engines. ○
B By complete combustion in car engines. ○
C By nitrogen and oxygen reacting together due to the heat of combustion reactions. ○
D By reactions between solid carbon and oxygen in car engines. ○

31 Iron pipes need protection from rusting.
What type of reaction is rusting?

A distillation ○
B electrolysis ○
C oxidation ○
D reduction ○

32 Sulfur dioxide (SO_2) has a range of industrial and domestic uses.
Which of the options below are common uses of sulfur dioxide?

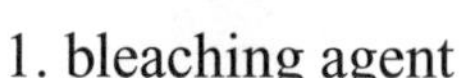

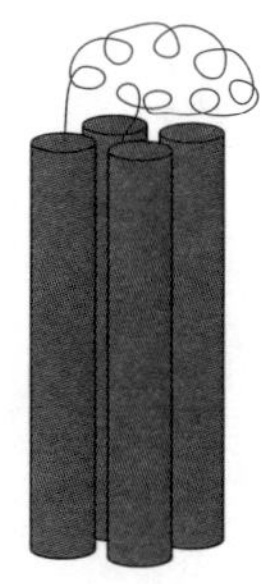

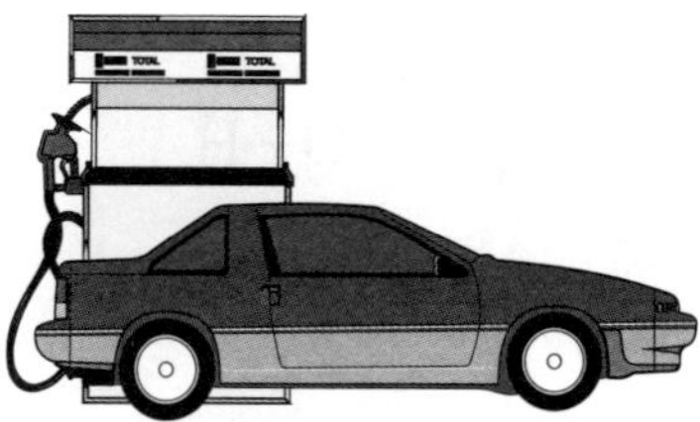

1. bleaching agent 2. explosives 3. food preservatives 4. fuel for cars

A 2 and 4 ⬭
B 3 and 4 ⬭
C 1 and 2 ⬭
D 1 and 3 ⬭

33 Calcium oxide reacts with water to give slaked lime, $Ca(OH)_2$:

$$CaO + H_2O \rightarrow Ca(OH)_2$$

What could be the pH of a solution of slaked lime?

A 12 ⬭
B 7 ⬭
C 5 ⬭
D 1 ⬭

34 Fractional distillation separates petroleum into fractions.
Which of the following fractions is extracted above gasoline in the fractionating column?

A Fuel oil ⬭
B Refinery gas ⬭
C Bitumen ⬭
D Naphtha ⬭

35 The table below shows the number of carbon atoms in four compounds that can be found in petroleum.

Which of the compounds would you expect to condense highest up a fractional distillation column?

	Name of compound	Number of carbon atoms
A ⬭	Lubricating oil	40
B ⬭	Gasoline	7
C ⬭	Diesel oil	20
D ⬭	Kerosene	16

Turn over ▶

36 Long-chain hydrocarbons can be processed to form short-chain hydrocarbons through cracking. Heptane (C_7H_{16}) can be cracked to form pentane (C_5H_{12}) and which of these molecules?

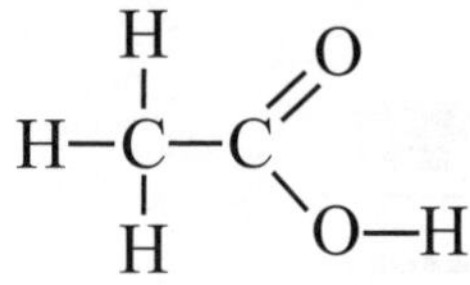

A ○

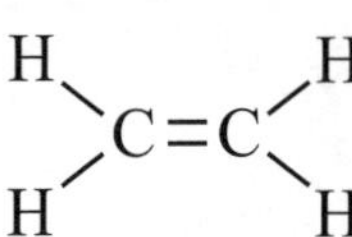

B ○

```
 H H
 | |
H−C−C−H
 | |
 H H
```

C ○

```
 H
 |
H−C−H
 |
 H
```

D ○

37 Which of the statements about poly(ethene) below is **true**?

A The monomer of poly(ethene) is ethene. ○
B The polymer of poly(ethene) is ethane. ○
C The monomer of poly(ethene) is ethane. ○
D The polymer of poly(ethene) is ethene. ○

38 Ethanol (C_2H_5OH) is an alcohol. It can be made by the fermentation of glucose ($C_6H_{12}O_6$). What is used in the fermentation process to convert glucose to ethanol?

A yeast ○
B ethanoic acid ○
C an oxidising agent ○
D oxygen ○

39 Which of these statements about plastic pollution is **false**?

A Burning plastics releases toxic gases such as HCl and CO_2. ○
B Addition polymers are non-biodegradable. ○
C Addition polymers contain very strong carbon-carbon bonds. ○
D It is easy and cheap to separate polymers for recycling. ○

40 Which of these substances is a synthetic polymer used to make clothing?

A nylon ○
B poly(ethene) ○
C bitumen ○
D naphtha ○

END OF QUESTIONS

Cambridge International GCSE Chemistry

Paper 2 Multiple Choice (Extended)

In addition to this paper you should have:
- A soft pencil and eraser.
- A calculator.
- A Periodic Table

Centre name					
Centre number					
Candidate number					

Time allowed:
- 45 minutes

Candidate name
Candidate signature

Instructions to candidates
- Write your name and other details in the spaces provided above.
- Use pencil to record your answers.
- For each question, clearly shade the oval next to your chosen answer. For example: ⬬
  If you wish to change your answer, use an eraser to remove your original answer.
- Do all rough work on the paper.

Information for candidates
- There are 40 marks available for this paper.
- Each question is worth one mark.

1 When a liquid becomes a gas, the particles ..... **1** ..... and move ..... **2** ..... .
Which pair of statements correctly completes the sentence above?

	1	**2**
A ⬭	lose energy	closer together
B ⬭	gain energy	further apart
C ⬭	lose energy	further apart
D ⬭	gain energy	closer together

2 A student is carrying out analysis on several dyes using chromatography.
His chromatogram is shown below.

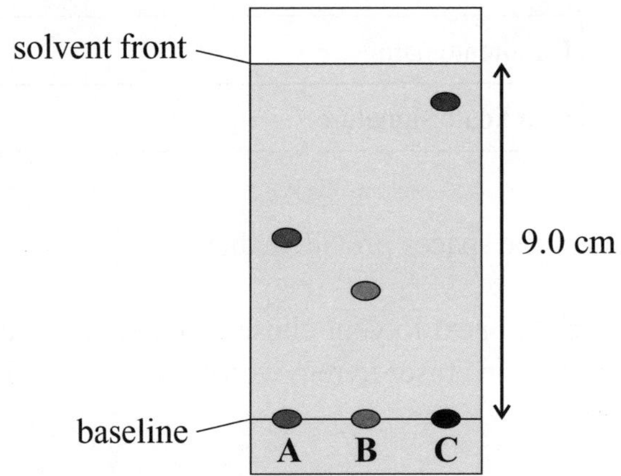

Dye **A** travelled 4.7 cm along the chromatogram.
What is the R_f value of Dye **A**?

A 0.52 ⬭
B 1.90 ⬭
C 0.43 ⬭
D 0.03 ⬭

3 The table below contains boiling point data for three common organic compounds.

Name	Boiling point / °C
methanol	65
hexane	69
propanone	56

A mixture of these compounds is separated by fractional distillation.
Which of the following statements is **true**?

A Propanone evaporates first and methanol evaporates last. ⬭
B Methanol evaporates first and hexane evaporates last. ⬭
C Hexane evaporates first and methanol evaporates last. ⬭
D Propanone evaporates first and hexane evaporates last. ⬭

4 Atoms contain protons, neutrons and electrons.
Where are each of these particles found?

	protons	neutrons	electrons
A ⬭	nucleus	shells	shells
B ⬭	nucleus	nucleus	nucleus
C ⬭	nucleus	nucleus	shells
D ⬭	shells	shells	nucleus

5 Some data about subatomic particles is shown in the table below.

Particle	Relative charge	Relative mass
x	+1	1
y	0	1
z	−1	0.0005

What is the correct identity of each particle?

	x	y	z
A ⬭	neutron	proton	electron
B ⬭	proton	neutron	electron
C ⬭	electron	neutron	proton
D ⬭	proton	electron	neutron

6 Potassium has 19 electrons. What is its electronic structure?

A 2, 8, 8, 1 ⬭
B 2, 8, 8 ⬭
C 8, 8, 2, 1 ⬭
D 2, 8, 8, 2 ⬭

7 Methane and water are both simple molecular compounds.
The table below shows their melting and boiling points.

Name	Melting point / °C	Boiling point / °C
Methane	–182	–161
Water	0	100

Based on this information, which compound has the stronger forces of attraction between molecules?

A methane ⬭
B water ⬭
C both the same strength ⬭
D can't tell from this information ⬭

8 Which of the following terms can be used to describe the electrons in metallic bonding?

A delocalised ⬭
B ionic ⬭
C covalent ⬭
D basic ⬭

9 A sodium ion has the formula Na^+. A phosphate ion has the formula PO_4^{3-}.
What is the formula of sodium phosphate?

A $NaPO_4$ ⬭
B Na_3PO ⬭
C $Na(PO_4)_3$ ⬭
D Na_3PO_4 ⬭

10 216 g of impure zinc oxide (ZnO) gives 130 g of zinc when heated with carbon.
What is the percentage purity of the zinc oxide?

A 25% ⬭
B 50% ⬭
C 75% ⬭
D 100% ⬭

11 A student dissolves 36.0 g of sodium chloride (NaCl) in water to make 400 cm^3 of solution.
What is the concentration of the solution?

A 31.5 mol/dm^3 ⬭
B 90 mol/dm^3 ⬭
C 0.0154 mol/dm^3 ⬭
D 1.54 mol/dm^3 ⬭

12 A concentrated aqueous solution of magnesium chloride is electrolysed using inert electrodes. What is produced at each electrode?

	Anode	Cathode
A ⬭	magnesium	oxygen gas
B ⬭	magnesium	chlorine gas
C ⬭	hydrogen gas	oxygen gas
D ⬭	hydrogen gas	chlorine gas

13 Which of these diagrams shows a correctly labelled representation of the reaction below?

$$C{\equiv}O + H\text{–}O\text{–}H \rightarrow O{=}C{=}O + H\text{–}H$$

$C{\equiv}O = 1072$ kJ/mol O–H = 459 kJ/mol C=O = 800 kJ/mol H–H = 436 kJ/mol

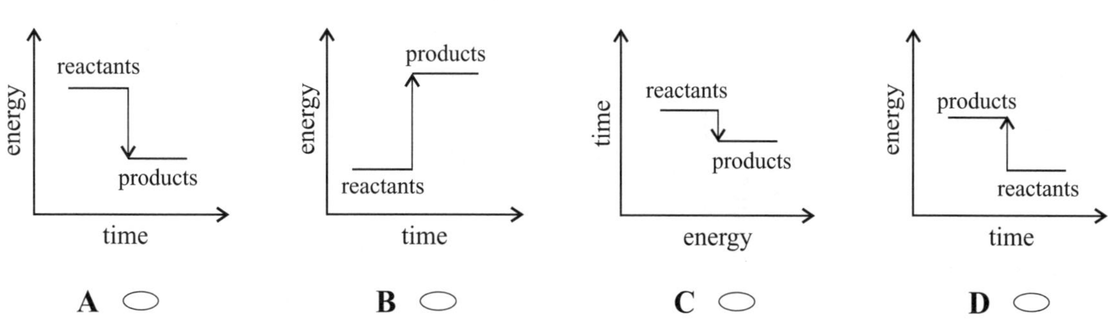

A ⬭ **B** ⬭ **C** ⬭ **D** ⬭

14 The diagram below shows a simplified fuel cell.

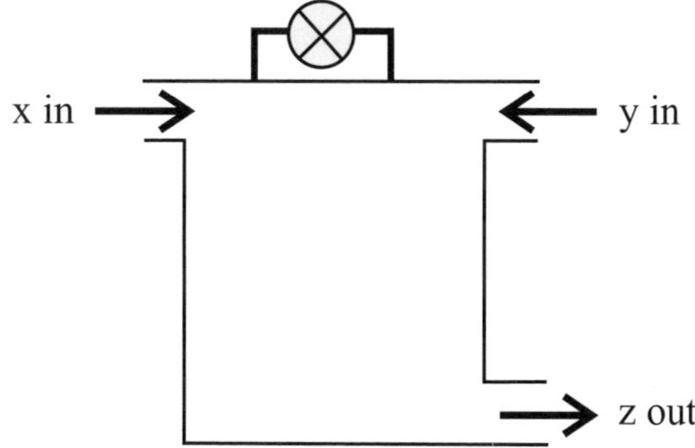

What are the reactants and products used in this fuel cell?

	x	y	z
A ⬭	oxygen	water	hydrogen
B ⬭	hydrogen	water	oxygen
C ⬭	water	hydrogen	oxygen
D ⬭	hydrogen	oxygen	water

15 Adding zinc metal to hydrochloric acid causes bubbles to form as hydrogen gas is released:

$$Zn + 2HCl \rightarrow ZnCl_2 + H_2$$

In the reaction above, which species is oxidised and which species is reduced?

	Oxidised	Reduced
A ⬭	hydrogen	zinc
B ⬭	zinc	hydrogen
C ⬭	zinc	chlorine
D ⬭	chlorinc	hydrogen

16 Photosynthesis is a photochemical reaction that produces glucose and oxygen.

$$6CO_2 + 6H_2O \rightarrow C_6H_{12}O_6 + 6O_2$$

The graph below shows the amount of oxygen produced over time in an experiment under constant conditions.

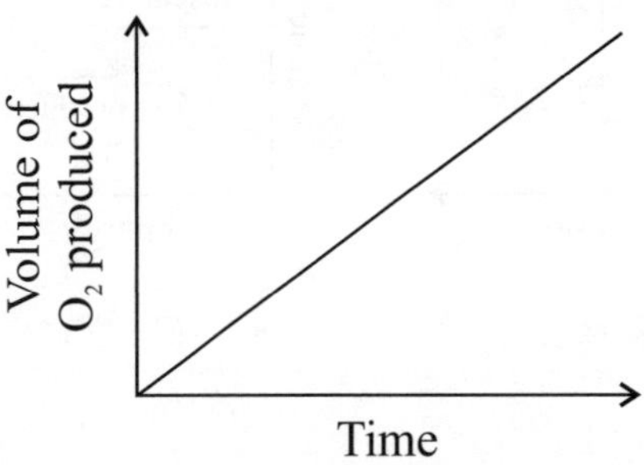

What would be the effect on the graph if the intensity of the light was increased?

A The gradient would increase. ⬭
B The gradient would decrease. ⬭
C There would be no change to the gradient. ⬭
D The graph line would go flat. ⬭

17 Nitrogen dioxide forms an equilibrium mixture with dinitrogen tetroxide in the following reaction: $2NO_{2(g)} \rightleftharpoons N_2O_{4(g)}$. The forward reaction is exothermic.
Which of the following conditions would result in the greatest shift of the equilibrium to the left?

	Temperature	Pressure
A ⬭	high	high
B ⬭	high	low
C ⬭	low	high
D ⬭	low	low

18 Insoluble salts can be made by precipitation reactions.
The table below can be used to work out the solubility of some metal salts.

	carbonate	chloride	nitrate
sodium	soluble	soluble	soluble
potassium	soluble	soluble	soluble
lead	insoluble	insoluble	soluble

Which of the following equations describes a precipitation reaction?

A $KOH + CO_2 \rightarrow K_2CO_3 + H_2O$ ⬭
B $KCl + NaNO_3 \rightarrow NaCl + KNO_3$ ⬭
C $2HCl + Na_2CO_3 \rightarrow 2NaCl + H_2O + CO_2$ ⬭
D $Pb(NO_3)_2 + 2NaCl \rightarrow PbCl_2 + 2NaNO_3$ ⬭

19 The following steps describe how you would produce a pure sample of magnesium sulfate, $MgSO_4$, from solid magnesium hydroxide (an insoluble salt) and sulfuric acid.
The steps are not in the correct order.

1 Gently heat the solution over a Bunsen burner to evaporate off some of the water.
2 Filter the solid off and leave it to dry.
3 Filter out the excess solid using a filter funnel and filter paper.
4 Add magnesium hydroxide to a flask containing sulfuric acid until no more of the magnesium hydroxide reacts.
5 Leave the solution to cool and crystallise.

Which is the correct order that these steps should be carried out in?

A 4, 1, 3, 2, 5 ⬭
B 1, 4, 2, 5, 2 ⬭
C 4, 3, 1, 5, 2 ⬭
D 3, 1, 2, 5, 4 ⬭

20 Which row contains the correct colours of the precipitates that form when aqueous sodium hydroxide is added to certain metal ions?

	Zn^{2+}	Fe^{2+}	Cu^{2+}
A ⬭	white	light blue	green
B ⬭	white	green	light blue
C ⬭	green	white	light blue
D ⬭	light blue	green	white

21 Which of these elements has the strongest metallic character?

A aluminium ⬭
B calcium ⬭
C iodine ⬭
D xenon ⬭

22 The table below gives melting and boiling point data for the first three Group VI elements.

Element	Melting point / °C	Boiling point / °C
oxygen	–218	–183
sulfur	115	445
selenium	221	685

What trends can you identify in the physical properties of Group VI elements?

	Melting point	Boiling point
A ⬭	decreases down the group	decreases down the group
B ⬭	increases down the group	increases down the group
C ⬭	increases down the group	doesn't change
D ⬭	no trend	no trend

23 The transition metals are metallic elements located in the centre of the periodic table.

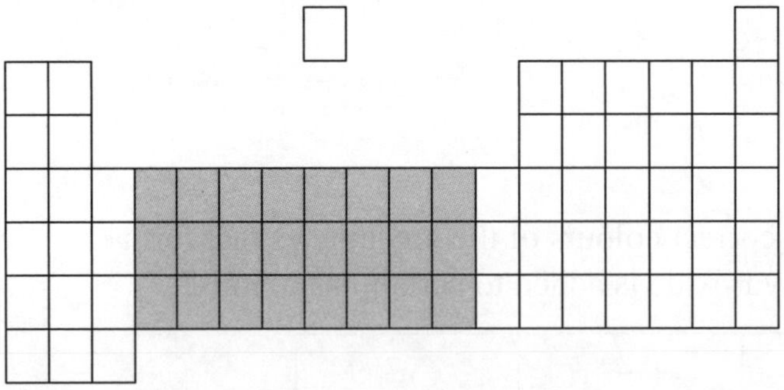

Which of these statements is **true** for transition metals but **not true** for all metals?

A They can exist in multiple oxidation states. ⬭
B Their ions only form colourless compounds. ⬭
C Most have high melting points. ⬭
D They are good electrical and thermal conductors. ⬭

24 Which of the following statements about Group VIII elements is **true**?

A Group VIII elements are reactive because they gain electrons easily.
B Group VIII elements only react with other Group VIII elements.
C Group VIII elements are inert because they don't gain or lose electrons easily.
D All Group VIII elements exist as diatomic gases.

25 Which of the statements below about metal reactivity is **incorrect**?

A The easier it is for a metal atom to form a positive ion, the less reactive it will be.
B A metal will displace a less reactive metal from a metal oxide.
C In a reactivity series, you will find a reactive metal above a less reactive metal.
D The more reactive a metal is, the faster its reaction with dilute acid will be.

26 A student is testing the reactivity of three metals, **X**, **Y** and **Z**.
According to the reactivity series, metal **Z** should be the most reactive.
However, metals **X** and **Y** appear to react more readily than **Z**.
What could be the identity of metal **Z**?

A potassium
B sodium
C iron
D aluminium

27 A student is asked to work out the equations for the extraction of aluminium from bauxite.
The student's answers are:

Cathode half-equation	$Al^{3+} + 3e^- \rightarrow Al$
Anode half-equation	$2O^{2-} \rightarrow O_2 + 2e^-$
Overall equation	$2Al_2O_{3(l)} \rightarrow 4Al_{(l)} + 3O_{2(g)}$

What error has the student made?

A The overall equation is not balanced.
B Aluminium does not form at the cathode.
C There should be 4 electrons produced in the anode half-equation.
D Oxygen exists as O^{3-} ions.

28 Which gas can be used to treat water to make it safe to drink?

A sulfur dioxide ○
B carbon monoxide ○
C chlorine ○
D carbon dioxide ○

29 Which of the following methods is the **best** method to use to prevent an iron bike chain from rusting?

A Painting ○
B Oiling ○
C Tin plating ○
D Galvanisation ○

30 In the Haber process, hydrogen and nitrogen gas are passed over iron to produce liquid ammonia. What would be the effect on the reaction rate and percentage yield if iron was removed from the reaction?

	Rate	Percentage Yield
A ○	would decrease	would decrease
B ○	would increase	would decrease
C ○	would decrease	no effect
D ○	would increase	no effect

31 A fertiliser manufacturer uses the Contact process to produce sulfuric acid. The second step of the Contact process involves the oxidation of sulfur dioxide, which is an exothermic process.

$$2SO_2 + O_2 \rightleftharpoons 2SO_3$$

The company must maintain suitable conditions for this reaction to be economical. Which statement below is **false**?

A Higher pressures will increase the yield of SO_3. ○
B Lower pressures are cheaper to maintain. ○
C High pressures will increase the rate of reaction. ○
D Using lower temperatures increases the reaction rate. ○

32 Which compound below completes the equation for the thermal decomposition of calcium carbonate to produce lime?

$$CaCO_{3(s)} \rightarrow CaO_{(s)} + \text{..........}$$

A Water

B Methane

C Sulfur dioxide

D Carbon dioxide

33 What is the general formula of the alkanes?

A C_nH_{2n}

B C_nH_{2n+1}

C C_nH_{2n+2}

D C_nH_{2n-1}

34 Three of the following structures belong to the same homologous series. Which structure belongs to a different homologous series?

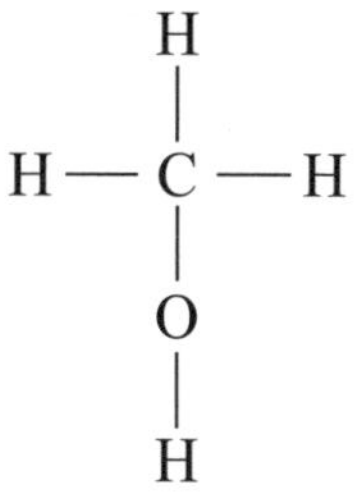

A 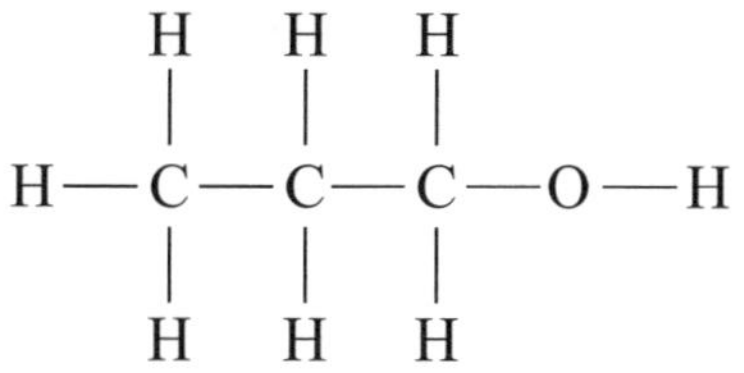 **B** 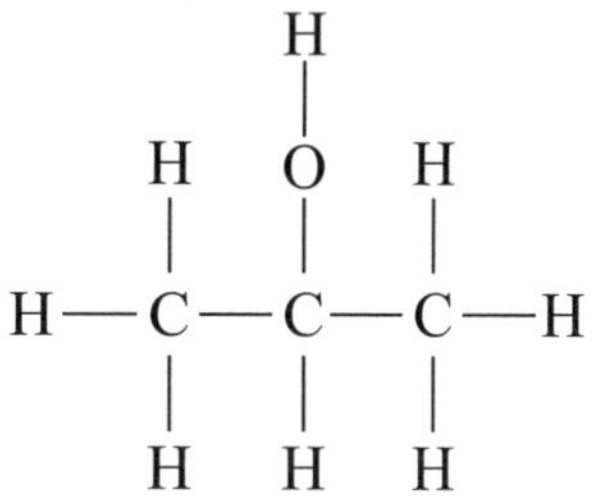 **C** 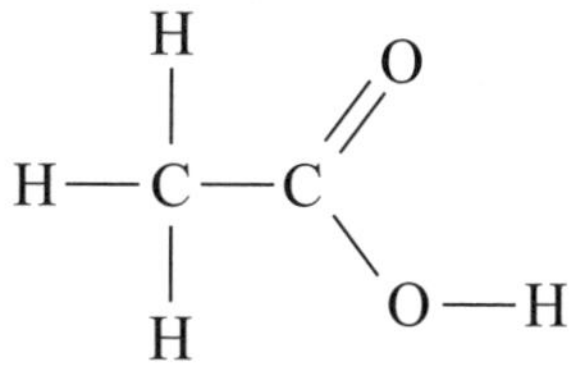 **D**

35 Which of the following molecules is **not** an isomer of the other three?

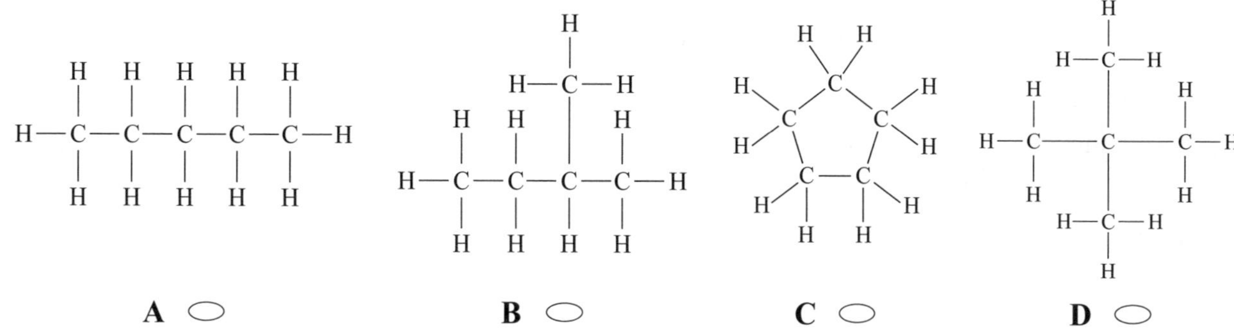

A **B** **C** **D**

36 Chlorine can react with ethane in the presence of ultraviolet light in the following reaction:

$$Cl_2 + C_2H_6 \rightarrow C_2H_5Cl + HCl$$

What name is given to this type of reaction?

A substitution

B oxidation

C combustion

D hydrogenation

37 Cracking breaks down the products of fractional distillation into smaller molecules.
The reaction below is an example of cracking.

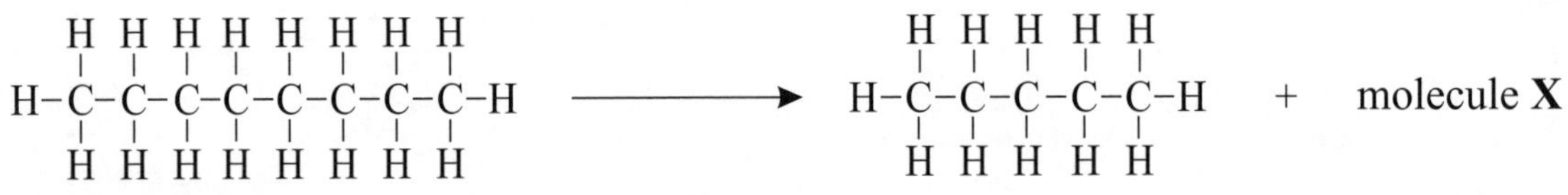

```
  H H H H H H H H                H H H H H
  | | | | | | | |                | | | | |
H-C-C-C-C-C-C-C-C-H  ------->  H-C-C-C-C-C-H   +   molecule X
  | | | | | | | |                | | | | |
  H H H H H H H H                H H H H H
```

Which of the following is the chemical name given to molecule **X**?

A propene

B propane

C butane

D ethene

38 A student is testing a mystery organic compound to find out what homologous series it belongs to.
Some of her findings are listed below:

- The compound is soluble in water.
- Its aqueous solution is pH 3.
- It reacts with ethanol to form an ester.

Which homologous series does the mystery compound belong to?

A alkene

B alkane

C carboxylic acid

D alcohol

39 Nylon is a common synthetic polymer.
What element can be placed in the circles to complete the structure of nylon?

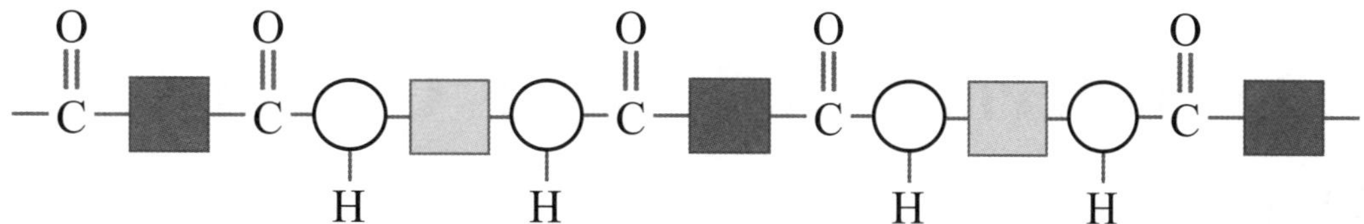

A carbon, C ⬭
B oxygen, O ⬭
C potassium, K ⬭
D nitrogen, N ⬭

40 Proteins can be broken down into their amino acid monomers by hydrolysis.
Which of the following statements accurately describes protein hydrolysis?

A The amide bond is heated until it breaks apart. ⬭
B The amide bond is broken apart by the addition of water. ⬭
C Electricity is used to break the amide bond. ⬭
D The amide bond is broken apart by the addition of methane. ⬭

END OF QUESTIONS

Cambridge International GCSE Chemistry

Paper 3 Theory (Core)

In addition to this paper you should have:
- A pen and pencil.
- A ruler.
- A calculator.
- A Periodic Table

Centre name					
Centre number					
Candidate number					

Time allowed:
- 1 hour 15 minutes

Candidate name	
Candidate signature	

Instructions to candidates
- Write your name and other details in the spaces provided above.
- Use blue or black ink to write your answers.
- Answer all questions in the spaces provided.
- Do all rough work on the paper.
- Cross out any work you do not want to be marked.
- In calculations, show clearly how you worked out your answers.

Information for candidates
- The marks available are given in brackets at the end of each question part.
- There are 80 marks available for this paper.

1 Atoms contain protons, neutrons and electrons.

(a) The following table shows the numbers of protons, neutrons and electrons present in six different atoms.

Atom	Number of protons	Number of neutrons	Number of electrons
A	5	6	5
B	7	7	7
C	6	8	6
D	6	6	6
E	10	10	10
F	4	5	4

Which **two** atoms are isotopes of the same element? Explain your answer.

....

....

....

[2]

(b) The nuclear symbol for an atom of selenium is shown below.

$$^{34}_{79}\mathrm{Se}$$

(i) How many protons and neutrons are there in this atom of selenium?

Protons = ...

Neutrons = ...

[2]

(ii) State the nucleon number of a selenium atom.

....

[1]

(iii) Draw the outer electron shell of a selenium atom.

[1]

(c) Atoms can bond with each other to form compounds.

(i) What is a compound?

....

....

[2]

(ii) Iron(II) sulfate is a compound with the formula $FeSO_4$.

Calculate the relative formula mass of iron(II) sulfate.

relative formula mass = ...

[2]

[Total 10 marks]

2 Petroleum can be split up into fractions using a fractionating column.
A diagram of a fractionating column is shown below.

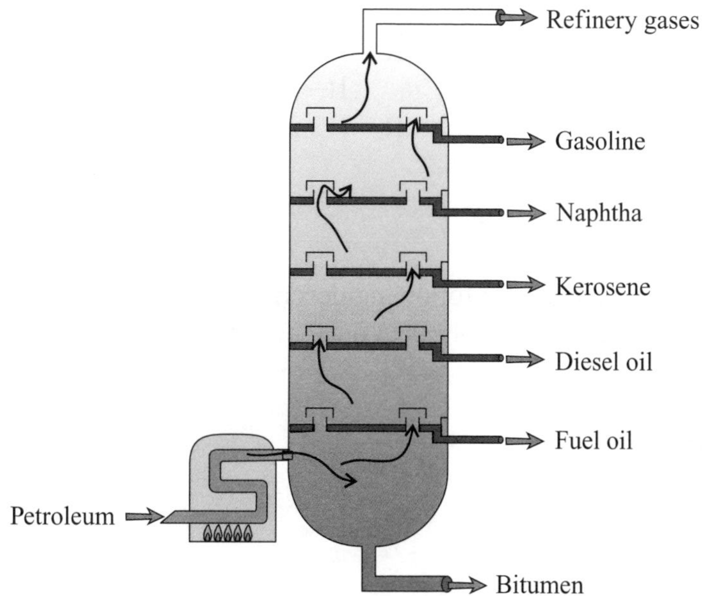

(a) Complete the following passage by choosing the correct words from the list.

condense	**distillation**	**increases**
evaporates	**decreases**	**freeze**

Petroleum is piped in at the bottom of the column.

The petroleum .... and rises up the column.

The temperature .... as you go up the column.

The various fractions .... at different levels.

[3]

(b) Name the process by which petroleum is separated into different fractions.

....

[1]

(c) A student has samples of two different fractions labelled **X** and **Y**.
One of the samples is gasoline and the other is diesel oil.

Fraction **X** has a boiling point of 40 °C.
Fraction **Y** has a boiling point of 250 °C.

Which fraction, **X** or **Y**, is gasoline?
Explain your answer.

....

....

....

[2]

Turn over ▶

(d) Below are 5 organic molecules, **A**–**E**.

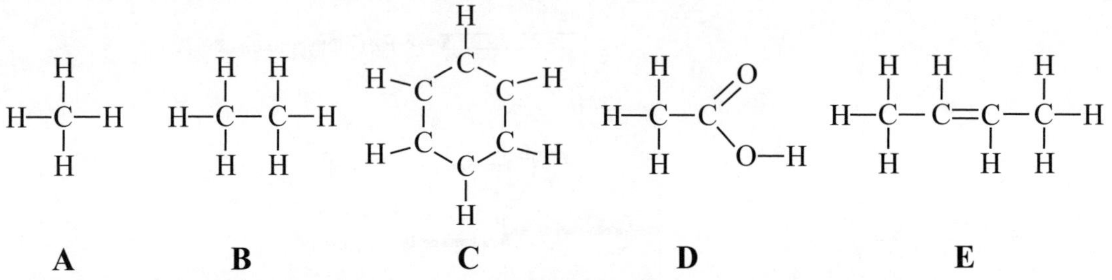

Choose a molecule that matches the following descriptions.
Each molecule may be used once, more than once or not at all.

Which molecule:

(i) is not a hydrocarbon, ...

[1]

(ii) is a saturated hydrocarbon, ...

[1]

(iii) is in the same homologous series as ethene, ...

[1]

(iv) is the main constituent of natural gas, ...

[1]

(v) has the formula C_6H_6? ....

[1]

(e) Cracking is used to break down long-chain alkanes into shorter alkanes, alkenes and hydrogen.

State the conditions required for cracking.

....

....

[2]

[Total 13 marks]

3 When fuels undergo combustion in engines, they release pollutants such as sulfur dioxide.

(a) Some data about the properties of sulfur dioxide is shown in the table below.

Melting point	Boiling point
−73 °C	−10 °C

(i) Predict the physical state of sulfur dioxide at −32 °C.

....

[1]

(ii) Describe the similarities and differences between the separation, arrangement and types of motion of the particles in liquid and gaseous sulfur dioxide.

....

....

....

....

....

[4]

(b) Combustion of fuels also releases carbon dioxide.

(i) Describe a way a chemist could test for carbon dioxide.

Test: ....

Result: ....

[2]

(ii) Give another source of carbon dioxide.

....

[1]

(c) The table below shows the concentration of pollutants in two cities, **A** and **B**.

City	Concentration of Pollutants (μg/m³)			
	Nitrogen dioxide	Carbon monoxide	Lead compounds	Sulfur dioxide
A	13.2	3023.6	0.4	8.9
B	306.4	8284.5	0.1	68.2

(i) In one city, hospitals have reported a number of patients with breathing difficulties and headaches after spending time in polluted areas.
Suggest which city this has happened in.
Explain your answer and suggest a reason for the difference between the two cities.

....

....

....
[2]

(ii) Give **one** risk to human health associated with carbon monoxide.

....
[1]

(iii) Limestone buildings in one of the cities have become damaged as a result of chemical weathering.
Which of the cities, **A** or **B**, is this likely to have occurred in?
Explain your answer using evidence from the table.

....

....

....
[2]

(d) Many people are now looking for greener alternatives to fossil fuels.
Which of the substances below could be used as a fuel?
Circle the correct answer.

Carbon dioxide (CO_2) **Hydrogen (H_2)** **Sulfur dioxide (SO_2)** **Water (H_2O)**

[1]
[Total 14 marks]

4 The dehydration of hydrated copper(II) sulfate is a reversible reaction.

$$CuSO_4{\bullet}5H_2O \rightleftharpoons CuSO_4 + 5H_2O$$

(a) Which direction will the reaction favour if heat is applied to the reaction?

....

[1]

(b) Copper(II) sulfate can be used as a chemical test for water.
Describe the colour change when water is added to anhydrous copper(II) sulfate.

....

[1]

(c) At a particular temperature, 8.4 g of $CuSO_4$ are produced from this dehydration reaction.
What mass of $CuSO_4{\bullet}5H_2O$ is required to produce this quantity of $CuSO_4$?

mass of $CuSO_4{\bullet}5H_2O$ = ...

[3]

(d) A student is using copper(II) sulfate to electroplate a fork.

(i) Suggest which electrode the fork should be used as.

....

[1]

(ii) Why is copper used for electroplating?

....

....

[2]

[Total 8 marks]

5 Aluminium can be obtained by electrolysis of its ore.
The overall equation for this reaction is:

$$2Al_2O_3 \rightarrow 4Al + 3O_2$$

(a) Is aluminium being oxidised or reduced in this reaction?
Explain your answer.

....

....

[1]

(b) Name the ore used as a source of aluminium in this process.

....

[1]

(c) Suggest which electrode the aluminium forms at.

....

[1]

(d) Give **two** advantages of recycling aluminium.

1. ....

....

....

2. ....

....

....

[2]

(e) Aluminium has a variety of useful chemical and physical properties.
Give a property of aluminium that makes it suitable for the manufacture of aircraft.

....

[1]

(f) A student reacts a small piece of aluminium in a test tube with dilute sulfuric acid and reports hearing a loud squeaky pop when holding a lighted splint over the test tube.

(i) What gas is responsible for this noise?

....

[1]

(ii) Sulfuric acid is manufactured from elemental sulfur.
Give a source of sulfur.

....

[1]

[Total 8 marks]

6 The table below shows some of the properties of four common metals.

Metal	Melting point (°C)	Density (g/cm^3)	Effect of heating in air	Ions formed
Magnesium	650	1.74	Burns very brightly	Mg^{2+}
Iron	1535	7.87	Produces sparks if powdered	Fe^{2+}, Fe^{3+}
Chromium	1860	7.19	Little reaction	Cr^{2+}, Cr^{3+}
Sodium	98	0.97	Burns very brightly	Na^+

(a) The properties of iron and chromium are typical of transition metals.
The properties of magnesium and sodium are typical of Group I and II metals.
Using the information in the table, suggest **three** differences between transition metals and the metals in Groups I and II.

1. ....

2. ....

3. ....
[3]

(b) Give **two** further properties that make transition metals different from other metals.

1. ....

2. ....
[2]

(c) A scientist adds each of the metals listed in the table to cold water. Only sodium reacts.
Use this information and the table above to order the metals from the most to least reactive.

Most reactive: ....

....

....

Least reactive: ....

[2]

(d) When a small piece of sodium is added to water, it fizzes around on the surface before dissolving to form a colourless solution.

(i) Complete the word equation for this reaction.

sodium + water → .... + ...

[2]

(ii) At the end of the reaction, the solution is tested with Universal indicator.
The solution turns purple.
What does this tell you about the solution?

....

[1]

(iii) Rubidium is lower than sodium in Group I of the periodic table.
Predict how the reaction of rubidium with water would differ from the reaction of sodium with water.

....

....

....

[1]

[Total 11 marks]

7 A scientist is investigating the composition of an ink.
The ink is made up of a solvent and a mixture of dyes.
The boiling points of the possible solvents are shown in the table.

Solvent	Boiling point (°C)
Toluene	111
Butanol	118
DMF	153

(a) Outline a method that the scientist could use to identify the solvent.

....

....

....
[2]

The scientist carries out paper chromatography on the ink and some reference dyes.
All the possible dyes that could be in the ink are used as reference dyes.
The chromatogram produced during the experiment is shown below.

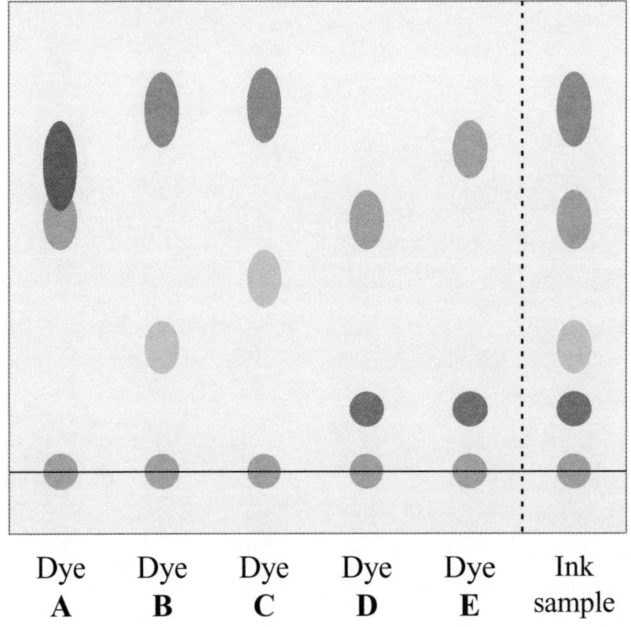

(b) The scientist says that dyes B and E are present in the ink.
Is the scientist correct?
Explain your answer.

....

....

....
[2]

[Total 4 marks]

8 Ethanol (C_2H_5OH) is an alcohol.
It can be made by the fermentation of glucose ($C_6H_{12}O_6$) using yeast.

(a) (i) Complete the symbol equation for the production of ethanol by fermentation.

$$C_6H_{12}O_6 \rightarrow \text{...........}\ C_2H_5OH + 2\ \text{...........}$$

[2]

(ii) Fermentation is carried out at 30 °C.
Explain why the reaction isn't carried out at a higher temperature.

....

....

....

[2]

(iii) Ethanol is one of the main components of wine.
The table below gives the percentage of each of the components that make up a bottle of wine.

Component	Percentage (%)
water	86
ethanol	....
glycerol	1
organic acids	0.5
volatile compounds	0.5

Complete the table by calculating the percentage of ethanol.

[1]

(b) Fractional distillation can be used to concentrate the dilute ethanol solution produced by fermentation. This involves heating the fermentation mixture to 78 °C so that the ethanol evaporates.

A student suggests that to speed up this process, the fermentation mixture should be heated to 100 °C. Explain why this won't lead to the collection of concentrated ethanol.

....

....

....

....

[3]

(c) Burning ethanol in excess oxygen produces carbon dioxide and one other product.
Name the other product of the complete combustion of ethanol.

....

[1]

Turn over ▶

(d) Ethanol can be oxidised to form ethanoic acid.

(i) Name the homologous series that ethanoic acid belongs to.

....

[1]

(ii) Draw the structure of ethanoic acid.

[1]

(iii) Ethanoic acid can undergo a reaction with metal carbonates.
State the expected observation when sodium carbonate breaks down in ethanoic acid.

....

[1]

[Total 12 marks]

END OF QUESTIONS

Cambridge International GCSE Chemistry

Paper 4 Theory (Extended)

In addition to this paper you should have:
- A pen and pencil.
- A ruler.
- A calculator.
- A Periodic Table

Centre name					
Centre number					
Candidate number					

Time allowed:
- 1 hour 15 minutes

Candidate name
Candidate signature

Instructions to candidates
- Write your name and other details in the spaces provided above.
- Use blue or black ink to write your answers.
- Answer all questions in the spaces provided.
- Do all rough work on the paper.
- Cross out any work you do not want to be marked.
- In calculations, show clearly how you worked out your answers.

Information for candidates
- The marks available are given in brackets at the end of each question part.
- There are 80 marks available for this paper.

1 The structure and bonding of elements and compounds affects their properties.

(a) Sodium and chlorine can react together to form an ionic compound (sodium chloride).
Write out the electronic structure for a sodium ion and a chloride ion.

sodium ion: ....

chloride ion: ....

[2]

(b) Describe the structure of sodium chloride.
Include a description of the forces that hold the structure together.

....

....

....

....

[2]

(c) The table below shows some properties of five substances, **A-E**.

Substance	Melting point in °C	Boiling point in °C	Does it conduct electricity when solid?	Does it conduct electricity when dissolved or molten?
A	–210	–196	No	No
B	–219	–183	No	No
C	801	1413	No	Yes
D	115	445	No	No
E	1083	2567	Yes	Yes

(i) Substance **A** consists of small, covalently bonded molecules.
Explain why it has a relatively low melting point.

....

....

[2]

(ii) Look at the table in part (c). One of the substances, **A-E**, is an ionic compound. Use the information in the table to suggest which of the substances is ionic. Explain your answer.

....

....

....

....

[2]

(d) This table contains information about some of the properties of diamond and graphite.

	Hardness	Melting point	Conducts electricity?	Uses
Diamond	Hard	High	No	Cutting tools
Graphite	Soft	High	Yes	Electrodes in batteries

Describe the structures of diamond and graphite and relate the structures to their given uses.

....

....

....

....

....

....

....

....

....

....

....

[4]

[Total 12 marks]

Turn over ▶

2 A student reacts four different metals with dilute sulfuric acid.
She controls all of the relevant variables to make sure that the test is fair.
She collects the gas given off by each reaction in a gas syringe.
The figure below shows all four reactions after 30 seconds

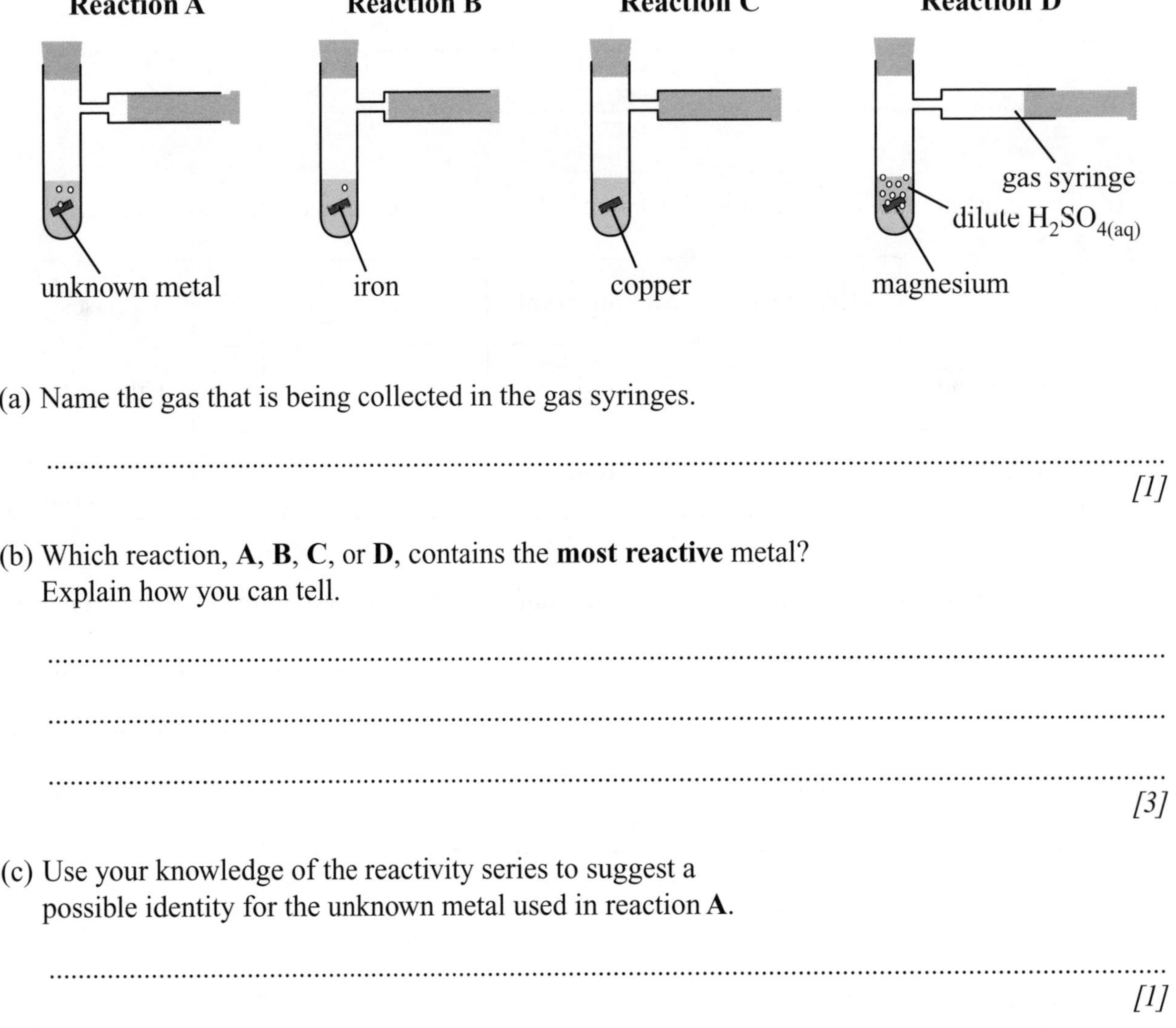

(a) Name the gas that is being collected in the gas syringes.

.... *[1]*

(b) Which reaction, **A**, **B**, **C**, or **D**, contains the **most reactive** metal?
Explain how you can tell.

....

....

.... *[3]*

(c) Use your knowledge of the reactivity series to suggest a possible identity for the unknown metal used in reaction **A**.

.... *[1]*

(d) In another experiment, the student placed pieces of different metals in metal salt solutions. She left them for 1 hour. The student then recorded whether any reaction had occurred.

The results of this experiment are shown below.

	Did any reaction occur with:		
	iron sulfate	magnesium sulfate	copper sulfate
iron	No	No	....
magnesium	....	No	Yes
copper	No	No	No

Complete the table by filling in the gaps.

[2]

(e) The equation for the reaction between magnesium and copper sulfate solution is:

$$Mg_{(s)} + CuSO_{4(aq)} \rightarrow MgSO_{4(aq)} + Cu_{(s)}$$

Write the ionic equation for this reaction.
Include state symbols in your answer.

....

[2]

(f) In the reaction described in part (e), which species was reduced?

....

[1]

[Total 10 marks]

3 A student added an excess of zinc oxide (ZnO) to dilute hydrochloric acid (HCl). They reacted to produce zinc chloride, a soluble salt.

(a) In addition to the zinc chloride, one other product is formed by this reaction. Name the other product of the reaction.

....

[1]

(b) Zinc oxide can react with both acids and bases. What term can be used to describe this type of oxide?

....

[1]

(c) Hydrogen chloride can react with ethene to form chloroethane. The bond energies in ethene, hydrogen chloride and chloroethane are given in the table below.

Bond	Bond energy / kJ/mol
H — C	414
C = C	614
H — Cl	431
C — C	347
C — Cl	339

$$H_2C{=}CH_2 + H{-}Cl \rightarrow H{-}CH_2{-}CH_2{-}Cl$$

Use the bond energies given in the table to calculate the energy change of this reaction.

energy change = ... kJ/mol

[3]

(d) Another student added solid calcium carbonate ($CaCO_3$) to dilute hydrochloric acid.

(i) Which gas was given off by the reaction in the student's experiment?

....

[1]

(ii) The solution formed at the end of the reaction is neutral.
Suggest a method you could use to test the pH of the solution.
State what you would expect to observe.

....

....

....

[2]

(e) Calcium carbonate can also be used in the production of lime.

What type of reaction is used to produce lime from calcium carbonate?

....

[1]

[Total 9 marks]

Turn over ▶

4 Iron can be extracted from hematite, Fe_2O_3, by reduction, using coke.
Here is the equation for this reaction:

$$Fe_2O_3 + 3C \rightarrow 2Fe + 3CO$$

(a) Explain, in terms of electrons, what is meant by a reduction reaction.

....
[1]

(b) Calculate the mass of iron that could be extracted from 40 g of Fe_2O_3.
Relative atomic masses, A_r: Fe = 56, O = 16.

Mass of iron = ... g
[4]

(c) Lead is below iron in the reactivity series.
Would you expect lead to be extracted by reduction with carbon?
Explain your answer.

....

....
[1]

(d) Iron is used to produce an alloy called steel.
Explain why steel is harder than iron.

....

....

....

....
[3]

(e) Chemical additives can be added to steel to change its properties.
Give an example of a substance which may be added to steel to alter its properties.

....
[1]

[Total 10 marks]

5 A student carried out an experiment to investigate the electrolysis of copper sulfate solution, $CuSO_{4\ (aq)}$, using inert carbon electrodes. The diagram shows how his experiment was set up.

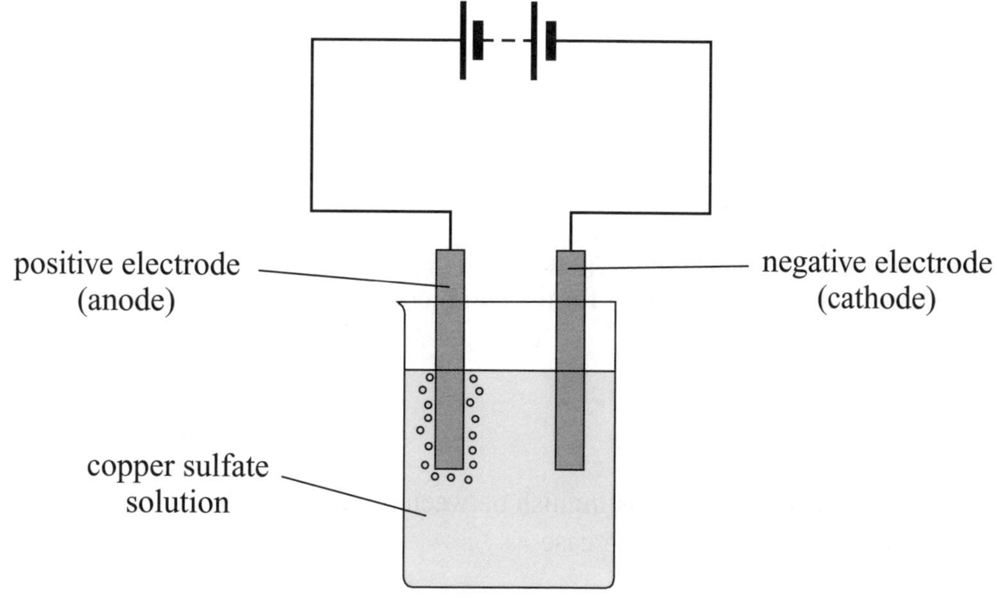

(a) Explain why a solution of copper sulfate can conduct electricity, but solid copper sulfate cannot.

....

....
[2]

(b) List the formulae of all **four** of the ions that are present in aqueous copper sulfate solution.

....

....
[1]

(c) The student repeated their experiment using copper electrodes.

Explain why the positive electrode decreased in mass in this experiment. Your answer should include the half-equation for the reaction taking place at the positive electrode.

....

....

....

....

....
[3]

[Total 6 marks]

6 Propane is an alkane.

(a) Draw the displayed formula of propane.

[1]

(b) Propane burns in the presence of oxygen.
Write the balanced symbol equation for the complete combustion of propane.

....

[2]

(c) Propene is an alkene.
Describe a test you could use to distinguish between propene and propane.
Say what you would observe in each case.

....

....

....

[3]

(d) Propene can be used as a monomer in addition polymerisation.
It forms the polymer poly(propene).
Draw the repeat unit of poly(propene).

[1]

(e) Alkenes can also be reacted with steam to form alcohols.
Give the name of the alcohol produced by reacting propene with steam.

....

[1]

[Total 8 marks]

7 The halogens make up Group VII of the periodic table.
The table below shows some of the physical properties of the first four halogens.

Halogen	Atomic number	Melting Point / °C	Boiling Point / °C	Colour at room temperature
Fluorine	9	–220	–188	very pale yellow
Chlorine	17		–34	green
Bromine	35	–7	59	
Iodine	53	114	185	dark grey

(a) Use the data in the table to predict the melting point of chlorine.
Explain your answer.

....

....

....
[2]

(b) Describe the appearance of bromine at room temperature.

....
[2]

(c) Explain how the group number of bromine in the periodic table is related to its electronic structure.

....

....

....
[2]

(d) Chlorine is bubbled through sodium iodide solution.
Describe the reaction that will occur, if any. Explain your answer in terms of the relative positions of chlorine and iodine in the periodic table.

....

....

....

....

....
[3]

(e) Chlorine can combine with hydrogen to form hydrogen chloride.
Explain why hydrogen chloride forms an acidic solution in water.

....

....

....
[2]

[Total 11 marks]

8 Carbon dioxide is a simple molecule whose displayed formula is shown below.

O=C=O

(a) Carbon dioxide can be formed from the thermal decomposition of magnesium carbonate.
Name the other product of this reaction.

....

[1]

(b) Complete this dot and cross diagram to show the bonding in carbon dioxide.
Show the outer shell electrons only.

O C O

[2]

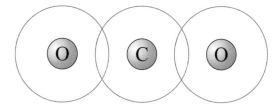

(c) What volume would 1.1 g of CO_2 gas occupy at room temperature and pressure?

volume of carbon dioxide = ... dm^3

[2]

(d) Carbon dioxide is a greenhouse gas.
Explain what is meant by the term greenhouse gas.

....

....

....

[2]

[Total 7 marks]

9 A student burns a piece of copper in air.

(a) The copper reacts with oxygen in the air to form copper oxide.
Use the data in the table below to find the empirical formula of the copper oxide.

Mass of empty container	28.00 g
Mass of container + mass of copper oxide	34.40 g
Mass of container + copper	33.12 g

Empirical formula = ...

[5]

(b) In another experiment, the student burns 1.08 g of magnesium in air.
She expected to produce 1.80 g of magnesium oxide.
The actual mass of magnesium oxide produced was 1.20 g.

Calculate the percentage yield of magnesium oxide.

Percentage yield = ... %

[2]

[Total 7 marks]

END OF QUESTIONS

Practice Paper 5

As part of your assessment, you will take either a practical test (Paper 5) or a written alternative to the practical test (Paper 6). You should check with your teacher which one of those options you'll be taking. Both options will test your knowledge of experimental skills and investigations. This practice paper is the equivalent of Paper 6 in the exams.

Cambridge International GCSE Chemistry

Paper 5 Alternative to Practical

In addition to this paper you should have:
- A pen and pencil.
- A ruler.
- A calculator.

Centre name					
Centre number					
Candidate number					

Time allowed:
- 1 hour

Candidate name
Candidate signature

Instructions to candidates
- Write your name and other details in the spaces provided above.
- Use blue or black ink to write your answers.
- Answer all questions in the spaces provided.
- Do all rough work on the paper.
- Cross out any work you do not want to be marked.
- In calculations, show clearly how you worked out your answers.

Information for candidates
- The marks available are given in brackets at the end of each question part.
- There are 40 marks available for this paper.

1 A student measured the volume of gas produced over time when lumps of zinc are reacted with dilute sulfuric acid.
The equation for the reaction is:

$$Zn + H_2SO_4 \rightarrow ZnSO_4 + H_2$$

(a) Draw and label an experimental set-up that the student could have used to collect and measure the volume of gas produced over time.

[2]

The graph below shows the student's results.

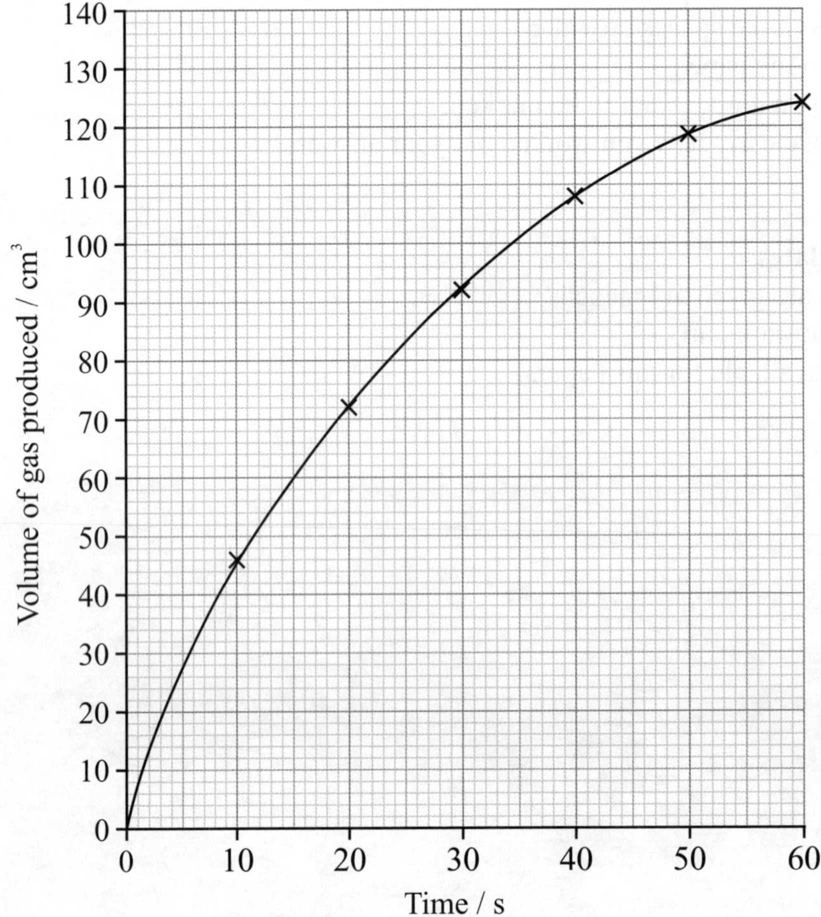

(b) Calculate the rate of reaction (in cm^3/s) for the reaction during the first 15 seconds using the formula:

$$\text{Rate} = \frac{\text{volume of gas produced (cm}^3\text{)}}{\text{time (s)}}$$

rate = ... cm^3/s
[2]

In a second experiment, the student added a catalyst to the acid.
The same amounts of zinc and dilute sulfuric acid were used as before.
The results are shown in the table below.

Time / s	Volume of gas produced / cm^3
	Experiment 2
0	0
10	60
20	94
30	112
40	122
50	124
60	124

(c) On the graph on the previous page:

- Plot the results for the second experiment.
- Draw a curve of best fit through the points.
- Label the line 'Experiment 2'.

[3]

(d) How can you can tell from the graph that the reaction rate of Experiment 2 is faster than Experiment 1?

....

.... *[1]*

(e) The reaction between zinc and sulfuric acid is exothermic.
The student confirms this by measuring the temperature of the solution before and after the reaction. The diagram below shows the thermometer that the student used.

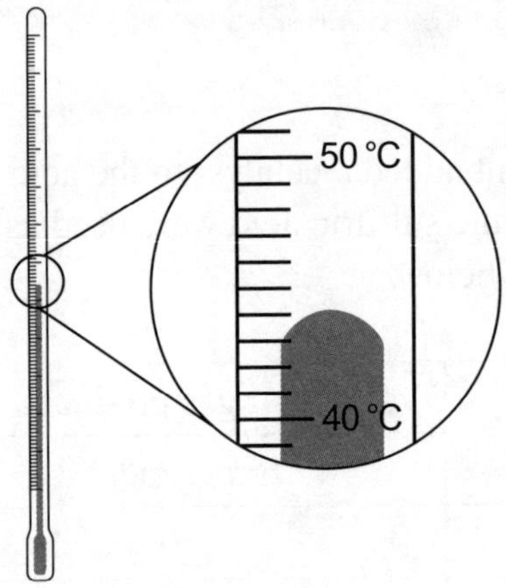

50 °C
40 °C

What temperature is shown on the thermometer?

.... *[1]*

[Total 9 marks]

2 A student is investigating the properties of vinegar. Ethanoic acid is found in vinegar.
The student reacted some of the vinegar with solid sodium carbonate.
The apparatus that he used is shown below.

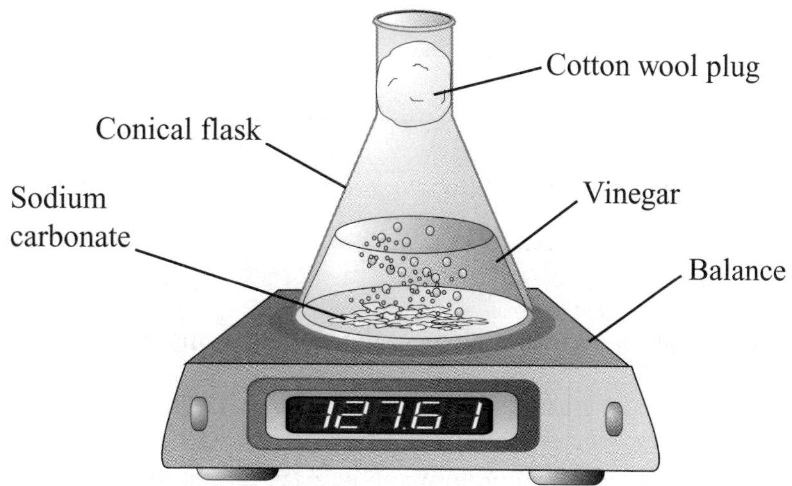

The student recorded the initial mass of the flask and then recorded it again after 60 s.
He repeated the experiment three times. His results are shown in the table.

	Initial Mass / g	Final Mass / g	Loss of Mass / g
Run 1	128.00	127.61	0.39
Run 2	128.50	127.95	0.55
Run 3	128.35	127.90	0.45

(a) Calculate the mean loss of mass after 60 s.

mean loss of mass = ... g
[2]

(b) (i) Why would it be inappropriate to use a mass balance that has a resolution of 1 g for this experiment?

....

....

....
[1]

Turn over ▶

(ii) The teacher asks the student to test the solid sodium carbonate that he was given to confirm that it contains sodium ions.

Name and describe a simple test the student could perform.

....

....

....

....

[3]

(iii) State what observation you would expect the student to make during this test.

....

....

[1]

(c) The student found that ethanoic acid reacts with ammonia to produce a colourless solution. He was asked to confirm that the solution contained ammonium ions.

Describe a test that the student could carry out to confirm this.

....

....

....

....

[3]

(d) The student also needed to identify the ions in two different metal halide solutions.

Describe a test the student could use to distinguish between solutions of a metal iodide and a metal bromide. Say what you would observe in each case.

....

....

....

[3]

[Total 13 marks]

3 A student has a small bottle of a colourless solution. Her teacher tells her it contains sulfate ions and an unknown cation. She is asked to perform some tests to confirm the contents of the bottle.

(a) The student tests the solution for sulfate ions using the method shown.

> <u>Method for testing for sulfate ions</u>
>
> 1. Place 3 cm^3 of your test solution in a test tube.
> 2. Add 3 cm^3 of hydrochloric acid.
> 3. Add 10 drops of Reagent **X** to the test tube and observe what happens.

The test solution does contain sulfate ions.
When she adds Reagent **X** to the test solution in step 3, a precipitate forms.

(i) Identify Reagent **X**.

....

[1]

(ii) State the colour of the precipitate that forms when Reagent **X** is added in step 3.

....

[1]

(b) The student adds a few drops of aqueous ammonia (NH_3) to the solution and a white precipitate forms. The student concludes from this that the cation must be zinc.

State why the student's conclusion could be wrong. Suggest a further test the student could do to confirm that the solution contains zinc ions.

....

....

....

....

....

[3]

[Total 5 marks]

4 A student wanted to find the concentration of a solution of sodium hydroxide. She decided to titrate 10.0 cm^3 of the sodium hydroxide solution with 4.90 g/dm^3 sulfuric acid solution to find the exact volume of sulfuric acid needed to neutralise the alkali.

(a) The student used methyl orange as an indicator rather than Universal indicator. Explain why Universal indicator should not be used for the student's titration.

....

....

....
[2]

(b) The student set up her apparatus as shown below.

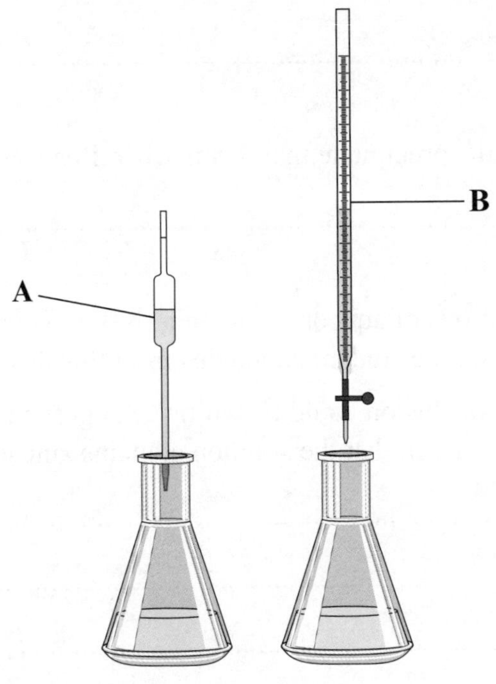

Name the pieces of equipment labelled **A** and **B**.

A: ....

B: ....
[2]

(c) When the student did the titration, the conical flask sat on a dark brown lab bench.
Explain how could this have affected the accuracy of her result.
Suggest what could she do to correct this problem.

....

....

....

[2]

(d) After correcting the problem described in part (c), the student repeated her titration.
She found that 8.80 cm^3 of the acid were needed to neutralise the sodium hydroxide solution.

Another student carries out a titration using the same sulfuric acid solution and 10.0 cm^3 of a sodium hydroxide solution with double the concentration.
What volume of acid will he need to neutralise this sample?

Volume = ... cm^3

[1]

[Total 7 marks]

Turn over ▶

5 A student wants to separate the components of a mixture.
The mixture is a white powder composed of barium sulfate and potassium iodide.
The table below shows some information about the two compounds in the mixture.

Name	Melting point / °C	Boiling point / °C	Appearance at room temperature	Soluble in water?
barium sulfate	1580	1600	white solid	no
potassium iodide	681	1330	white solid	yes

Describe an experimental method that would allow the student to obtain a pure solid sample of each of the salts using common laboratory apparatus.

....

....

....

....

....

....

....

....

....

....

....

....

....

....

....

[Total 6 marks]

END OF QUESTIONS

Section 1 — The Particulate Nature of Matter

Page 5

Warm-Up Questions

1) The particles are randomly arranged and free to move past each other, but they tend to stick closely together.
2) When you heat a gas, the particles have more energy, so they move faster. They will hit the container walls harder and more frequently. This produces a larger force on the walls, creating more pressure.
3) Brownian motion

Exam Questions

1 a) D ***[1 mark]***
b) condensation ***[1 mark]***
c) The particles gain energy ***[1 mark]*** and vibrate more ***[1 mark]***. This weakens the forces that hold the solid together ***[1 mark]***. At the point of melting, many of the particles have enough energy to break free from their positions ***[1 mark]***.

2 a) Diffusion is when a substance moves from an area of higher concentration to an area of lower concentration ***[1 mark]***.
b) Iodide ions have a smaller mass than lead ions ***[1 mark]***, so the iodide ions diffused across the dish faster than the lead ions ***[1 mark]***. When the ions met, the iodide ions had moved further than the lead ions (so the solid lead iodide formed closer to the end of the dish where the lead nitrate was added) ***[1 mark]***.

Section 2 — Experimental Techniques

Page 13

Warm-Up Questions

1) E.g. burette / (volumetric) pipette / measuring cylinder
2) A pure substance is a substance that only contains one compound or one element.
3) Impurities in a substance will result in it boiling over a wider temperature range, and at a higher temperature than the pure substance.
4) fractional distillation
5) crystallisation

Exam Questions

1 a) The boiling points of water and methanoic acid are too close together to allow them to be separated by simple distillation ***[1 mark]***.
b)

Temperature on thermometer	Contents of the flask	Contents of the beaker
30 °C	both liquids	no liquid
65 °C	water	propanone
110 °C	no liquid	both liquids

[3 marks for whole table correct, otherwise 1 mark for each correct row.]

2 a) All of the inks have separated into at least two different substances, so none of them can be pure ***[1 mark]***.
b) C ***[1 mark]*** because the spots in the chromatogram for C match those in sunrise yellow ***[1 mark]***.
c) R_f = distance travelled by substance in sunrise yellow ÷ distance travelled by solvent
$R_f = 9.0 \div 12.0 = 0.75$
[2 marks for correct answer, otherwise 1 mark for using the correct formula to calculate R_f]

Section 3 — Atoms, Elements and Compounds

Page 20

Warm-Up Questions

1) relative mass = 1, relative charge = 0
2) The total number of protons and neutrons in the nucleus of the atom.
3) electrons = 19, protons = 19, neutrons = 39 – 19 = 20
4) a) 2
b) 8

Exam Questions

1 a) 3 shells ***[1 mark]***
b) chlorine ***[1 mark]***

You want the element in Period 3 and Group VII here — that's chlorine.

2 a) 2,8,6 ***[1 mark]***
b)

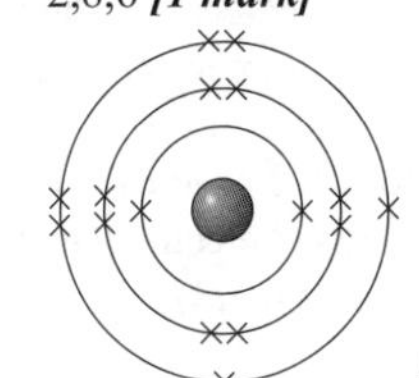

[1 mark]

3 a) Any one of: lithium / potassium / rubidium / caesium / francium ***[1 mark]***
b) 1 ***[1 mark]***

4 a) Isotopes are atoms of the same element ***[1 mark]***, which have the same proton number but a different nucleon number ***[1 mark]***.
b) protons = 6 ***[1 mark]***, neutrons = 7 ***[1 mark]***, electrons = 6 ***[1 mark]***
c) It has a different proton number from carbon ***[1 mark]***.

Page 27

Warm-Up Questions

1) A substance that is made of two or more different elements which are chemically joined (bonded) together.
2) An alloy is a mixture of a metal with other elements.
3) By the atom losing electrons.
4) 2

Exam Questions

1

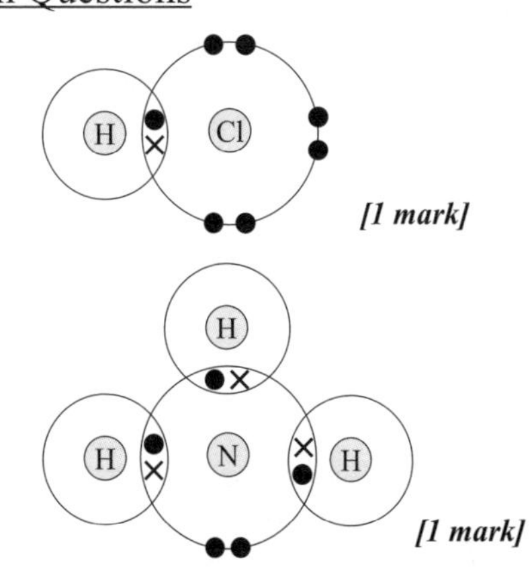

[1 mark]

[1 mark]

2 a) Element **Q** is a non-metal. You can tell this because it is to the right of/above the dividing line between metals and non-metals ***[1 mark]***.
b) Any two from: e.g. has a dull appearance / has a low melting point / forms oxides that are acidic / has poor electrical conductivity ***[2 marks]***.

3 a) Sodium will lose the electron from its outer shell to form a positive ion ***[1 mark]***. Fluorine will gain an electron to form a negative ion ***[1 mark]***.

b) Ionic compounds have a giant ionic lattice structure ***[1 mark]***. The ions form a closely packed regular arrangement of alternating positive and negative ions ***[1 mark]***, held together by strong electrostatic forces of attraction between oppositely charged ions ***[1 mark]***.

Page 31

Warm-Up Questions

1) false

The ions in ionic compounds are held together by extremely strong ionic bonds. It takes a large amount of energy to break these bonds so ionic compounds do not readily form gases.

2) covalent bonds between atoms
3) A lattice of positive ions in a 'sea' of electrons.

Exam Questions

1 a) The layers of carbon atoms that make up graphite are held together weakly ***[1 mark]***. The layers can easily slide over each other, making graphite soft and slippery ***[1 mark]***.

b) Each carbon atom in graphite has a delocalised electron/an electron that is able to move ***[1 mark]***. Diamond does not have any delocalised electrons and therefore cannot conduct electricity ***[1 mark]***.

The delocalised electrons carry an electrical charge and can move freely through the material.

c) In diamond, each carbon atom forms four covalent bonds in a rigid lattice structure ***[1 mark]***. This makes diamond very hard, so it would be good at cutting other substances ***[1 mark]***.

2 a) ionic compound ***[1 mark]***

b) E.g. by heating them, as giant macromolecular structures have a much higher melting point ***[1 mark]*** so the giant macromolecular compound would not melt but the simple molecular compound would ***[1 mark]***.

3 a) MgO is an ionic compound, so when it melts its ions are free to move and carry an electric charge ***[1 mark]***. Oxygen is a simple molecule and does not contain ions or free electrons to carry a charge ***[1 mark]***.

b) There are strong bonds between the ions in ionic compounds which take a lot of energy to overcome ***[1 mark]***. Melting simple molecules only involves breaking weak intermolecular forces which does not require much energy ***[1 mark]***.

4 a) E.g. copper is a good electrical conductor as it contains delocalised electrons ***[1 mark]*** which are free to move and are able to carry an electrical charge ***[1 mark]***.

b) The copper atoms in a lattice are arranged into layers, which are able to slide over each other ***[1 mark]***.

Section 4 — Stoichiometry

Page 35

Warm-Up Questions

1) $MgCO_3$
2) sodium hydroxide + hydrochloric acid → sodium chloride + water

$NaOH + HCl \rightarrow NaCl + H_2O$

3) K_2CO_3

Exam Questions

1 a) $H_2SO_4 + 2NH_3 \rightarrow (NH_4)_2SO_4$
[1 mark for reactants and products correct, 1 mark for correctly balancing the equation.]

b) 8 ***[1 mark]***

2 a) oxygen/O_2 ***[1 mark]***

b) $CH_4 + \mathbf{2O_2} \rightarrow CO_2 + \mathbf{2H_2O}$
[1 mark for 2O₂, 1 mark for 2H₂O.]

c) 1 more carbon atom ***[1 mark]***, 2 more hydrogen atoms ***[1 mark]***.

3 a) $H^+_{(aq)} + OH^-_{(aq)} \rightarrow H_2O_{(l)}$
[1 mark for both reactants correct, 1 mark for product correct.]

b) $3NO_{2\,(g)} + H_2O_{(l)} \rightarrow 2HNO_{3\,(aq)} + NO_{(g)}$
[1 mark for correct reactants and products, 1 mark for correctly balancing the equation, 1 mark for state symbols].

Page 40

Warm-Up Questions

1) The average mass of naturally occurring atoms of an element on a scale where the ^{12}C atom has a mass of exactly 12 units.
2) moles = mass ÷ M_r = 90 ÷ 18 = 5.0 moles
3) M_r = mass ÷ moles = 87.0 ÷ 0.500 = 174
4) The reactant that gets used up in a reaction and therefore limits the amount of product formed.
5) percentage purity = (7.8 ÷ 12) × 100 = 65%

Exam Questions

1 C ***[1 mark]***

M_r of $CaCl_2$ = 40 + (2 × 35.5) = 111

2 $M_r(NO) = 30$ $\quad M_r(NO_2) = 46$
So moles of NO = 15 ÷ 30 = 0.5 mol ***[1 mark]***
From the equation, 2 moles of NO is produced from 2 moles of NO_2. So 0.5 mol of NO reacts to form 0.5 mol of NO_2.
So mass of NO_2 = 0.5 × 46 = 23 g ***[1 mark]***.

3 $M_r(C_9H_8O_4) = (12 \times 9) + (1 \times 8) + (16 \times 4) = 180$
mass = moles × M_r = 12.4 × 180 = 2232 g
[2 marks for the correct answer, otherwise 1 mark for calculating the M_r of $C_9H_8O_4$.]

4 a) $M_r(CuO) = 64 + 16 = 80$ ***[1 mark]***
So moles of CuO = 4.0 ÷ 80 = 0.05 mol
From the equation, 1 mole of Cu is produced for every 1 mol of CuO that reacts. So 0.05 mol CuO reacts to form 0.05 mol Cu ***[1 mark]***.
So theoretical yield of Cu = number of moles × M_r = 0.05 × 64 = 3.2 g ***[1 mark]***.

b) Percentage yield = (2.9 ÷ 3.2) × 100 ***[1 mark]***
= 90.625 = 91% (2 s.f.) ***[1 mark]***

If you got the answer to part (a) wrong, you can still have full marks in (b) for correctly using your incorrect answer from (a).

Page 45

Warm-Up Questions

1) CH_2O
2) $M_r(CH_2) = 12 + (2×1) = 14$
42 ÷ 14 = 3
So $CH_2 \times 3 = C_3H_6$
3) number of moles = concentration × volume
= 0.10 × (25 ÷ 1000) = 0.0025 mol
4) false

All gases have a molar volume of 24 dm^3 at RTP.

Exam Questions

1 a) mass of manganese =
(mass of container + manganese) − (mass of container)
= 84.88 − 36.48 = 48.40 ***[1 mark]***

b) number of moles: Mn = 48.40 ÷ 55 = 0.88
O = 14.08 ÷ 16 = 0.88
simplest whole number ratio:
(0.88 ÷ 0.88) : (0.88 ÷ 0.88) = 1 : 1
empirical formula: MnO
[3 marks for correct answer, otherwise 1 mark for calculating the moles of both manganese and oxygen, 1 mark for correct whole number ratio.]

2 a) volume = moles ÷ concentration
= 2 ÷ 7.4 = 0.27 dm^3 ***[1 mark]***

You may also be asked to give your answer in cm^3, in which case 0.27 x 1000 = 270 cm^3

b) 750 cm^3 ÷ 1000 = 0.75 dm^3
concentration = moles ÷ volume
= 3 ÷ 0.75 = 4 mol/dm^3 ***[1 mark]***

c) $M_r(Na_2SO_4) = (23 \times 2) + 32 + (16 \times 4) = 142$
mass in 1 dm^3 = moles in 1 dm^3 × M_r = 4 × 142 = 568 g
concentration in g/dm^3 = 568 g/dm^3
[2 marks for correct answer, otherwise 1 mark for calculating the M_r of Na_2SO_4]

3 $M_r(CaCO_3) = 40 + 12 + (3 \times 16) = 100$ ***[1 mark]***
no. of moles of $CaCO_3$ = 25 ÷ 100 = 0.25 ***[1 mark]***
1 mole of CO_2 is formed for every mole of $CaCO_3$ that reacts.
So 0.25 moles of $CaCO_3$ reacts to form 0.25 moles of CO_2.
Volume of CO_2 = 0.25 × 24 dm^3 ***[1 mark]*** = 6.0 dm^3 ***[1 mark]***

Section 5 — Electricity and Chemistry

Pages 54-55

Warm-Up Questions

1) Electrolysis is the breakdown of an ionic compound, molten or in aqueous solution, by the passage of electricity.
2) the cathode/negative electrode
3) hydrogen and oxygen
4) copper

Exam Questions

1 a) lead ***[1 mark]*** and bromine ***[1 mark]***

b) A silver liquid (lead) would form below one electrode ***[1 mark]*** and bubbles of brown vapour (bromine) would be released at the other electrode ***[1 mark]***.

2 a) The cathode is the object you want to electroplate ***[1 mark]***.

b) E.g. atoms from the anode are gradually losing electrons and moving into the solution ***[1 mark]***.
So the anode will decrease in mass and will need replacing if it gets used up ***[1 mark]***.

3 a) hydrogen ***[1 mark]***

b) chlorine ***[1 mark]***

c) Inert electrodes are used because they will not react with the electrolyte ***[1 mark]***.

d) $2H^+ + 2e^- \rightarrow H_2$ ***[1 mark]***

e) Copper is less reactive than hydrogen ***[1 mark]***.

4 a) $\mathbf{Al^{3+} + 3e^- \rightarrow Al}$ ***[1 mark]***

b) bauxite ***[1 mark]***

c) The oxygen made at the positive electrode reacts with the carbon (to make carbon dioxide) ***[1 mark]***.

5 a) Metal 2, Metal 3, Metal 1 ***[1 mark]***. E.g. Zinc is less reactive than all 3 metals, so the most reactive metal will make the cell with the greatest voltage, since there will be the biggest difference in reactivity ***[1 mark]***.
So the order of reactivity is simply the order of the size of voltage of the cells from lowest to highest ***[1 mark]***.

b) Metal 1 would be oxidised ***[1 mark]***.

6 a) i) Cu^{2+}, SO_4^{2-}, H^+, OH^- ***[1 mark]***

ii) E.g. carbon/platinum ***[1 mark]***

b) Copper is transferred from the anode to the cathode ***[1 mark]***. Over time, the anode gets lighter because copper atoms from the anode lose electrons and enter the solution as ions ***[1 mark]***. The cathode gets heavier because the copper ions are gaining electrons, forming atoms, which creates a coating of copper on the cathode ***[1 mark]***.

c) Potassium is more reactive than hydrogen ***[1 mark]*** so hydrogen is produced at the cathode ***[1 mark]***. At the anode, oxygen will be formed ***[1 mark]*** because the bromide ions are at a low concentration ***[1 mark]***.

Section 6 — Chemical Energetics

Page 59

Warm-Up Questions

1) A reaction which gives out energy to the surroundings
2) A reaction which takes in energy from the surroundings
3) Endothermic

Exam Questions

1 Diagram B ***[1 mark]***

2 a) It releases useful energy (heat) ***[1 mark]***.

b) E.g. hydrogen, uranium-235 ***[1 mark]***

3 a) C – H and O = O ***[1 mark]***

b) (4 × 414) + (2 × 494) = 2644 kJ/mol

This is the amount of energy required to break the bonds in CH_4 and $2O_2$.

(2 × 800) + (4 × 459) = –3436 kJ/mol

This is the amount of energy released by forming the bonds in CO_2 and $2H_2O$.

2644 – 3436 = –792 kJ/mol
[4 marks for correct answer, otherwise 1 mark for finding the energy needed to break the bonds in the reactants, 1 mark for finding the energy released by forming bonds in the products, 1 mark for subtracting the energy released by forming bonds from the energy required to break bonds.]

Section 7 — Chemical Reactions

Pages 68-69

Warm-Up Questions

1) physical change
2) In flour mills, very fine particles of flour are suspended in the air. The particles have a high surface area to volume ratio and are highly flammable, so a small spark could lead to a combustion reaction with a very high reaction rate (i.e. an explosion).
3) true
4) Enzymes help to speed up chemical reactions in living cells.

Exam Questions

1 a) 17 cm^3 ***[1 mark]***

b) Manganese(IV) oxide was the most effective catalyst ***[1 mark]*** because it led to the greatest volume of oxygen being produced over the time period measured / increased the rate of reaction by the greatest amount ***[1 mark]***.

2 a) i) E.g. the gas is released directly into the room and may be toxic/hazardous ***[1 mark]***.

ii) E.g. measure the volume of gas given off using a gas syringe ***[1 mark]***.

b) i) E.g. Mix the reactants, observe a mark through the solution ***[1 mark]*** and measure how long it takes for the mark to disappear (as the precipitate forms) ***[1 mark]***.
The student should carry out the reaction with the reactants at different temperatures and record the time taken at each temperature ***[1 mark]***. For each temperature, the student should heat both reactants to the correct temperature before they are mixed together, using a water bath ***[1 mark]***.

ii) E.g. the higher the temperature, the faster the rate of reaction will be ***[1 mark]***. This is because a higher temperature makes the particles move faster, so they collide more frequently ***[1 mark]***, and it gives the particles more energy, so more particles will collide with enough energy to react ***[1 mark]***.

3 a) i) photosynthesis ***[1 mark]***

ii) oxygen ***[1 mark]***

b) The rate of glucose production is lower in dim light than in bright sunlight ***[1 mark]***. The reaction needs energy from sunlight to occur, so less light means less of the reactant particles will have enough energy to react when they collide ***[1 mark]***.

You would also get the marks for writing this the opposite way around (i.e. that the rate is higher in bright sunlight than dim light).

4 a) E.g.

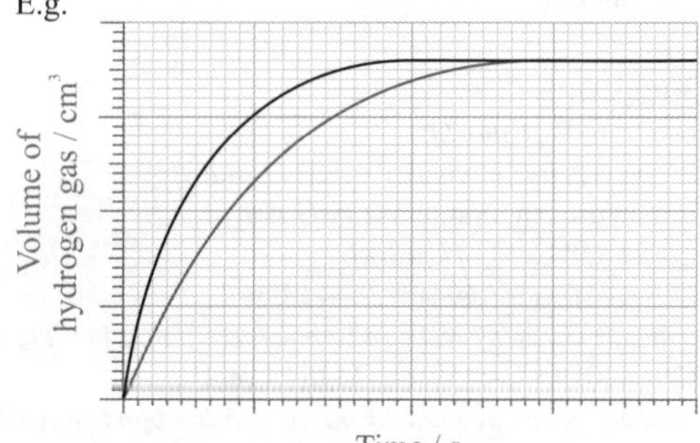

[1 mark for curve with steeper gradient at the start of the reaction, 1 mark for final volume being the same as for the other curve but reaching it in less time.]

b) There are more particles in a given volume/the particles are closer together ***[1 mark]***, so the collisions between particles are more frequent ***[1 mark]***.

c) The rate would increase ***[1 mark]***.

d) Smaller pieces have a higher surface area to volume ratio ***[1 mark]***. So for the same volume of solid, the particles around it will have more surface to collide with and collisions will be more frequent ***[1 mark]***.

e) E.g. changing the temperature / adding a catalyst ***[1 mark]***.

Page 74

Warm-Up Questions

1) A reaction that can go in both directions (so the products can react to form the reactants).

2) By adding water.

3) The forward reaction of a reversible reaction is going at the same rate as the backward reaction.

4) Yes. Zn loses two electrons to become Zn^{2+} (its oxidation state increases from 0 to +2), so it is oxidised. Cu^{2+} gains two electrons to become Cu (its oxidation state decreases from +2 to 0), so it is reduced. Both oxidation and reduction are happening at the same time, so it's a redox reaction.

Exam Questions

1) a) It's a reversible reaction. / It can go in both directions ***[1 mark]***.

b) water ***[1 mark]***

2) a) Oxygen is being lost from iron oxide. / The iron(III)/Fe^{3+} ions in the iron oxide are gaining electrons ***[1 mark]***.

If you are taking the Core assessment, you don't need to worry about knowing the answer in terms of electron transfer — just stating that oxygen is lost will be fine.

b) carbon ***[1 mark]***

Carbon gains oxygen in this reaction to form carbon dioxide, meaning it is oxidised. This means it acts as the reducing agent.

3) The first student's reaction conditions are better ***[1 mark]***, because: The forward reaction is endothermic ***[1 mark]*** so raising the temperature will cause the equilibrium to increase the rate of the forward reaction in order to decrease the temperature / counteract the change in temperature ***[1 mark]***. There are more moles of gas on the right-hand side of the equation ***[1 mark]***, and a lower pressure will encourage the reaction that produces more moles of gas ***[1 mark]***.

Section 8 — Acids, Bases and Salts

Page 82

Warm-Up Questions

1) neutral

2) A substance that reacts with an acid to produce a salt and water.

3) sulfuric acid + magnesium oxide → magnesium sulfate + water

4) Strong acids ionise almost completely in water, so a large proportion of the acid molecules break apart to release H^+ ions. Weak acids do not fully ionise, so only a small proportion of the acid molecules break apart to release H^+ ions.

5) An oxide that will react with both acids and bases to form a salt and water.

6) E.g. filter the reaction mixture to remove the excess insoluble base. Heat the remaining solution gently (using a Bunsen burner) to evaporate off some of the water and make a saturated solution. Leave the solution to cool and allow the salt to crystallise. Filter off the solid salt and leave the crystals to dry.

Exam Questions

1 a) H^+ ions/hydrogen ions ***[1 mark]***

b) neutralisation ***[1 mark]***

2 D ***[1 mark]***

Metal oxides form basic solutions and pH 13 is the only basic pH given.

3 a) The student should measure out a set amount of acid into a conical flask using a pipette and add a few drops of indicator to the acid ***[1 mark]***. Then they should slowly add alkali to the acid, using a burette, until the reaction reaches the end-point / the indicator changes colour ***[1 mark]***. Then the student should carry out the reaction using exactly the same volumes of alkali and acid but with no indicator (so the resulting solution is just the soluble salt and water) ***[1 mark]***.

b) The student has poured too much solution into the funnel / the level of the solution goes above the filter paper ***[1 mark]***. This means that some of the solid could pass down the sides of the filter paper and into the conical flask below, reducing the amount of solid that's extracted from the solution ***[1 mark]***.

Page 88

Warm-Up Questions

1) potassium/K^+

2) light blue

3) An insoluble green precipitate forms.

4) Hold a piece of damp red litmus paper over the test tube. If ammonia is present, the paper will turn blue.

Exam Questions

1

Flame colour	Metal ion
blue-green	**Cu^{2+}**
red	Li^+
yellow	**Na^+**

[3 marks]

2 a) Hydrogen produces a "squeaky pop" ***[1 mark]*** with a lighted splint ***[1 mark]***.

b) Oxygen relights ***[1 mark]*** a glowing splint ***[1 mark]***.

3 a) iron(II) iodide ***[1 mark for iron(II), 1 mark for iodide]***

b) No, the student is not correct. The sample produced a white precipitate with hydrochloric acid and barium chloride solution, so he can be sure that it contains sulfate ions ***[1 mark]***. Calcium does produce a white precipitate with a few drops of sodium hydroxide ***[1 mark]***, but so do aluminium and zinc, so he cannot be sure that it contains calcium ions ***[1 mark]***.

Section 9 — The Periodic Table

Page 95

Warm-Up Questions

1) sodium

Potassium and sodium are both in Group I of the periodic table. Calcium is in Group II. Elements in the same group have similar properties, so the properties of potassium should be more like sodium than calcium.

2) 1
3) more reactive
4) It increases.
5) green
6) Group VIII/Group 8/Group 0
7) They have a full outer shell of electrons, so they don't easily give up or gain electrons.
8) Any two from: e.g. high melting point / high density / form coloured compounds / have catalytic activity.

Exam Questions

1 a) Highest (X): fluorine ***[1 mark]***
Lowest (Y): iodine ***[1 mark]***

Halogens at the top of Group VII are more reactive than those at the bottom of the group.

b) E.g. (–188 + 58.8) ÷ 2 = –129.2 ÷ 2 = –64.6 °C
[1 mark for any value between –100 °C and 0 °C.]

The actual boiling point of chlorine is –34 °C.

2 a) transition metals ***[1 mark]***
b) To the right of the line ***[1 mark]***. Since it does not conduct electricity, it must be a non-metal ***[1 mark]***.

Section 10 — Metals

Page 101

Warm-Up Questions

1) The layers of atoms in a pure metal can slide over each other.
2) hydrogen/H_2
3) true
4) The more reactive metal will more readily form positive ions/cations and will bind more strongly to oxygen than the less reactive metal.

Exam Questions

1 a) C, A, D, B
[1 mark for putting C as the most reactive and B as the least reactive. 1 mark for putting A and D in the correct order.]
b) i) zinc oxide ***[1 mark]***
ii) Metal X was sodium, because it reacted vigorously with cold water ***[1 mark]***.
c) Copper carbonate will react ***[1 mark]***.
$CuCO_3 \rightarrow CuO + CO_2$ ***[1 mark]***

Page 107

Warm-Up Questions

1) false
2) hematite, coke and limestone
3) zinc blende
4) E.g. it costs money to collect and separate for recycling.
5) It's unreactive and a good thermal conductor.

Exam Questions

1 a) electrolysis ***[1 mark]***
b) No, because sodium is more reactive than carbon ***[1 mark]***.
2 a) $Fe_2O_3 + 3CO \rightarrow 2Fe + 3CO_2$ ***[1 mark for all reactants and products correct, 1 mark for correctly balancing the equation.]***
b) Oxygen is being lost from iron oxide ***[1 mark]***.
c) $CaO + SiO_2 \rightarrow CaSiO_3$ ***[1 mark]***
d) It is drained off as molten slag ***[1 mark]***.
3 a) To lower the melting point of the aluminium oxide ***[1 mark]***.
b) Aluminium and oxygen ***[1 mark]***.
c) E.g. aircraft manufacturing / food containers ***[1 mark]***

Section 11 — Air, Water, Sulfur and Carbonates

Page 113

Warm-Up Questions

1) Add a few drops of the sample being tested to blue anhydrous cobalt(II) chloride. If it turns pink, water is present in the sample.
2) oxygen and water

Exam Questions

1 C ***[1 mark]***
2 a) Any two from: e.g. drinking water / cooking / cleaning / heating / watering plants ***[1 mark for each correct answer]***
b) First, large bits of material are removed by a wire mesh ***[1 mark]***, then sand and gravel beds filter out any other solid bits ***[1 mark]***.
3 a) Fossil fuels can contain sulfur compounds ***[1 mark]***.
b) E.g. it kills plants/animals / damages buildings and statues / makes metals corrode ***[1 mark]***.
4 a) Sacrificial protection involves attaching a metal that is more reactive than steel to the ship ***[1 mark]***. The more reactive metal will be oxidised more easily than steel ***[1 mark]***, so it will corrode instead of the steel ***[1 mark]***.
b) No, the zinc layer acts as sacrificial protection as well as a barrier / the zinc is more reactive than iron ***[1 mark]*** so it will be oxidised in preference to iron, even if it's scratched ***[1 mark]***.

Page 118

Warm-Up Questions

1) ammonia gas, a salt and water
2) iron catalyst
3) E.g. carbon dioxide and methane
4) true

Exam Questions

1 a) phosphorus ***[1 mark]*** and potassium ***[1 mark]***
b) E.g. fertilisers provide/replace missing elements in the soil that are essential for plant growth ***[1 mark]***. This helps to increase crop yield ***[1 mark]***.
2 a) photosynthesis ***[1 mark]***
b) respiration ***[1 mark]***
3 a) A: reaction of hydrocarbons and steam ***[1 mark]***
B: air ***[1 mark]***
b) If the pressure was higher the process may become too dangerous/expensive to maintain ***[1 mark]***.

Page 121

Warm-Up Questions

1) food preservative
2) E.g. in car batteries / making detergents/fertiliser/paints/dyes.
3) calcium carbonate
4) E.g. neutralising acidic soil / flue gas desulfurisation

Exam Questions

1 C ***[1 mark]***

2 a) sulfur dioxide + oxygen $\rightleftharpoons$ sulfur trioxide
[1 mark for the correct reactants and 1 mark for the correct product].

b) Temperature: 450 °C ***[1 mark]***
Pressure: 2 atmospheres ***[1 mark]***
Catalyst: vanadium(V) oxide catalyst ***[1 mark]***

Section 12 — Organic Chemistry

Page 130

Warm-Up Questions

1) False — naphtha condenses higher in the column than fuel oil.
2) carbon and hydrogen
3) propanoic acid
4) Structural isomers are molecules with the same molecular formula but with their atoms arranged differently.

Exam Questions

1 A ***[1 mark]***

2 a) i) jet fuel ***[1 mark]***
ii) making chemicals/used in the chemical industry ***[1 mark]***
iii) making roads ***[1 mark]***

b) Shorter hydrocarbons have a lower boiling point and so remain as gases for longer ***[1 mark]***.

3 a) $CH_4 + \mathbf{2}O_2 \rightarrow CO_2 + 2\mathbf{H_2O}$
[1 mark for 2 in front of O_2, 1 mark for identifying water as other product].

b) $C_3H_8 + Cl_2 \rightarrow C_3H_7Cl + HCl$ ***[1 mark]***
UV light ***[1 mark]***

4 a) E.g.

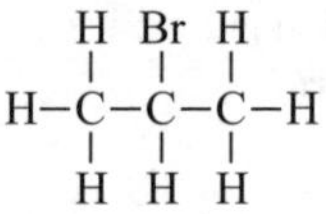

```
   H  Br  H
   |   |  |
H—C—C—C—H
   |   |  |
   H  H  H
```

[1 mark]

The bromine atom needs to be attached to the middle carbon atom. If the bromine is attached to either of the end carbons, it's the same structure as the one in the question.

b)

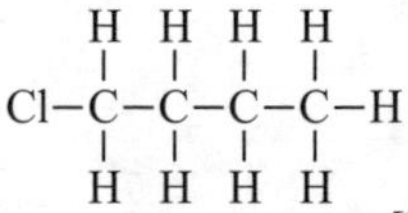

```
    H  H  H  H
    |  |  |  |
Cl—C—C—C—C—H
    |  |  |  |
    H  H  H  H
```

[1 mark]

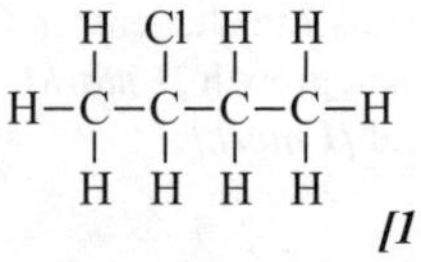

```
   H  Cl  H  H
   |   |  |  |
H—C—C—C—C—H
   |   |  |  |
   H  H  H  H
```

[1 mark]

Don't worry if your answer doesn't look identical to what's shown here — as long as you drew an isomer with the Cl attached to one of the end carbons, and an isomer where it's attached to one of the middle carbons, you'd get the marks.

Pages 138-139

Warm-Up Questions

1) They contain C=C double bonds which can open up to make more bonds.
2) addition polymerisation
3) Eg. the temperature must be around 30 °C and the reaction must be carried out under anaerobic conditions.
4) ethyl ethanoate

Exam Questions

1 a) Cracking is the breaking up of long-chain hydrocarbons ***[1 mark]*** to form short-chain hydrocarbons/ alkanes and alkenes (and hydrogen) ***[1 mark]***.

b) silica (SiO_2) / alumina (Al_2O_3) ***[1 mark]***

c) hydrogen gas ***[1 mark]***

2 a)

Method	Reaction	Catalyst
A	$C_2H_4 + \mathbf{H_2O} \rightarrow C_2H_5OH$	**phosphoric acid**
B	$C_6H_{12}O_6 \rightarrow 2CO_2 + \mathbf{2}C_2H_5OH$	**yeast/enzymes**

[4 marks — 1 mark for each correct answer]

b) fermentation ***[1 mark]***

c)

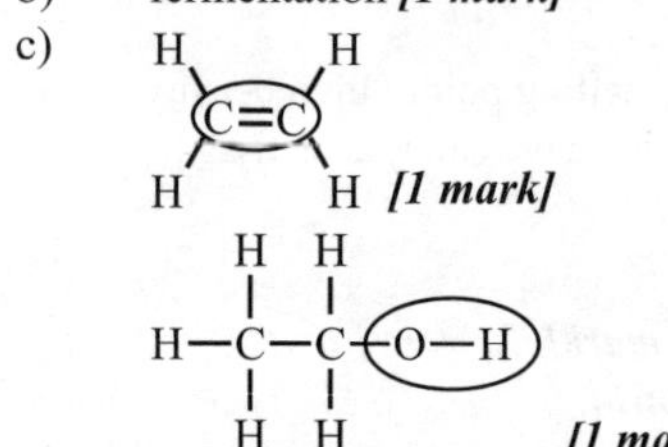

3 a) Shake the hydrocarbon with bromine water ***[1 mark]***. If the solution turns from orange to colourless, then alkenes are present ***[1 mark]***.

b) $C_3H_6 + Br_2 \rightarrow C_3H_6Br_2$ ***[1 mark]***

You'd also get the mark if you wrote the product as $CH_2BrCHBrCH_3$.

4 a) ethanoic acid ***[1 mark]***

b)

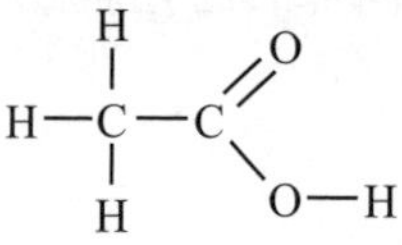

```
   H
   |      O
H—C—C//
   |    \
   H     O—H
```

[1 mark]

c) The pH of the solution would decrease ***[1 mark]***.

5 a) propanol/propan-1-ol/propan-2-ol ***[1 mark]***

b) $CH_3CH_2CH_2CH_2OH$ ***[1 mark]***

c)

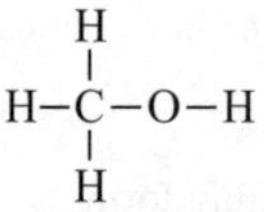

```
   H
   |
H—C—O—H
   |
   H
```

[1 mark]

6 a) i) ethanol ***[1 mark]***
ii) E.g. acidified potassium manganate(VII) ***[1 mark]***

b) butyl ethanoate ***[1 mark]***, water ***[1 mark]***

7

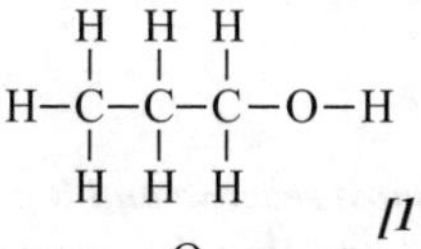

```
   H  H  H
   |  |  |
H—C—C—C—O—H
   |  |  |
   H  H  H
```

[1 mark]

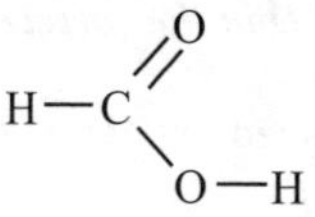

```
      O
     //
H—C
     \
      O—H
```

[1 mark]

Page 144

Warm-Up Questions

1) two
2) true
3) Not easily broken down by microorganisms.

Exam Questions

1 a) Any three from: e.g. packaging / fabrics / gadgets / vehicles ***[3 marks]***

b) E.g. they take up space in landfill. / Burning them produces carbon dioxide, which contributes to global warming ***[1 mark]***.

2 a) amide bonds ***[1 mark]***

b) hydrolysis ***[1 mark]***

3 a) condensation polymerisation ***[1 mark]***
b) addition polymerisation ***[1 mark]***
c) condensation polymerisation ***[1 mark]***
4 a) The reaction produces a mixture (of sugar molecules) ***[1 mark]***. Chromatography is required to separate and identify each of the products ***[1 mark]***.
b) Apply a locating agent to the chromatogram ***[1 mark]***.
c) (simple) sugar molecules ***[1 mark]***

Page 145
Revision Summary Questions

4) C_2H_5OH
5) butan-1-ol

Paper 1 Multiple Choice (Core)

Pages 157-168

1 D ***[1 mark]***
2 A ***[1 mark]***
3 C ***[1 mark]***
4 D ***[1 mark]***
5 D ***[1 mark]***
6 B ***[1 mark]***
7 A ***[1 mark]***
8 C ***[1 mark]***
9 A ***[1 mark]***
10 C ***[1 mark]***
11 D ***[1 mark]***
The compound contains 2 carbon atoms, 3 hydrogen atoms, 1 chlorine atom and 2 oxygen atoms.
12 C ***[1 mark]***
M_r of MgF_2 = 24 + (2 × 19) = 62
13 B ***[1 mark]***
14 D ***[1 mark]***
15 C ***[1 mark]***
16 B ***[1 mark]***
17 B ***[1 mark]***
Reaction Y produced twice as much gas in the same amount of time, so the amount of $CaCO_3$ must have doubled and the amount of acid stayed the same.
18 C ***[1 mark]***
19 A ***[1 mark]***
20 D ***[1 mark]***
21 B ***[1 mark]***
22 C ***[1 mark]***
Melting point decreases down the group, so the melting point of sodium must be lower than 180 °C and higher than 63 °C.
23 B ***[1 mark]***
24 B ***[1 mark]***
25 C ***[1 mark]***
26 A ***[1 mark]***
27 D ***[1 mark]***
28 D ***[1 mark]***
29 C ***[1 mark]***
30 A ***[1 mark]***
31 C ***[1 mark]***
32 D ***[1 mark]***
33 A ***[1 mark]***
Calcium oxide is a basic oxide, so it will react with water to produce a solution with a pH greater than 7.
34 B ***[1 mark]***
35 B ***[1 mark]***
36 B ***[1 mark]***
The second molecule has 7 – 5 = 2 carbons and 16 – 12 = 4 hydrogens.
37 A ***[1 mark]***
38 A ***[1 mark]***
39 D ***[1 mark]***
40 A ***[1 mark]***

Paper 2 Multiple Choice (Extended)

Pages 169-181

1 B ***[1 mark]***
2 A ***[1 mark]***
4.7 ÷ 9.0 = 0.522.... = 0.52
3 D ***[1 mark]***
4 C ***[1 mark]***
5 B ***[1 mark]***
6 A ***[1 mark]***
7 B ***[1 mark]***
8 A ***[1 mark]***
9 D ***[1 mark]***
10 C ***[1 mark]***
A_r of Zn = 65, so 130 g of Zn = 130 ÷ 65 = 2 moles.
M_r of ZnO = 65 + 16 = 81
2 moles of ZnO are needed to produce 2 moles of Zn, so the mass of ZnO in the impure sample must be 2 × 81 = 162 g.
(162 ÷ 216) × 100 = 75%
11 D ***[1 mark]***
M_r of NaCl = 23 + 35.5 = 58.5
so 36.0 g of NaCl = 36.0 ÷ 58.5 = 0.615... moles.
0.615... ÷ 0.400 = 1.538... = 1.54 mol/dm^3
12 D ***[1 mark]***
13 A ***[1 mark]***
Energy required to break bonds = 1072 + (2 x 459) = 1990 kJ/mol
Energy released from bonds forming = (2 x 800) + 436 = –2036 kJ/mol
Overall energy change = 1990 – 2036 = –46 kJ/mol
The energy change is negative so the reaction is exothermic. Option A correctly shows an energy level diagram for an exothermic reaction.
14 D ***[1 mark]***
15 B ***[1 mark]***
16 A ***[1 mark]***
17 B ***[1 mark]***
18 D ***[1 mark]***
Using the table, reaction D is the only reaction that produces an insoluble salt ($PbCl_2$).
19 C ***[1 mark]***
20 B ***[1 mark]***
21 B ***[1 mark]***
22 B ***[1 mark]***
23 A ***[1 mark]***
24 C ***[1 mark]***
25 A ***[1 mark]***
26 D ***[1 mark]***
27 C ***[1 mark]***
28 C ***[1 mark]***
29 B ***[1 mark]***
30 C ***[1 mark]***
31 D ***[1 mark]***
32 D ***[1 mark]***
33 C ***[1 mark]***
34 D ***[1 mark]***
35 C ***[1 mark]***
36 A ***[1 mark]***
37 A ***[1 mark]***
Molecule X has (8 – 5 =) 3 carbon atoms and (18 – 12 =) 6 hydrogen atoms, so its molecular formula must be C_3H_6 (which is propene).
38 C ***[1 mark]***
39 D ***[1 mark]***
40 B ***[1 mark]***

Paper 3 Theory (Core)

Pages 182-196

1 a) C and D ***[1 mark]***. They are the only pair to have the same number of protons but a different number of neutrons ***[1 mark]***.

b) i) Protons = 34 ***[1 mark]***
Neutrons = 79 – 34 = 45 ***[1 mark]***
Remember: number of protons = proton (atomic) number, number of neutrons = nucleon (mass) number – proton number
ii) 79 ***[1 mark]***
iii)
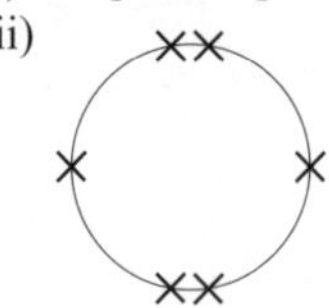
[1 mark]
Selenium is in Group VI of the periodic table, so it has 6 electrons in its outer shell.

c) i) A compound is a substance made of two or more different elements ***[1 mark]*** that are chemically bonded together ***[1 mark]***.
ii) $M_r = 56 + 32 + (4 \times 16) = 152$
[2 marks for correct answer, otherwise 1 mark for using the correct A_r values]

2 a) Petroleum is piped in at the bottom of the column. The petroleum **evaporates** and rises up the column. The temperature **decreases** as you go up the column. The various fractions **condense** at different levels.
[3 marks — 1 mark for each correct answer]
b) fractional distillation ***[1 mark]***
c) Fraction X is gasoline. The higher up the fractionating column a fraction condenses, the lower the boiling point ***[1 mark]***. Gasoline condenses higher on the fractionating column than diesel oil, so gasoline has a lower boiling point than diesel oil ***[1 mark]***.
d) i) D ***[1 mark]***
ii) A/B ***[1 mark]***
iii) E ***[1 mark]***
iv) A ***[1 mark]***
v) C ***[1 mark]***
e) A high temperature ***[1 mark]*** and a catalyst ***[1 mark]***.

3 a) i) liquid ***[1 mark]***
ii) The particles in both liquids and gases are randomly arranged ***[1 mark]***. Particles in a liquid are close together, while the particles in a gas are far apart from each other ***[1 mark]***. The particles in both liquids and gases are free to move around / are not held in fixed positions ***[1 mark]***. The particles in gases are able to travel long distances in straight lines, while the particles in liquids flow past each other ***[1 mark]***.
b) i) Test: Bubble the gas through limewater ***[1 mark]***.
Result: Carbon dioxide will turn the limewater cloudy/milky ***[1 mark]***.
ii) E.g. respiration / reaction between an acid and a carbonate / thermal decomposition of carbonate ***[1 mark]***.
c) i) City B, as it has the higher concentration of nitrogen dioxide / pollutants ***[1 mark]***. The difference might be because of higher amounts of traffic in City B ***[1 mark]***.
ii) E.g. fainting/coma/death ***[1 mark]***
iii) City B, as it has the higher concentration of nitrogen dioxide and sulfur dioxide ***[1 mark]***. These pollutants mix with clouds and form acids, which fall as acid rain and can damage limestone buildings ***[1 mark]***.
d) hydrogen (H_2) ***[1 mark]***

4 a) forwards ***[1 mark]***
b) The white copper(II) sulfate will turn blue ***[1 mark]***.
c) M_r of $CuSO_4 = 64 + 32 + (4 \times 16) = 160$
M_r of $CuSO_4 \cdot 5H_2O = 160 + 5 \times (2 + 16) = 250$
$(8.4 \div 160) \times 250 = 13.1$ g
[3 marks for the correct answer, otherwise 1 mark for the correct M_r of $CuSO_4$ and 1 mark for the correct M_r of $CuSO_4 \cdot 5H_2O$].
d) i) cathode ***[1 mark]***
ii) Copper is unreactive ***[1 mark]***, so it protects other metals from corrosion ***[1 mark]***.

5 a) The aluminium is reduced because it loses oxygen ***[1 mark]***.
b) bauxite ***[1 mark]***
c) The cathode / the negative electrode ***[1 mark]***.
d) Any two from: e.g. Recycling reduces waste going to landfill / Recycling requires less energy than extracting aluminium from its ore / Recycling is cheaper than extracting aluminium from its ore / Recycling reduces the need to mine aluminium ore, so it reduces damage to the landscape caused by mining / Recycling preserves natural resources, so it is more sustainable. ***[1 mark for each valid advantage]***
e) E.g. strong/low density ***[1 mark]***
f) i) hydrogen/H_2 ***[1 mark]***
ii) E.g. volcanoes / hot springs / mining / removal from fuels ***[1 mark]***

6 a) Any three from: e.g. transition metals have higher melting points than Group I and II metals / transition metals have higher densities than Group I and II metals / transition metals can form ions with different charges but Group I and II metals can't / transition metals react less vigorously when heated in air than Group I and II metals ***[3 marks]***.
Questions like this are easy marks — all you're asked to do is find information from the table — the answers are right there in front of you.
b) E.g. transition metals have catalytic properties (as metals or compounds) ***[1 mark]***, transition metal compounds are usually coloured ***[1 mark]***.
c) From most to least reactive: sodium, magnesium, iron, chromium ***[2 marks for all four metals in correct order, 1 mark for two metals in the correct order]***.
d) i) sodium + water → **sodium hydroxide** + **hydrogen**
[1 mark for each correct product]
ii) It is alkaline / has a pH greater than 10 ***[1 mark]***.
iii) E.g. there would be a more violent reaction / the reaction would be faster / it would explode ***[1 mark]***.

7 a) They could separate the solvent from the ink by fractional distillation ***[1 mark]*** then use the boiling point to identify the substance by comparing it to the values in the table ***[1 mark]***.
b) Dye B is present in the ink, as all the spots present in dye B appear in the ink sample ***[1 mark]***. Dye E is not present in the ink, as not all the spots in dye E are present in the ink sample ***[1 mark]***.

8 a) i) $C_6H_{12}O_6 \rightarrow \mathbf{2}C_2H_5OH + \mathbf{2CO_2}$
[1 mark for CO_2, 1 mark for correct balancing]
ii) Yeast contains an enzyme that speeds up/catalyses the fermentation reaction ***[1 mark]***. At higher temperatures, the yeast enzyme would be denatured/destroyed and the reaction would stop ***[1 mark]***.
iii) 100 – 86 – 1 – 0.5 – 0.5 = 12% ***[1 mark]***
b) E.g. 100 °C is the boiling point of water ***[1 mark]***. Heating the fermentation mixture to 100 °C would evaporate some/all of the water as well as the ethanol, so they wouldn't separate out ***[1 mark]***. The collected vapours would be an ethanol solution that was the same or only slightly more concentrated than the fermentation mixture ***[1 mark]***.
c) water ***[1 mark]***
d) i) carboxylic acids ***[1 mark]***
ii)
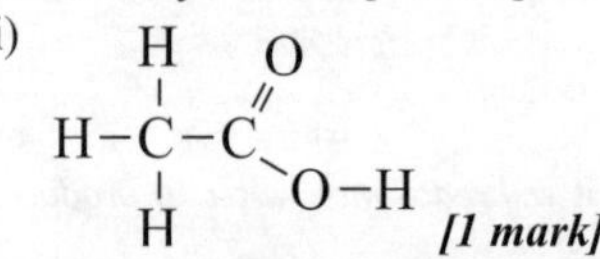

[1 mark]
iii) Fizzing / bubbles (of gas) ***[1 mark]***.
Ethanoic acid reacts in the same way as other acids, so it will react with a carbonate to produce a salt, water and carbon dioxide gas. When you're asked for an observation, make sure you write what you would see — the name of the gas is not an observation.

Paper 4 Theory (Extended)

Pages 197-210

Exam Questions

1 a) Sodium (Na^+): 2,8 ***[1 mark]***
Chlorine (Cl^-) = 2,8 ***[1 mark]***

b) Sodium chloride is a giant lattice made up of alternating Na^+ and Cl^- ions ***[1 mark]*** held together by the strong forces of attraction between oppositely charged ions ***[1 mark]***.

c) i) The molecules in substance A are only attracted to each other by weak intermolecular forces ***[1 mark]*** which don't need much energy to break/overcome ***[1 mark]***.

ii) Substance C ***[1 mark]***. It has a high melting and boiling point and can conduct electricity when molten or dissolved but not when solid ***[1 mark]***.

d) Diamond is made up of a network of carbon atoms that each form four covalent bonds ***[1 mark]***.
The strong covalent bonds hold the atoms in a rigid lattice, making diamond very hard, which makes it suitable for use in cutting tools ***[1 mark]***.
Each carbon atom in graphite forms three covalent bonds, creating sheets of carbon atoms ***[1 mark]***.
Only three out of each carbon's four outer electrons are used in bonds, so graphite has lots of free/delocalised electrons and can conduct electricity, making it suitable for use as an electrode ***[1 mark]***.

2 a) hydrogen/H_2 ***[1 mark]***

b) Reaction D ***[1 mark]***. The most reactive metal will react fastest with the acid ***[1 mark]***. In reaction D, the largest volume of gas has been collected in the syringe / the most bubbles are being given off ***[1 mark]***.

c) e.g. zinc ***[1 mark]***

You would get this mark if you named any metal between magnesium and iron in the reactivity series.

d) Gap for reaction of copper sulfate with iron: yes ***[1 mark]***
Gap for reaction of iron sulfate with magnesium: yes ***[1 mark]***

e) $Mg_{(s)} + Cu^{2+}_{(aq)} \rightarrow Mg^{2+}_{(aq)} + Cu_{(s)}$ ***[1 mark for the correct reactants, 1 mark for the correct products.]***

f) Cu^{2+} / copper ions ***[1 mark]***

Remember, when you're talking about oxidation and reduction in terms of electrons, reduction is the gain of electrons. In this reaction, the copper ions went from being positively charged ions to neutral atoms — so they must have gained electrons.

3 a) water/H_2O ***[1 mark]***

b) amphoteric ***[1 mark]***

c) Energy required to break bonds =
$614 + (4 \times 414) + 431 = 2701$ kJ/mol ***[1 mark]***
Energy released by forming new bonds =
$(5 \times 414) + 347 + 339 = -2756$ kJ/mol ***[1 mark]***
Energy change = $2701 - 2756 = -55$ kJ/mol ***[1 mark]***

d) i) carbon dioxide ***[1 mark]***

ii) E.g. test a sample of the solution using universal indicator paper/solution / litmus indicator. If the universal indicator turns green / the litmus turns purple, then the solution is neutral. ***[1 mark for any sensible method you could use to test the pH of the solution, 1 mark for a correct, matching observation of what that method would show if the solution was neutral.]***

e) thermal decomposition ***[1 mark]***

4 a) A reaction in which electrons are gained ***[1 mark]***.

b) M_r of $Fe_2O_3 = (2 \times 56) + (3 \times 16) = 160$
Moles of Fe_2O_3 = mass ÷ M_r = 40 ÷ 160 = 0.25
From the balanced equation you know that 2 moles of Fe_2O_3 produce 4 moles of Fe. So 0.25 moles of Fe_2O_3 will produce $0.25 \times 2 = 0.50$ moles of Fe
Mass of Fe = moles × A_r = $0.50 \times 56 = 28$ g
[4 marks for correct answer, otherwise 1 mark for M_r of Fe_2O_3, 1 mark for number of moles of Fe_2O_3, 1 mark for number of moles of Fe.]

c) Yes, because if lead is below iron in the reactivity series, it must also be below carbon/less reactive than carbon ***[1 mark]***.

d) In iron, the atoms are arranged in regular layers.
These layers can easily slide over each other, making iron soft ***[1 mark]***. Steel contains some carbon atoms, which disrupt the layers of iron atoms because they are a different size ***[1 mark]***. This makes it more difficult for the atoms to slide over each other, so steel is harder ***[1 mark]***.

e) e.g. carbon, chromium, nickel ***[1 mark]***

5 a) In a solution of copper sulfate, the ions are free to move (and carry an electric charge) ***[1 mark]***.
When copper sulfate is solid, the ions are held in fixed positions and can't move ***[1 mark]***.

b) Cu^{2+}, SO_4^{2-}, H^+, OH^- ***[1 mark]***

c) At the positive electrode, copper/Cu atoms from the electrode lose electrons and form copper ions/Cu^{2+} ions ***[1 mark]***.
The half-equation for this reaction is: $Cu \rightarrow Cu^{2+} + 2e^-$ ***[1 mark]***. As the reaction continues, the electrode loses mass as more copper atoms become ions and enter the solution ***[1 mark]***.

6 a)

```
  H H H
  | | |
H-C-C-C-H
  | | |
  H H H
```

[1 mark]

b) $C_3H_8 + 5O_2 \rightarrow 3CO_2 + 4H_2O$
[1 mark for correct reactants and products, 1 mark for correct balancing]

c) Add a few drops of bromine water to both compounds and shake ***[1 mark]***. With propane, nothing will happen ***[1 mark]***. Propene will turn the solution from orange to colourless ***[1 mark]***.

d)

```
   H   H
   |   |
 — C — C —
   |   |
 H3C   H
```

[1 mark]

e) propanol ***[1 mark]***

7 a) E.g. –113 °C ***[1 mark for any answer between –150 °C and –70 °C]***. Melting point increases down the group, so chlorine will have a melting point about halfway between the melting points of fluorine and bromine ***[1 mark]***.

b) It is a red-brown liquid ***[1 mark for colour, 1 mark for state]***.

c) The group number is equal to the number of electrons in the outer electron shell ***[1 mark]***.
Bromine is in Group VII (7), so a bromine atom has seven electrons in its outer shell ***[1 mark]***.

d) Chlorine will displace the iodine in solution to form sodium chloride solution ***[1 mark]***. This happens because chlorine is higher up Group VII than iodine ***[1 mark]***, which means that chlorine is more reactive ***[1 mark]***.

e) When hydrogen chloride is dissolved in water, the hydrogen chloride molecules split up into H^+ ions and Cl^- ions ***[1 mark]***. It is the H^+ ions that make the solution acidic ***[1 mark]***.

8 a) magnesium oxide ***[1 mark]***

b)

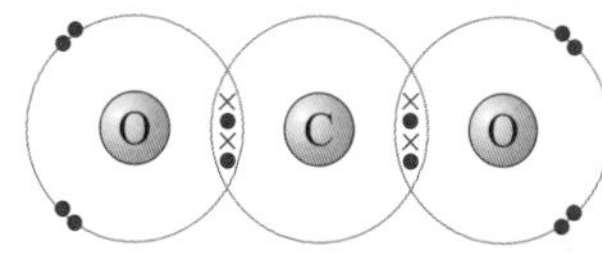

[1 mark for two bonding pairs between the carbon and each oxygen and 1 mark for each oxygen atom having two lone pairs and the carbon atom having none.]

c) M_r of $CO_2 = 12 + (2 \times 16) = 44$
moles of CO_2 = 1.1 g ÷ 44 g/mol = 0.025 mol
1 mole of gas occupies 24 dm^3 at RTP.
So, volume of $CO_2 = 0.025 \times 24\ dm^3 = 0.60\ dm^3$
[2 marks for correct answer, otherwise 1 mark for finding the number of moles of CO_2.]

d) A greenhouse gas is one that absorbs heat that would normally be radiated from the Earth into space ***[1 mark]*** and re-radiates some of it back towards the Earth ***[1 mark]***.

9 a) Mass of Cu: $33.12 - 28.00 = 5.12$
Mass of O: $34.40 - 33.12 = 1.28$
Number of moles: Cu = $5.12 \div 64 = 0.08$
O = $1.28 \div 16 = 0.08$
Simplest whole number ratio:
$(0.08 \div 0.08) : (0.08 \div 0.08) = 1:1$
Empirical formula: CuO
[5 marks for correct answer, otherwise 1 mark for calculating the mass of Cu, 1 mark for calculating the mass of O, 1 mark for correct number of moles of each element, 1 mark for finding the simplest whole number ratio.]

b) percentage yield = $(1.20 \div 1.80) \times 100 = 66.7\%$ ***[2 marks for correct answer, otherwise 1 mark for correct working.]***

Paper 5 Alternative to Practical

Pages 211-220

1 a) E.g.

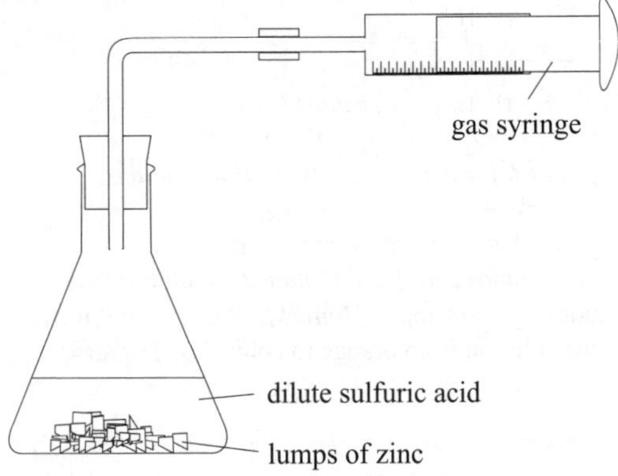

[2 marks — 1 mark for showing dilute sulfuric acid and lumps of zinc in a flask and 1 mark for showing a suitable way of collecting all of the gas produced.]

You'd still get the marks if you drew a set-up which involved collecting the gas over water — for example, using a measuring cylinder filled with water and upturned in a beaker of water.

b) Volume of gas produced in first 15 s = 60 cm^3
rate = volume of gas produced ÷ time = $60 \div 15 = 4\ cm^3/s$
[2 marks for correct answer, otherwise 1 mark for a volume of 60 cm³.]

c)

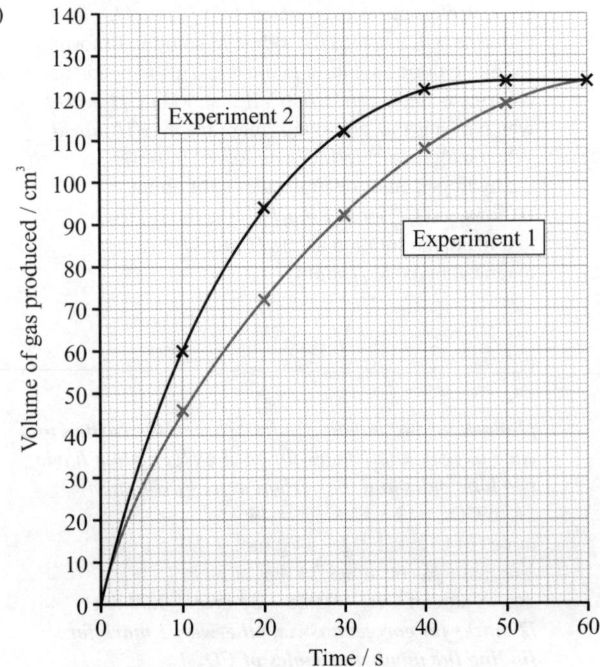

[2 marks for all points correctly plotted, or 1 mark for at least 5 points correctly plotted. 1 mark for a sensible curve of best fit.]

d) The graph for experiment 2 has a steeper slope at the beginning. / The reaction is complete (the line flattens) in less time ***[1 mark]***.

e) 44 °C ***[1 mark]***

2 a) $(0.39 + 0.55 + 0.45) \div 3 = 0.46$ g (2 s.f.)
[2 marks for correct answer, otherwise 1 mark for writing a correct expression that could be used to find the mean.]

b) i) The loss of mass for each run is less than 1 g ***[1 mark]***.
ii) A flame test ***[1 mark]***. Dip a nichrome wire/loop ***[1 mark]*** into the solid then place it into a blue Bunsen burner flame ***[1 mark]***.
iii) If sodium ions are present the substance would burn with a yellow flame ***[1 mark]***.

c) Add some sodium hydroxide to the solution and gently heat it ***[1 mark]***. Hold a piece of damp red litmus paper over the solution ***[1 mark]***. If the paper turns blue, ammonium ions are present in the original solution ***[1 mark]***.

d) Add dilute nitric acid, followed by a few drops of silver nitrate solution to the metal halide solutions ***[1 mark]***. The metal bromide would produce a cream precipitate ***[1 mark]***, and the metal iodide would produce a yellow precipitate ***[1 mark]***.

3 a) i) barium nitrate ***[1 mark]***
ii) white ***[1 mark]***

b) She cannot be certain it is zinc, since aluminium also gives a white precipitate under these conditions ***[1 mark]***. E.g. the student could add more aqueous ammonia to the sample until it is in excess ***[1 mark]***. If it contains zinc ions, the precipitate will redissolve ***[1 mark]***.

If the solution contained aluminium ions instead of zinc ions, adding more ammonia wouldn't redissolve the white precipitate.

4 a) In a titration you need to see a single, clear colour change at the point when the acid is neutralised ***[1 mark]***. Universal indicator changes colour gradually as the pH changes, so it is not suitable for a titration ***[1 mark]***.

b) **A**: pipette ***[1 mark]***
B: burette ***[1 mark]***

c) The dark colour of the lab bench would make it hard to spot the exact moment when the indicator changes colour ***[1 mark]***. This problem could be prevented by e.g. placing the conical flask on a white tile/a piece of white paper ***[1 mark]***.

d) $8.80\ cm^3 \times 2 = 17.60\ cm^3$ ***[1 mark]***

If the concentration of sodium hydroxide is doubled, the volume of sulfuric acid will need to be doubled too (because twice the amount of acid will be needed to neutralise the sodium hydroxide).

5 Any six from:
- Mix the powder with distilled/deionised water.
- Filter the mixture through a filter paper in a funnel and collect the liquid part of the mixture in a flask.
- Wash the solid barium sulfate with distilled/deionised water, then dry the salt.
- Gently heat the solution from the flask in an evaporation dish.
- Heat until crystals start to form.
- Allow the solution to cool, then filter out the crystals.
- Dry the crystals by leaving them in a warm place / using a drying oven / using a desiccator.

[6 marks — 1 mark for each valid point.]

Mixing the powder with water will dissolve the potassium iodide, but not the barium sulfate. The potassium iodide solution will then pass through the filter paper, leaving solid barium sulfate in the paper. The barium sulfate is then washed to remove any remaining traces of potassium iodide. To get solid pure potassium iodide from the solution, you need to crystallise the solution.

Glossary

acid	A substance with a pH of less than 7. (Extended) A proton donor, i.e. a source of hydrogen ions.
acidic oxide	An oxide that will react with a base to form a salt and water.
activation energy	The minimum amount of energy needed to break the bonds in the reactants and start the reaction.
alkali	A base that's soluble in water. The solution formed has a pH greater than 7.
alloy	A mixture of a metal with other elements.
amphoteric oxide	An oxide that will react with both acids and bases to form a salt and water.
anion	An ion with a negative charge.
Avogadro's constant	The number of atoms or molecules in a mole of substance. Equal to 6.02×10^{23}.
base	A substance that reacts with an acid to produce a salt and water. (Extended) A proton acceptor that can neutralise acids.
basic oxide	An oxide that will react with an acid to form a salt and water.
boiling	When a substance changes state from liquid to gas. This happens at the boiling point of the substance.
Brownian motion	The random zigzag movement of any particle suspended in a liquid or gas.
catalyst	A substance which increases the rate of reaction without being chemically changed or used up.
cation	An ion with a positive charge.
compound	A substance made of two or more different elements which are chemically bonded together.
concentration	The amount of substance in a given volume of solution.
condensation	When a substance changes state from gas to liquid.
covalent bond	A chemical bond between two atoms involving a shared pair of electrons.
diatomic molecule	A molecule made up of two atoms.
diffusion	When a substance moves from an area of higher concentration to an area of lower concentration.
dissolve	To mix with a liquid and form a solution.
electrolysis	The breakdown of an ionic compound, molten or in aqueous solution, by electricity.
element	A substance that only contains one type of atom.
empirical formula	The smallest whole number ratio of atoms in a compound.
endothermic reaction	A reaction that takes in energy from the surroundings, usually in the form of heat.
enzyme	Biological catalysts that speed up the chemical reactions in living cells.

Glossary

equilibrium	When the forward and backward reactions in a reversible reaction are going at exactly the same rate.
evaporation	A change of state that happens when particles escape from the surface of a liquid and become gas particles. It happens at temperatures below the boiling point of the liquid.
exothermic reaction	A reaction that gives out energy to the surroundings, usually in the form of heat.
freezing	When a substance changes state from liquid to solid.
functional group	A group of atoms that determine how a compound typically reacts.
group	A column on the periodic table, containing elements with similar properties.
homologous series	A family of similar compounds with similar chemical properties due to the presence of the same functional group.
hydrocarbon	A compound only containing atoms of carbon and hydrogen.
insoluble	Does not dissolve in a solvent.
ion	A charged particle formed when an atom (or group of atoms) gains or loses electrons.
ionic bond	An electrostatic attraction that occurs between oppositely charged ions.
isomer	A molecule that has the same molecular formula as another molecule but a different arrangement of atoms.
isotopes	Different atoms of the same element which have the same proton number but different nucleon numbers.
limiting reactant	The reactant that's used up in a reaction, so limiting the amount of product formed.
melting	When a substance changes state from solid to liquid.
metallic bonding	A lattice of positive ions in a 'sea of electrons'.
mixture	Two or more substances that are not chemically bonded together.
molar gas volume	The space that one mole of a gas takes up (24 dm^3 at room temperature and pressure).
mole	The amount of substance that contains 6.02×10^{23} particles.
monomer	A small molecule that can be combined with other small molecules to form a polymer.
neutral oxide	An oxide that doesn't react with either acids or bases.
nucleon number	The total number of protons and neutrons in the nucleus of an atom. Also known as the mass number.
nucleus	The positively-charged centre of an atom, consisting of protons and neutrons.
ore	A compound found naturally in the Earth's crust that can be used as a source of metal.
organic molecule	A covalently bonded molecule containing carbon.
oxidation	(Core) The gain of oxygen. (Extended) The loss of electrons.

Glossary

oxidising agent	A substance that can oxidise another substance during a redox reaction.
period	A row on the periodic table.
polymer	A large molecule made up of small repeating units (called monomers).
precipitate	A solid that forms in a solution during a chemical reaction.
proton number	The number of protons in the nucleus of an atom. Also known as the atomic number.
pure substance	A substance that is completely made up of a single element or compound.
rate of reaction	How fast the reactants in a reaction are changed into products.
recycling	The process of converting waste materials into new products.
redox reaction	A reaction in which electrons are transferred from one substance to another (from the oxidised species to the reduced species).
reducing agent	A substance that can reduce another substance during a redox reaction.
reduction	(Core) The loss of oxygen. (Extended) The gain of electrons.
relative atomic mass	The average mass of naturally occurring atoms of an element on a scale where the ^{12}C atom has a mass of exactly 12 units.
relative molecular mass	The sum of the relative atomic masses of all the atoms in the molecular formula of a compound.
reversible reaction	A reaction which can run in either direction, so the products can react to form the reactants.
salt	An ionic compound formed in a neutralisation reaction between an acid and a base.
saturated hydrocarbon	A hydrocarbon that contains only single bonds between the carbon atoms.
saturated solution	A solution in which no more solute will dissolve at that temperature.
soluble	Does dissolve in a solvent.
solute	A substance dissolved in a solvent to form a solution.
solution	A mixture made up of one or more substances (solutes) dissolved in a liquid (the solvent).
solvent	A liquid in which another substance (a solute) can be dissolved.
strong acid/base	An acid or base that ionises almost completely in solution.
sublimation	A change of state where a substance goes directly from a solid to a gas.
thermal decomposition	The breakdown of a substance into simpler substances when heated.
unsaturated hydrocarbon	A hydrocarbon that contains a double bond between two carbon atoms.
volatility	The ability of a substance to become a gas.
weak acid/base	An acid or base that doesn't fully ionise in solution.

Index

Index

The Periodic Table

Atomic (proton) number → 5 (upper number in each box)

Relative atomic mass → 11 (lower number in each box)

Periods	Group I	Group II											Group III	Group IV	Group V	Group VI	Group VII	Group VIII
1								1 H Hydrogen 1										2 He Helium 4
2	3 Li Lithium 7	4 Be Beryllium 9											5 B Boron 11	6 C Carbon 12	7 N Nitrogen 14	8 O Oxygen 16	9 F Fluorine 19	10 Ne Neon 20
3	11 Na Sodium 23	12 Mg Magnesium 24											13 Al Aluminium 27	14 Si Silicon 28	15 P Phosphorus 31	16 S Sulfur 32	17 Cl Chlorine 35.5	18 Ar Argon 40
4	19 K Potassium 39	20 Ca Calcium 40	21 Sc Scandium 45	22 Ti Titanium 48	23 V Vanadium 51	24 Cr Chromium 52	25 Mn Manganese 55	26 Fe Iron 56	27 Co Cobalt 59	28 Ni Nickel 59	29 Cu Copper 64	30 Zn Zinc 65	31 Ga Gallium 70	32 Ge Germanium 73	33 As Arsenic 75	34 Se Selenium 79	35 Br Bromine 80	36 Kr Krypton 84
5	37 Rb Rubidium 85	38 Sr Strontium 88	39 Y Yttrium 89	40 Zr Zirconium 91	41 Nb Niobium 93	42 Mo Molybdenum 96	43 Tc Technetium —	44 Ru Ruthenium 101	45 Rh Rhodium 103	46 Pd Palladium 106	47 Ag Silver 108	48 Cd Cadmium 112	49 In Indium 115	50 Sn Tin 119	51 Sb Antimony 122	52 Te Tellurium 128	53 I Iodine 127	54 Xe Xenon 131
6	55 Cs Caesium 133	56 Ba Barium 137	57-71 Lanthanoids	72 Hf Hafnium 178	73 Ta Tantalum 181	74 W Tungsten 184	75 Re Rhenium 186	76 Os Osmium 190	77 Ir Iridium 192	78 Pt Platinum 195	79 Au Gold 197	80 Hg Mercury 201	81 Tl Thallium 204	82 Pb Lead 207	83 Bi Bismuth 209	84 Po Polonium —	85 At Astatine —	86 Rn Radon —
7	87 Fr Francium —	88 Ra Radium —	89-103 Actinoids															

CISI41